Printed at the Mathematical Centre, 49, 2e Boerhaavestraat, Amsterdam.

The Mathematical Centre, founded the 11-th of February 1946, is a non-profit institution aiming at the promotion of pure mathematics and its applications. It is sponsored by the Netherlands Government through the Netherlands Organization for the Advancement of Pure Research (Z.W.O), by the Municipality of Amsterdam, by the University of Amsterdam, by the Free University at Amsterdam, and by industries.

MATHEMATICAL CENTRE TRACTS 65

J. DE VRIES

TOPOLOGICAL TRANSFORMATION GROUPS 1

A CATEGORICAL APPROACH

MATHEMATISCH CENTRUM AMSTERDAM 1975

AMS(MOS) subject classification scheme (1970): 54-02, 54H15, 18B99, 18C15, 43A

ISBN 90 6196 113 0

PREFACE

The theory of topological transformation groups (ttgs) forms a fascinating and comprehensive realm in the world of mathematics, bordering on the domains of topology, abstract harmonic analysis, ergodic theory, geometry and differential equations. We intend to lead the reader over a more or less artificial path between a number of "vantage points" which afford a "scenic view" of this landscape. These "points" are the notes which conclude the subsections. Without pretending completeness we indicate there the relationship of the material in the subsection to other literature. We shall now present a short description of the path mentioned above which the reader must follow. First of all, we have chosen to take a mainly categorical point of view, with the aim of unifying parts of the existing theory of ttgs. However, our aim could not fully be realized since more category theory had to be included than was originally planned. In a subsequent volume we intend to deal with a number of topics which could only be mentioned in the notes of this volume.

In Chapter I we give some basic material on ttgs. We claim no originality for its content, except for theorem 2.3.15: for any locally compact Hausdorff group G the dimension of $L^2(G)$ equals the weight of G.

After this prelude, we describe several categories of ttgs in Chapter II. As in a fugue, we always deal systematically with the same theme in each category. This theme can be described as follows: facts about a certain category of ttgs should be expressed in terms of the underlying categories of topological groups and topological spaces. (Although this tactic will probably hurt the feelings of every pure category theorist, it is a consequence of their wish that each "working mathematician" should try to use category theory for the description of the objects he is studying.) Thus, in §3 we describe the category **TTG** of all ttgs. In accordance with the policy indicated above, we try to do this by proving certain preservation and reflection properties of the obvious forgetful functor $K: TTG \to TOPGRP \times TOP$. For limits and monomorphisms everything works well, because the functor K is monadic, i.e. TTG can be identified with the category of all algebras over a certain monad in TOPGRP × TOP. For colimits, things go wrong; nevertheless, epimorphisms are preserved and reflected by K. In addition, TTG is cocomplete. In order to prove cocompleteness, we had to generalize a known construction which is related to "induced representations".

In §4, we consider some subcategories of TTG, defined by imposing certain restrictions on the phase groups and the phase spaces of ttgs. It is felt to be a serious omission that in this volume sparse attention could be paid to the much more interesting subcategories which arise from restrictions on actions. This subject is only touched upon in connection with certain reflective subcategories of TTG.

In TTG, the "group component" and the "space component" of a morphism have the same direction. In §6, we define a category TTG_*, which has the same object class as TTG, but in which the two components of a morphism have opposite directions. Thus, we obtain a functor $K_*: TTG_* \to TOPGRP^{op} \times TOP$. Although K_* has quite nice properties with respect to colimits, the category TTG_* is not cocomplete; neither is it complete. Therefore, we consider in §6 also the category $k\text{-}TTG_*$ which is defined similarly to TTG_*, except that its objects are k-ttgs. (Roughly speaking, all cartesian products have to be replaced by products in the category KR of all k-spaces.). The study of these objects is initiated in §5, where we consider the category k-TTG (morphisms similar to those in TTG). There we show that k-TTG is well-behaved with respect to limits; it is a category of algebras over a certain monad in KR. In §6, we show that $k\text{-}TTG_*$ (morphisms similar to those in TTG_*) is well-behaved with respect to colimits; it is a category of coalgebras over a certain comonad in $KRGRP^{op} \times KR$. Combining these results, it follows that the category $k\text{-}KR^G$ (for a fixed k-group G) is well-behaved in both respects. This result extends to the category TOP^G of all (ordinary) ttgs with phase group a fixed locally compact group G.

The final remarks in Chapter II concern the existence of cogenerators in TTG_*. This is the starting point for the considerations in Chapter III. However, the categorical point of view in this chapter is hidden under the surface of variations on another theme. This theme is the question of whether a given class of G-spaces (i.e. ttgs with a common phase group G, mostly locally compact) admits a comprehensive object, i.e. an object (not necessarily in the given class) in which all G-spaces in question can be embedded in one way or another. Here the main difference between our results and earlier ones (among others, by P.C. BAAYEN and J. DE GROOT) is that we obtain comprehensive objects which are G-spaces, whereas in the older results only G_d-spaces were obtained. To be honest, most of those G_d-spaces turned out to be G-spaces, and that is just what we prove in §8. In other words, the methods used in §8 are modifications of older ones. In addition, our methods and our categorical starting point made it possible to give a more unified treatment of the subject.

The internal reference system is self-explaining; a reference like "cf. p.q.r" means that the reader may find some useful information (or sometimes, material for comparison) in the r'th sub-subsection of subsection q in section p. For references to the literature, we used two methods. References to research papers are by the name(s) of the author(s), followed by the year of publication between brackets. On the other hand, references to books and monographs are by a two-letter abbreviation of the author's name between square brackets. This is due to the fact that originally we planned to refer only to a limited number of standard text books, namely the following ones: for topology, the books by Bourbaki [Bo], Dugundji [Du] and Engelking [En], for topological groups the work of Hewitt and Ross [HR], for topological transformation groups the book by Gottschalk and Hedlund [GH] and, finally, for category theory the text book of Mac Lane [ML]. Unfortunately, the list of books expanded, and it took some efforts to keep it at a reasonable length.

This book is a revised version of the author's Ph.D. thesis, written at the Free University at Amsterdam under the supervision of prof.dr. P.C. Baayen The author wishes to thank dr. A.B. Paalman-De Miranda for reading large parts of the manuscript and for her valuable suggestions. The author is indebted to the "Wiskundig Seminarium" of the Free University and to the Mathematisch Centrum at Amsterdam for giving him the opportunity to do this research. Finally, I would like to thank the reproduction staff of the Mathematisch Centrum for the excellent way in which they realized this book. In particular, I mention Mrs. C.J. Klein Velderman-Los and Mrs T. Bays-Renforth, who typed the manuscript.

CONTENTS

PREFACE i

CONTENTS iv

CHAPTER I: BASICAL CONCEPTS 1

§0. PREREQUISITES 1

0.1 General remarks and conventions 1

0.2 Topology 3

0.3 Topological groups 10

0.4 Category theory 12

§1. GENERALITIES ON TTGS 24

1.1 Definitions and terminology 24

1.2 Topological homeomorphism groups 32

1.3 Orbit space and enveloping semigroup 37

1.4 Morphisms and comorphisms 42

1.5 Operations on ttgs 49

§2. ACTIONS OF GROUPS ON SPACES OF FUNCTIONS 54

2.1 Action of a group G on $C_c(G,Y)$ 55

2.2 Action of a group G on $C_u(G,Y)$ 59

2.3 Action of a locally compact Hausdorff group G on $L^p(G)$ for $1 \leq p < \infty$ 66

2.4 Weighted translations in $L^2(G)$ 72

CHAPTER II: CATEGORIES OF TOPOLOGICAL TRANSFORMATION GROUPS 83

§3. THE CATEGORIES TTG AND TOP^G. 83

3.1 Limits in TTG. 83

3.2 Limits in TOP^G. 94

3.3 Induced actions. 97

3.4 Colimits in TTG AND TOP^G. 105

§4. SUBCATEGORIES OF TTG 118
4.1 Limits, monomorphisms and epimorphisms 118
4.2 Applications 125
4.3 Reflective subcategories of TTG. 128
4.4 Some particular reflections. 137

§5. K-ACTIONS OF K-GROUPS ON K-SPACES. 150
5.1 General remarks on k-spaces and k-groups 150
5.2 The category k-TTG 155
5.3 The category k-KR^G. 161

§6. THE CATEGORIES TTG_* AND k-TTG_* 164
6.1 The category TTG_*. 164
6.2 The category k-TTG_*. 171
6.3 Actions of locally compact Hausdorff groups. 180
6.4 Cogenerators in TTG_* 184

CHAPTER III: COMPREHENSIVE OBJECTS AND LINEARIZATIONS 189

§7. COMPREHENSIVE OBJECTS IN TOP^G. 189
7.1 General remarks. 190
7.2 The comprehensive object $\langle G, C_c(G\times G, X_0), \tilde{r}\rangle$. 194
7.3 Compactifications of G-spaces 205

§8. LINEARIZATION OF ACTIONS 213
8.1 General remarks on linearization 214
8.2 Strict linearizations in Fréchet spaces and in Hilbert spaces. 216

APPENDIX A Pseudocompactness for topological groups. 226

APPENDIX B Weight functions on sigma-compact locally compact Hausdorff groups. 229

APPENDIX C The weight of $C_c(X)$ 234

BIBLIOGRAPHY. 236

INDEX. 246

LIST OF SYMBOLS. 250

CHAPTER I
BASICAL CONCEPTS

0 - PREREQUISITES

Although all terminology and notation in this treatise will be essentially standard, we inevitably have to include some notational conventions and state some known facts for easy reference. In subsection 0.1 some general remarks about notation are made. Then, in subsections 0.2, 0.3 and 0.4 we collect some notions from topology, topological groups and category theory, respectively. Here the choice of what has been inserted is mainly governed by the desire to avoid as much as possible repetitions of similar arguments. This principle is responsible for a number of trivial remarks in subsections 0.2, 0.3 and 0.4. Sometimes this tendency to unification will give rise to slightly sophisticated proofs in the main text, or to references which are, strictly speaking, superfluous. In addition, we tried to make this treatise as self-contained as possible by limitation of the number of text-books and research papers which are referred to in the main text. A few specialized topics are dealt with in appendices.

0.1. General remarks and conventions

The following logical symbols will be used: $\Rightarrow$ (implication), $\Leftrightarrow$ (equivalence), & (conjunction), $\exists$ (existential quantifier), $\forall$ (universal quantifier). In order to reduce the number of parentheses, we shall often write $\forall x,y \in X$ instead of $\forall (x,y) \in X\times X$, and $\forall x : \Phi(x)$ instead of $\forall x[\Phi(x)]$. The sign $\vdots$ is read "such that"; if it immediately precedes a quantifier, it will be omitted.

Expressions like $P := Q$ or $Q =: P$ are used when the expression Q defines P.

Next we make some agreements with respect to sets and functions. In the following list, A, X and Y denote sets.

$A \subset X$	:	A is a proper subset of X;
$A \subseteq X$	:	$A \subset X$ or $A = X$;
$X \sim A$	:	$= \{x \in X \,\vdots\, x \notin A\}$;
1_X	:	identity mapping on X;
$\|X\|$	:	the cardinality of the set X.

If f is a function on X with values in Y, we write $f\colon X \to Y$ or $x \mapsto f(x)\colon X \to Y$. We shall use the following terminology when $f\colon X \to Y$ is a function:

domain of f	:	X;
codomain of f	:	Y;
$f(x)$, $f[x]$, fx	:	value of f at $x \in X$;
range of f	:	$f[X] := \{f(x) \,\vdots\, x \in X\}$;
image of A under f	:	$f[A] := \{f(x) \,\vdots\, x \in A\}$;
inverse image of Z under f	:	$f^{\leftarrow}[Z] := \{x \in X \,\vdots\, f(x) \in Z\}$;
restriction of f to A	:	$f\|_A\colon A \to Y$.

If $f\colon X \to Y$ is a function and $A \subseteq X$, then for typographical reasons the restriction of f to A will sometimes be denoted $f\colon A \to Y$. We shall not introduce a special notation for corestrictions. If we wish to consider a corestriction, we shall use phrases like "consider $f\colon X \to Z$" (corestriction to $Z \subseteq Y$), or "consider $f\colon A \to Z$" (restriction to $A \subseteq X$ and corestriction to $Z \subseteq Y$, where $f[A] \subseteq Z$).

Compositions of functions are denoted $f \circ g$ or fg; to be sure, if $f\colon X \to Y$ and $g\colon Z \to X$, then $f \circ g(z) := f(g(z))$ for $z \in Z$.

If $\pi\colon X \times Y \to Z$ is a function then for each $(x,y) \in X \times Y$ we write

$$\pi^x(y) := \pi(x,y) =: \pi_y(x).$$

Obviously this convention defines functions $\pi^x\colon Y \to Z$ and $\pi_y\colon X \to Z$.

The cartesian product of a family $\{X_j \,\vdots\, j \in J\}$ of sets will be denoted by $\mathbb{P}\{X_j \,\vdots\, j \in J\}$ or simply $\mathbb{P}_j X_j$; its elements are denoted by $(x_j)_j$. Notations like $\Pi_j X_j$ are reserved for products (in the categorical sense) in the category under consideration.

Some fixed symbols denoting sets are:

$\mathbb{C}$	:	the set of complex numbers;
$\mathbb{R}$	:	the set of real numbers;
$\mathbb{Z}$	:	the set of all integers;
$\mathbb{N}$	:	$= \{n \,\vdots\, n \in \mathbb{Z}\ \&\ n \geq 1\}$;
$\mathbb{Q}$	:	the set of rational numbers;

$\mathbb{T}$: $= \{z \,\vdots\, z\in\mathbb{C} \;\&\; |z|=1\}$;

$\mathbb{F}$: the unspecified scalar field of a vector space (in this treatise, always $\mathbb{F} = \mathbb{R}$ or $\mathbb{F} = \mathbb{C}$).

Parts of the text)1 between braces can be skipped without further ado. Braces are also used to indicate alternative reading: if in a certain passage there are several pairs of braces, then all these pairs can be replaced by the word "respectively". Thus the phrase "if P{Q} then R{S}" means "if P, resp. Q, then R, resp. S".

0.2. Topology

0.2.1. In this section we embody some definitions and notational conventions which are not universally agreed upon. Otherwise, the reader is referred to [Bo], [Du] or [En].

In general a topological space $(X,\mathcal{T})$, i.e. a set X endowed with a topology $\mathcal{T}$, will be denoted only by the symbol X. A similar convention holds for uniform spaces. Some notations (where $A \subseteq X$ and $x \in X$):

$\mathcal{T}\text{-cl}_X(A)$, $\text{cl}_X(A)$, $\text{cl}(A)$: closure of A in $(X,\mathcal{T})$,
$\mathcal{T}\text{-int}_X(A)$, $\text{int}_X(A)$, $\text{int}(A)$: interior of A in $(X,\mathcal{T})$,
neighbourhood of A {of x} : a set $U \subseteq X$ with $A \subseteq \text{int}(U)$ $\{x \in \text{int}(U)\}$,
$\mathcal{V}_A$ $:= \{U \,\vdots\, U\subseteq X \;\&\; A\subseteq\text{int}(U)\}$,
$\mathcal{V}_x$ $:= \{U \,\vdots\, U\subseteq X \;\&\; x\in\text{int}(U)\}$.

Our use of the concepts *regular, completely regular, normal, paracompact, compact* and *locally compact* is, that they do *not* incorporate the T_1-separation axiom. So T_3 = regular&T_1, $T_{3\frac{1}{2}}$ = completely regular&T_1, T_4 = normal&T_1. A $T_{3\frac{1}{2}}$-space will also be called a *Tychonov space*. In contradistinction to the above convention, a *k-space* will always be assumed to be a Hausdorff space. Thus, a k-space is just the same as a *compactly generated space* in the terminology of [ML].

0.2.2. For easy reference we present here some well-known properties of continuous functions with respect to compactness. The proofs are completely standard, hence they are omitted:

)1 Here, of course, mathematical formulae have to be excluded.

Let X, Y *and* Z *be topological spaces, let* $f\colon X\times Y\to Z$ *be a continuous function, and let* A *and* B *be compact subsets of* X *and* Y, *respectively. Then:*

(i) $\forall W\in \mathcal{V}_{f[A\times B]}\ \ \exists (U,V)\in \mathcal{V}_A\times\mathcal{V}_B : f[U\times V]\subseteq W.$

(ii) *If the topology of* Z *is generated by a uniformity* $\mathcal{U}$, *then for all* $y\in Y$ *and* $\gamma\in\mathcal{U}$ *there exists* $V\in\mathcal{V}_y$ *such that*

$$(f(x,y),f(x,v))\in\gamma \quad \textit{for all } x\in A \textit{ and } v\in V.$$

Thus, $\{f^x : x\in A\}$ *is an equicontinuous set of mappings on* Y.

0.2.3. If T_1 and T_2 are topologies on a set X then we say that T_2 is *finer* than T_1 (or T_1 is *weaker* than T_2) if $T_1\subseteq T_2$.

If X is a set and if for each $i\in J$ we have a mapping $f_i\colon X\to Y_i$ (J a set, each Y_i a topological space), then the *weak topology* defined by the mappings f_i is, by definition, the weakest topology on X making each f_i continuous. If X is endowed with this weak topology, then it is well-known that for any topological space Z, a mapping $g\colon Z\to X$ is continuous iff $f_i g\colon Z\to Y_i$ is continuous for each $i\in J$.

The "dual" notion of a weak topology is the finest topology on a set X making all members of a set of functions $f_i\colon Y_i\to X$ continuous (each Y_i a topological space). Then a function $g\colon X\to Z$ is continuous iff each $gf_i\colon Y_i\to Z$ is (Z any topological space).

In this context it is useful to recall that a continuous surjection $f\colon X\to Z$ is called a *quotient mapping* if the topology of Z is the finest one making f continuous.

0.2.4. Let X and Y be topological spaces, R and S equivalence relations on X and Y, respectively, and let $r\colon X\to X/R$, $s\colon Y\to Y/S$ denote the quotient mappings. Then $R\times S := \{((x,y),(x',y')) : (x,x')\in R \ \& \ (y,y')\in S\}$ is an equivalence relation on $X\times Y$, and there is an obvious bijection $f\colon X\times Y/R\times S \to (X/R)\times(Y/S)$ such that $fq = r\times s$, q denoting the quotient mapping of $X\times Y$ onto $X\times Y/R\times S$. Plainly, f is continous. Moreover, it is easy to see that f is a homeomorphism iff $r\times s : X\times Y\to (X/R)\times(Y/S)$ is a quotient mapping. Now a repeated application of the lemma below shows the following:

If r *and* s *are either open or perfect (one of them open and the other perfect*[1] *is also allowed) then* $r\times s$ *is a quotient mapping, and* f *is a*

[1] A *perfect* mapping is what [Bo] calls a *proper* mapping: a continuous function $f\colon X\to Y$ is perfect whenever it is closed and, in addition, each fiber $f^{\leftarrow}[y]$ is compact ($y\in Y$).

homeomorphism. This holds true also if the codomain of one of the maps r *and* s *and the domain of the other one are locally compact Hausdorff spaces.*

Incidentally, conditions implying that a quotient space is T_2 are given in [Du], Chap. VII, 1.6 and 1.7; cf. also [En], Theorem 2.4.5.

LEMMA. *Let* $f: X \to Y$ *be a quotient mapping and let* Z *be any topological space. Each of the following conditions implies that* $1_Z \times f: Z \times X \to Z \times Y$ *is a quotient mapping:*

(i) f *is an open mapping;*

(ii) f *is a perfect mapping;*

(iii) Z *is a locally compact* T_2*-space;*

(iv) $Z \times Y$ *is a* k*-space.*

PROOF. We give only brief indications or references to proofs.

(i): This is easy (cf. [Bo], Chap. I, §5.3, Cor. to Prop. 8).

(ii): This is a straightforward application of 0.2.2(i). Alternatively, by [Bo], Chap. I, §10.1, Prop. 4, $1_Z \times f$ is perfect, hence a quotient mapping.

(iii): Cf. [Du], Chap. XII, 4.1.

(iv): Replace in the proof referred to in (iii) the application of [Du], Chap. XII, Theorem 3.1 by its Corollary 3.2. Alternatively, see the proof of Theorem 4.4 in N.E. STEENROD [1967]. □

0.2.5. The following example shows that $1_Z \times f$ is not necessarily a quotient mapping if f is. There exist other examples in the literature, but we shall need this particular example, where Z is a topological group.

Take $Z := \mathbb{Q}$, with its usual topology. Let $X := [0,1] \times \mathbb{N}$, and let $Y := X/R$, where R is the equivalence relation defined by

$$((x,n),(x',n')) \in R \Leftrightarrow \begin{cases} \text{either } x = x',\ n = n' \\ \text{or } \quad x = x' = 0. \end{cases}$$

So X is a countable disjoint union of unit intervals, and Y consists of a countable set of unit intervals with a common begin point p. Let $f: X \to Z$ denote the quotient mapping[1], and let Y be given the quotient topology. We claim that on $\mathbb{Q} \times Y$ the quotient topology induced by $1_{\mathbb{Q}} \times f : \mathbb{Q} \times X \to \mathbb{Q} \times Y$ is strictly finer than the product topology on $\mathbb{Q} \times Y$. Thus, with this product topology on $\mathbb{Q} \times Y$, $1_{\mathbb{Q}} \times f$ is not a quotient mapping.

---

[1] Thus, $p = f(0,n)$ for all $n \in \mathbb{N}$.

{Indication of proof: for each $n \in \mathbb{N}$, take as $V_n \subset \mathbb{Q}\times[0,1]$ the set that can be pictured as follows:

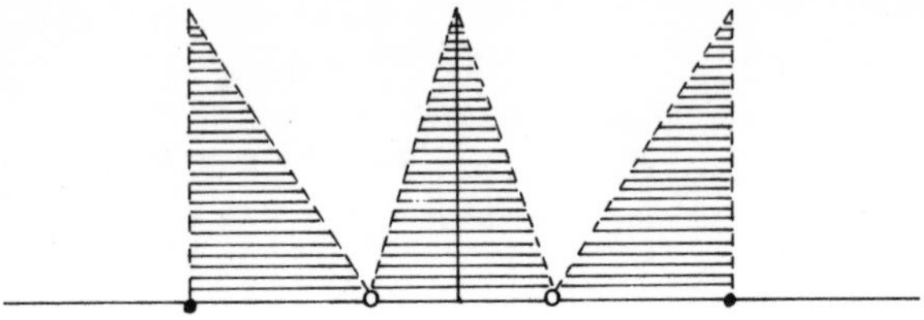

Identifying $\mathbb{Q}\times X$ with $(\mathbb{Q}\times[0,1])\times\mathbb{N}$, we see that the set $V := \{(t,x,n) \,\vdots\, n\in\mathbb{N}\ \&\ (t,x)\in V_n\}$ is open in $\mathbb{Q}\times X$. Since $(1_{\mathbb{Q}}\times f)^{\leftarrow}(1_{\mathbb{Q}}\times f)[V] = V$, it follows that $(1_{\mathbb{Q}}\times f)[V]$ is a neighbourhood of the point $(0,p)$ in $\mathbb{Q}\times Y$ with respect to the quotient topology induced by $1_{\mathbb{Q}}\times f$. However, if it were a neighbourhood of this point in the product topology, then there would be a real number $a > 0$ and an open subset W of Y such that $\{t\in\mathbb{Q} \,\vdots\, -a < t < a\} \times f^{\leftarrow}[W] \subseteq V$. But this is impossible.}

0.2.6. Let X and Y be topological spaces. Then $\mathbf{C}(X,Y)$ shall denote the set of all continuous functions on X with values in Y. In this set we shall consider the following topologies:

(i) The *point-open topology*: this is the weakest topology in $\mathbf{C}(X,Y)$ making each evaluation $\delta_x\colon f \mapsto f(x)\colon \mathbf{C}(X,Y)\to Y$ continuous $(x\in X)$, i.e. it is the relative topology of $\mathbf{C}(X,Y)$ in Y^X with its product topology. If $\mathbf{C}(X,Y)$ is endowed with this topology, we write $\mathbf{C}_p(X,Y)$.

(ii) The *compact-open topology:* This is the topology having as a subbase all sets of the form

$$N(K,U) := \{f \,\vdots\, f\in\mathbf{C}(X,Y)\ \&\ f[K]\subseteq U\},$$

where $K\subseteq X$ is compact and $U\subseteq Y$ is open. If $\mathbf{C}(X,Y)$ is endowed with this topology, we write $\mathbf{C}_c(X,Y)$.

If the topology in Y is generated by a uniformity $\mathcal{U}$, then the topology of $\mathbf{C}_c(X,Y)$ is generated by the uniformity in $\mathbf{C}(X,Y)$ having as a subbase all sets of the form

$$M(K,\alpha) := \{(f,g)\in\mathbf{C}(X,Y)\times\mathbf{C}(X,Y) \,\vdots\, (f(x),g(x))\in\alpha \text{ for all } x\in K\},$$

where $K\subseteq X$ is compact and $\alpha\in\mathcal{U}$. In this case, a local base at $f\in\mathbf{C}_c(X,Y)$ is formed by the family of all sets $M(K,\alpha)[f]$ (K and α as before). For simplicity, we shall use the following notation:

$$U_f(K,\alpha) := M(K,\alpha)[f]$$
$$= \{g \in C(X,Y) : (f(x),g(x)) \in \alpha \text{ for all } x \in K\}.$$

(iii) The *topology of uniform convergence:* Y is supposed to be a uniform space with uniformity $\mathcal{U}$, and the topology under consideration is the one generated by the uniformity in $C(X,Y)$ having as a subbase the family of all sets $M(X,\alpha)$ with $\alpha \in \mathcal{U}$ (where $M(X,\alpha)$ is defined as in (ii) with $K = X$). If $C(X,Y)$ is endowed with this topology, we shall write $C_u(X,Y)$.

If $A \subseteq C(X,Y)$, then we shall always write A_p, A_c or A_u if we consider the point-open topology, the compact-open topology or the topology of uniform convergence on A, respectively.[1] Sometimes, this notation will slightly be modified. Thus, we write $C^*_p(X,Y)$, $C^*_c(X,Y)$, etc. instead of $(C^*(X,Y))_p$, $(C^*(X,Y))_c$, etc. Here $C^*(X,Y)$ is defined as follows:

$$C^*(X,Y) := \{f \in C(X,Y) : cl_Y f[X] \text{ is compact}\}.$$

0.2.7. If X, Y and Z are topological spaces, then we shall need several times the following facts. For proofs, cf. [Du], Chap. XII.

(i) If Y is *locally compact Hausdorff*, then the composition-mapping

$$\omega:(f,g) \mapsto f\circ g : C_c(Y,Z)\times C_c(X,Y) \to C_c(X,Z)$$

is continuous. If Y is not locally compact, then ω is separately continuous.

(ii) If Y is *locally compact Hausdorff*, then the evaluation mapping

$$\delta:(f,y) \mapsto f(y) : C_c(Y,Z)\times Y \to Z$$

is continuous.[2]

(iii) If $f \in C(X\times Y,Z)$, then the mapping

$$\bar{f}:x \mapsto f^x: X \to C_c(Y,Z)$$

is continuous.[3] Conversely, *if either* Y *is locally compact* T_2 *or* $X\times Y$ *is a k-space* and $f: X\times Y\to Z$ is any function such that $f^x \in C_c(Y,Z)$ for all $x \in X$, then continuity of $\bar{f}:x \mapsto f^x:X \to C_c(Y,Z)$ implies that $f \in C(X\times Y,Z)$. In addition, then the mapping

---

[1] Equations like $A_p = A_c$ express that the corresponding topologies on A coincide.

[2] This result is an immediate consequence of (iii) below.

[3] This is an easy corollary of 0.2.2(i).

$$f \mapsto \bar{f}: C_c(X\times Y,Z) \to C_c(X,C_c(Y,Z))$$

is a homeomorphism; in particular, it is a bijection.

Concerning (ii) above we have to make the following remark, which is due to R. ARENS [1946b]: *if* Y *is completely regular and* $\delta:(f,y)\mapsto f(y)$: $C_c(Y,[0,1])\times Y \to [0,1]$ *is continuous, then* Y *is locally compact*. A close examination of the proof reveals that $C(Y,[0,1])$ can be replaced by any of its subsets which separates points and closed subsets of Y. Consequently, if Y is a uniform space with uniformity $\mathcal{U}$, and if $UC(Y,[0,1])$ denotes the set of all uniformly continuous functions from Y into [0,1], then the lemma below can be used in order to prove that *continuity of the restricted evaluation* δ: $UC_c(Y,[0,1])\times Y \to [0,1]$ *already implies that* Y *is locally compact*.

<u>LEMMA</u>. *Let* Y *be a uniform space. Then for any* $y \in Y$ *and any closed set* $S \subseteq Y$ *such that* $y \notin S$ *there exists* $f \in UC(Y,[0,1])$ *such that* $f(y) = 1$ *and* $f(s) = 0$ *for all* $s \in S$.

<u>PROOF</u>. Cf. [Is], Theorem I.13. One may also have a close examination of the proof of Cor. 3 to [En], Theorem 8.1.4. Cf. also [Ke], Th. 6.15. □

0.2.8. It will be convenient to have the following well-known statements at hand, leading up to a proof of the ASCOLI theorem. Let X be any topological space and let Y be a uniform space. Then:

(i) If $A \subseteq C(X,Y)$ is equicontinuous at $x \in X$, then the closure of A in Y^X is equicontinuous at x as well.

(ii) If $A \subseteq C(X,Y)$ is equicontinuous on X, then $A_p = A_c$.

(iii) If $A \subseteq C(X,Y)$ satisfies the condition that

$$x \in X \Rightarrow A \text{ equicontinuous at } x \;\&\; cl_Y A[x] \text{ is compact},$$

then the closure of A in $C_c(X,Y)$ is compact. In this situation the closure of A in $C_c(X,Y)$ equals the closure of A in Y^X and the point-open and compact-open topologies coincide on it.

There is a converse to (iii), namely the following one: if X has the property that the evaluation mapping δ: $C_c(X,Y)\times X \to Y$ is continuous on all sets $B \times X$, where B is a compact subset of $C_c(X,Y)$, then every relatively compact subset A of $C_c(X,Y)$ satisfies the condition in (iii). {In fact, only equicontinuity of A needs a proof, and this is just 0.2.2(ii).}

Notice that the above mentioned condition on X is fulfilled if X is a *locally compact* T_2*-space, or more generally, if* X *is a k-space:* then $B \times X$ is a k-space for every compact $B \subseteq C_c(X,Y)$ (cf. [Du], Chap. XII, Th. 4.4), so that 0.2.7(iii) gives the desired result[1].

0.2.9. Let $\mathbb{F}$ denote either $\mathbb{R}$ or $\mathbb{C}$. Then we shall write $C(X) := C(X,\mathbb{F})$ and $C^*(X) := C^*(X,\mathbb{F})$ for any topological space X. Thus, $C^*(X)$ is just the set of bounded continuous $\mathbb{F}$-valued functions on X. The topology in $C^*_u(X)$ is generated by the norm $\|..\|_X$. Here we define, for each $A \subseteq X$ and $f \in C^*(X)$,

$$\|f\|_A := \sup\{|f(x)| : x \in A\};$$

instead of $\|..\|_X$ we write mostly $\|..\|$.

If $f \in C(X)$, then the *support* of f is defined to be $supp(f) := cl_X\{x : x \in X \ \&\ f(x) \neq 0\}$. The following subspace of $C^*(X)$ will be of importance to us: $C_{00}(X) := \{f \in C(X) : supp(f) \text{ is compact}\}$.

0.2.10. A *cardinal invariant* in topology is an assignment of a cardinal number to each topological space in such a way that equal cardinal numbers are assigned to homeomorphic spaces. We shall use the following cardinal invariants: the weight w, the local weight ℓw, the density d and the Lindelöf degree L. They are defined as follows: if X is a topological space, then

the *weight* of X is

$$w(X) := \min\{|\mathcal{B}| : \mathcal{B} \text{ is an open base for } X\};$$

the *local weight of* X *at* x is

$$\ell w(X,x) := \min\{|\mathcal{V}| : \mathcal{V} \text{ is a local base at } x\};$$

the *local weight* of X is

$$\ell w(X) := \sup\{\ell w(X,x) : x \in X\};$$

the *density* of X is

$$d(X) := \min\{|A| : cl\, A = X\};$$

---

[1] See also R.W. BAGLEY & J.S. YANG [1966].

the *Lindelöf degree* of X is

$$L(X) := \min\{\kappa \,\vdots\, \text{each open covering of X has a subcovering of cardinality } \kappa\}.$$

For a systematical treatment of these and other cardinal invariants we refer to [Ju]. However, the following relations are well-known and easy to prove (for (2), see [En], Theorem 1.1.6):

(1) $d(X) \leq w(X) \leq 2^{|X|}$;)1

(2) $L(X) \leq w(X)$;

(3) $d(X)\cdot \ell w(X) \leq w(X)$.

It can be shown by examples that the inequality in (3) may be strict. However, in metrizable spaces X one has always equality in (3).

If A is a *dense* subspace of a T_3-space X, then it is not difficult to prove that $\ell w(A) = \ell w(X)$. In general however, $w(A) \leq w(X)$, and $d(A) \geq d(X)$. Consequently, $d(X)\cdot \ell w(X) \leq d(A)\cdot \ell w(A) \leq w(A) \leq w(X)$. If X is metrizable, then $d(X)\cdot \ell w(X) = w(X)$, and we obtain the following result:

If A *is a dense subspace of a metrizable space* X, *then* $w(A) = w(X)$.

0.3. Topological groups

0.3.1. For all basical knowledge about topological groups we refer to [HR], Vol. I, or to [Bo], Chap. III. In particular, results from [HR], §1-§8 will be used mostly without explicit reference. Some notational conventions in a topological group G which we shall use:

e_G, e	: the unit of G;
$\lambda(G)$, λ	: the multiplication mapping $(s,t) \mapsto st$: $G\times G \to G$;
G_d	: the group G endowed with its discrete topology;
G/H{G\H}	: the space of all right {left} cosets of a subgroup H of G.

Note the difference between the expressions G\H and $G \sim H$ (cf. 0.1).

)1 In locally compact T_2-spaces X one has even $w(X) \leq |X|$; cf. [En], Theorem 3.6.9. See also [Ju], 2.2.

0.3.2. The *left uniformity* in a topological group G is the uniformity generated by all sets of the form $\{(s,t) \in G\times G : s^{-1}t \in U\}$ with $U \in \mathcal{V}_e$. The topology of G is generated by its left uniformity. Similarly, the *right uniformity* is the uniformity generated by all sets $\{(s,t) \in G\times G : st^{-1} \in U\}$ with $U \in \mathcal{V}_e$. The right uniformity of G is also compatible with the topology of G. In general, the left and the right uniformity in a topological group do not coincide.

We shall use these uniformities mainly in order to introduce the following classes of functions. Let X be a uniform space with uniformity $\mathcal{U}$. Then a function f: G→X is said to be *left{right} uniformly continuous* whenever it is uniformly continuous with respect to the left{right} uniformity on G. The set of all left{right} uniformly continuous functions on G to X is denoted LUC(G,X) {RUC(G,X)}. Thus, if f: G→X is a function, then $f \in$ LUC(G,X) iff

$$\forall \alpha \in \mathcal{U},\ \exists U \in \mathcal{V}_e \ : \ s^{-1}t \in U \Rightarrow (f(s),f(t)) \in \alpha,$$

and $f \in$ RUC(G,X) iff

$$\forall \alpha \in \mathcal{U},\ \exists U \in \mathcal{V}_e \ : \ st^{-1} \in U \Rightarrow (f(s),f(t)) \in \alpha.$$

We write LUC(G) and RUC(G) instead of LUC(G,$\mathbb{F}$) and RUC(G,$\mathbb{F}$), where $\mathbb{F}$ is either $\mathbb{R}$ or $\mathbb{C}$. In addition, $LUC^*(G,X) := LUC(G,X) \cap C^*(G,X)$ and similarly, $RUC^*(G,X) := RUC(G,X) \cap C^*(G,X)$.

0.3.3. We shall use integration theory on locally compact Hausdorff groups with respect to Haar measure. Here we shall follow [HR], Chap. II, III. Some notations and conventions about this topic will be presented in 2.3.1.

Only a modest amount of knowledge is required about this topic: we need existence of Haar measure and some elementary facts from integration theory, up to the FUBINI theorem and the LEBESGUE theorem on interchangeability of limits and integrals.

In this context, a certain knowledge of functional analysis is needed. For this, we refer to [Sc] or [HR], Appendix B. The following notation will be used: if X is a Banach space, then L(X) {GL(X)} denotes the set of all bounded {invertible bounded} linear operators on X.

0.4. Category theory

0.4.1. For all undefined notions from category theory the reader is referred to [ML], the first six chapters. One of the most notable conventions is, that the set of all morphisms with domain X and codomain Y in a category **LTG** is denoted **LTG**(X,Y). No rule without exceptions, and the most important one here is the category **TOP**, where morphism sets are denoted C(X,Y). Other deviations from the notation used in [ML] are the shape of certain arrows (we use only →, also if [ML] writes ⇀ or ↛) and brackets (e.g. we denote monads with (H,η,μ) where [ML] writes $\langle H,\eta,\mu\rangle$, etc.). However, the author believes that this will cause no confusion. Yet another deviation from [ML] is that by a *diagram* we always understand a *small* diagram. Consequently, our term {*co*}*complete* means *small* {co}complete.

For the reader's convenience, we present here a listing of the categories which we shall use frequently:

SET : Objects, all (small) sets; morphisms, all functions between them.

TOP : Objects, all topological spaces; morphisms, all continuous functions between them.

HAUS : Full subcategory of **TOP** with as its objects all Hausdorff spaces.

COMP : Full subcategory of **HAUS** with as its objects all compact Hausdorff spaces.

KR : Full subcategory of **HAUS** determined by all k-spaces.

GRP : Objects, all groups; morphisms, all homomorphisms.

TOPGRP : Objects, all topological groups; morphisms, all continuous morphisms of groups.

HAUSGRP : The full subcategory of **TOPGRP** determined by all Hausdorff groups.

COMPGRP : The full subcategory of **HAUSGRP** determined by all compact Hausdorff groups.

KRGRP : cf. 5.1.7 for its definition.

0.4.2. For easy reference we present here some of the various equivalent formulations of adjointness (cf. also [ML], pp. 78-81).

Let **A** and **X** be categories. An *adjunction from* **X** *to* **A** is a triple (F,G,φ), where $F: \mathbf{X} \to \mathbf{A}$ and $G: \mathbf{A} \to \mathbf{X}$ are functors, while φ is a function which assigns to each pair of objects $X \in \mathbf{X}$, $A \in \mathbf{A}$ a bijection

$$(1) \qquad \varphi_{X,A}: \mathbf{A}(FX,A) \to \mathbf{X}(X,GA)$$

which is natural in X and A. Given such an adjunction, the functor F is said to have a *right adjoint* G, and G is said to have a *left adjoint* F. The following characterizations of adjointness will be used:

(i) A functor $G: A \to X$ has a left adjoint F iff for each object $X \in X$ there exist an object $F_0X \in A$ and a *universal arrow* $\eta_X: X \to GF_0X$ from X to G. This means that η_X is a morphism in X such that for every object $A \in A$ and every morphism $f: X \to GA$ in X there exists a *unique* morphism f' in A such that the following diagram commutes:

(2)

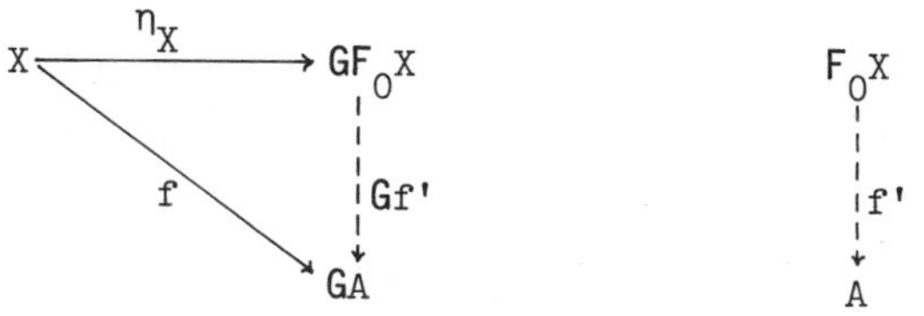

{Then the functor F has object function F_0; F can be defined on a morphism $h: X \to Y$ in X, using universality of η_X, in such a way that $G(Fh) \circ \eta_X = \eta_Y \circ h$. Obviously, the morphisms η_X for $X \in X$ are the components of a natural transformation $\eta: I_X \to GF$.}

(ii) A functor $F: X \to A$ has a right adjoint G iff for each object $A \in A$ there exist an object $G_0A \in X$ and a universal arrow $\varepsilon_A: FG_0A \to A$ from F to A. This means that ε_A is a morphism in A such that for every object $X \in X$ and every morphism $g: FX \to A$ in A there exists a *unique* morphism g' in X making the following diagram commutative:

(3)

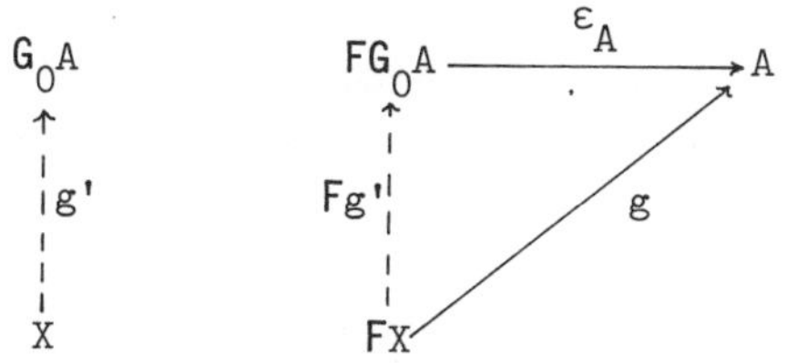

In this way, a natural transformation $\varepsilon: FG \to I_A$ is obtained.

In the above situations, φ and $\varphi^{\leftarrow}$ can be determined either by

(4) $$\varphi_{X,A}g = Gg \circ \eta_X: X \to GA$$

if $g: FX \to A$, or by

(5) $\varphi^{\leftarrow}_{X,A} f = \varepsilon_A \circ Ff\colon FX \to A$

if $f\colon X \to GA$. In fact, in diagram (2) we have $f' = \varphi^{\leftarrow}_{X,A} f$, and in diagram (3), $g' = \varphi_{X,A} g$.

The natural transformations η and ε are called the *unit* and the *counit* of the adjunction. The adjunction (F,G,φ) will often be denoted (F,G,η,ε).

0.4.3. If A is a subcategory of X and the inclusion functor $G\colon A \to X$ has a left adjoint F, then A is called a *reflective subcategory* of X. If η is the unit of adjunction, then for each $X \in X$, $\eta_X\colon X \to GFX$ is called *the reflection of* X *in* A (in concrete categories, the inclusion functor G is usually suppressed here). If E is a class of epimorphisms in X and each η_X is in E, then A is called an *E-reflective subcategory of* X.

We wish to formulate a theorem giving sufficient conditions for a subcategory A of a "nice" category X to be reflective. Let E{M} denote a class of epimorphisms {monomorphisms} in X that is closed under composition with isomorphisms. Then X is said to have *the E-M-factorization property* whenever each morphism f in X factorizes as $f = m e$ with $m \in M$ and $e \in E$. The category X is said to be *co-E-small* whenever for each object $X \in X$ there exists a subset E_X of E with the property that for each $e' \in E$ with domain X there are an element $e \in E_X$ and an isomorphism f in X such that $e' = f e$. Finally, a subcategory A of X is said to be *closed under the formation of M-subobjects {of products}* in X provided for each $m\colon X \to A$ in M the condition $A \in A$ implies $X \in A$ {each product in X of A-objects is again in A}. Now the following theorem can be proved (cf. [He], 10.2.2(c); see also [HS], 37.1):

<u>THEOREM</u>. *Let* A *be a full subcategory of* X *closed under isomorphisms in* X. *Let* E *and* M *be as above and suppose that* X *is co-E-small and has the E-M-factorization property. Assume that* X *has all products and consider the following conditions:*

(i) A *is E-reflective in* X.

(ii) A *is closed under the formation of products and M-subobjects in* X.

Then always (ii) ⇒ (i). *If, in addition, the E-M-factorization is unique (up to isomorphism) and if both* E *and* M *are closed under compositions, then we have also* (i) ⇒ (ii).

<u>PROOF</u>. (outline).

(i) ⇒ (ii): That A is closed under the formation of M-subobjects in X follows from [HS], 36.13. For products, cf. 0.4.4 below.

(ii) $\Rightarrow$ (i): Since X is co-$\mathcal{E}$-small, there exists for any $X \in \mathsf{X}$ a set $\mathcal{E}_X$ with the above mentioned property. For $f \in \mathcal{E}_X$, let A_f be the codomain of f. Let $A_0 := \Pi\{A_f \,\vdots\, f \in \mathcal{E}_X \;\&\; A_f \in \mathsf{A}\}$ (product in X). The induced morphism $g\colon X \to A_0$ admits an $\mathcal{E}$-$\mathcal{M}$-factorization, say $X \xrightarrow{e} A_1 \xrightarrow{m} A_0$. Then $e\colon X \to A_1$ is the desired reflection of X in A. □

Of course, the above theorem is an extension of the FREYD adjoint functor theorem for the particular case of an inclusion functor. The condition of co-$\mathcal{E}$-smallness replaces the "solution set condition" in FREYD's theorem. Cf. [ML], p.117.

0.4.4. For easy reference we collect here some preservation and reflection properties of functors. First, notice that monomorphisms and limits are related in the following way: a morphism $f\colon X \to Y$ in a category X is monic iff

(6) $$\begin{array}{ccc} X & \xrightarrow{1_X} & X \\ {\scriptstyle 1_X}\big\downarrow & & \\ X & & \end{array} \qquad \text{is a limiting cone for} \qquad \begin{array}{ccc} & & X \\ & & \big\downarrow{\scriptstyle f} \\ X & \xrightarrow{f} & Y \end{array}$$

Thus, if a functor preserves all limits, it preserves all monomorphisms. Similar for colimits and epimorphisms.

Now let $F\colon \mathsf{X} \to \mathsf{A}$ be a functor. Then the following statements can be proved:

(i) If F is faithful, it reflects monomorphisms and epimorphisms. Cf. [Pa], Lemma 1 in Section 2.12.[1]

(ii) If F has a left{right} adjoint, it preserves all limits and monomorphisms {all colimits and all epimorphisms}. Cf. [ML], Chap. V, §5, Th. 1.

(iii) Suppose F is left adjoint to a full and faithful functor $G\colon \mathsf{A} \to \mathsf{X}$. If $D\colon \mathsf{J} \to \mathsf{A}$ is a diagram such that the diagram $GD\colon \mathsf{J} \to \mathsf{X}$ has a limit {colimit} in X, then D has a limit {colimit} in A. Cf. [Pa], Prop. 4 in Section 2.14. A straightforward proof can easily be given, using the fact that in the given situation $\varepsilon_X\colon FGX \to X$ is an isomorphism in A (ε is the counit of adjunction).

(iv) If D is a diagram in X such that FD has a limit in A, and F creates the limit of D, then F preserves the limit of D (indeed, limits are

[1] In [ML], Exercise 9 on p.21, "carries ... to" should be replaced by "reflects".

unique up to isomorphism). In particular, if F creates all limits and A is complete, then X is complete and F preserves all limits.

As an application of (ii) and (iii) we mention the following well-known statement (cf. also [He], p. 88):

If A *is a full and reflective subcategory of* X, *closed with respect to isomorphisms in* X, *then limits in* A *can be calculated in* X. That is, if a diagram D in A has a limit in X, then this limit is completely included in A, and it is the limit of D in A. Conversely, a limit of D in A is also limit of D in X. *In particular, if* X *is complete then so is* A. *Moreover, if* X *is cocomplete then so is* A (use again (iii)). *In the latter case, the colimit of a diagram in* A *is obtained as the reflection in* A *of the colimit of that diagram in* X.

0.4.5. A *monad* in a category C is a triple (H,η,μ), consisting of a functor $H: C \to C$ and two natural transformations,

$$\eta: I_C \to H; \quad \mu: H^2 \to H,$$

such that the following diagrams commute:

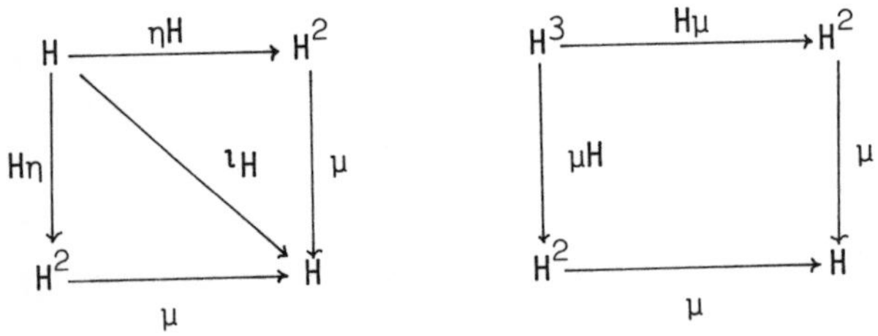

If (F,G,η,ε) is an adjunction from C to a category D, then the *monad, defined by this adjunction* is the monad $(GF,\eta,G\varepsilon F)$ in C (cf. [ML], p.134). The following construction shows that, conversely, every monad is defined by an adjunction. For proofs, we refer the reader to [ML], Chap. VI, §2.

Let (H,η,μ) be a monad in a category C. Then *an* H*-algebra* is a pair (X,π), consisting of an object X in C and a morphism $\pi: HX \to X$ in C such that the following diagrams commute:

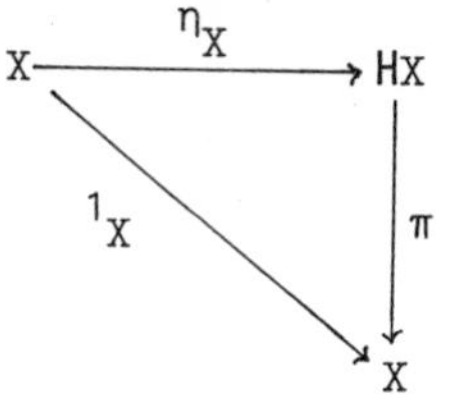

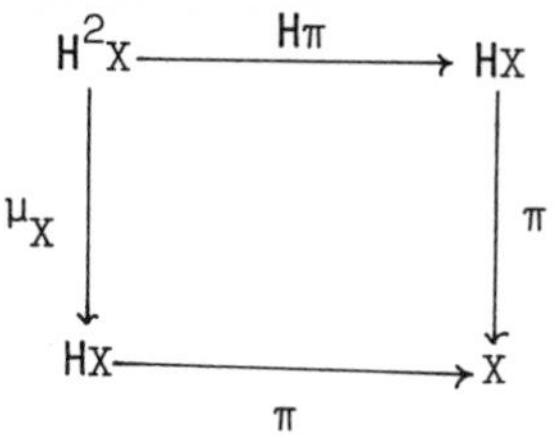

If (X,π) and (Y,σ) are H-algebras, then a morphism $f\colon X \to Y$ in C is called a *morphism of* H-*algebras*, from (X,π) to (Y,σ), whenever the following diagram commutes:

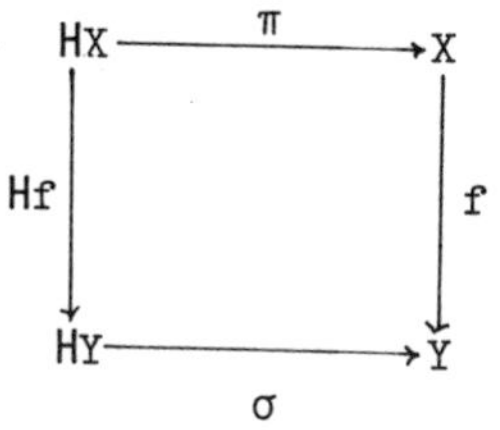

Since composites (in C) of morphisms of H-algebras are again morphisms of H-algebras, it is obvious that in this way we obtain a category: *the category* C^H *of all* H-*algebras*.

There is an obvious "forgetful" functor $G^H\colon C^H \to C$, namely

$$G^H\colon \begin{cases} (X,\pi) \longmapsto X & \text{on objects} \\ f \longmapsto f & \text{on morphisms.} \end{cases}$$

In the other direction, there is a functor $F^H\colon C \to C^H$, defined by

$$F^H\colon \begin{cases} X \longmapsto (HX,\mu_X) & \text{on objects} \\ f \longmapsto Hf & \text{on morphisms.} \end{cases}$$

The H-algebra $F^H X := (HX,\mu_X)$ is called the *free* H-algebra on X. Notice that $G^H \circ F^H = H$. The following theorem can be proved (cf. [ML], p.136):

0.4.6. THEOREM. *The functor* F^H *is left adjoint to* G^H, *and the monad defined by this adjunction is just the original monad* (H,η,μ). □

The *unit* for the adjunction of F^H and G^H is the natural transformation $\eta\colon I_C \to G^H F^H = H$. Its *counit* ξ is given by the morphisms

$$\xi_{(X,\pi)} := \pi\colon (HX,\mu_X) \to (X,\pi)$$

in C^H, for every H-algebra (X,π).

0.4.7. It follows from the preceding theorem that $G^H\colon C^H \to C$ preserves all limits and monomorphisms, and that $F^H\colon C \to C^H$ preserves all colimits and epimorphisms (cf. 0.4.4). For G^H, more can be shown, namely

THEOREM. *The functor* $G^H\colon C^H \to C$ *creates all limits.*

PROOF. Cf. [ML], Exercise 2, p.138. For a detailed proof, the reader is referred to E. MANES [1969 b]. □

If C is complete, then the preceding theorem implies that C^H is complete. In that case, the facts that G^H creates and preserves all limits and that G^H preserves and reflects all monomorphisms may be expressed by saying that *"limits and monomorphisms in* C^H *can be calculated in* C*".*

0.4.8.[)1] Let (H,η,μ) and (H',η',μ') be monads in C. Then a natural transformation $\theta\colon H \to H'$ is called *a morphism of monads, from* (H,η,μ) *to* (H',η',μ') whenever $\theta\eta = \eta'$ and $\theta\mu = \mu'\theta^2$, that is, whenever for each object $X \in C$ the following diagrams commute:

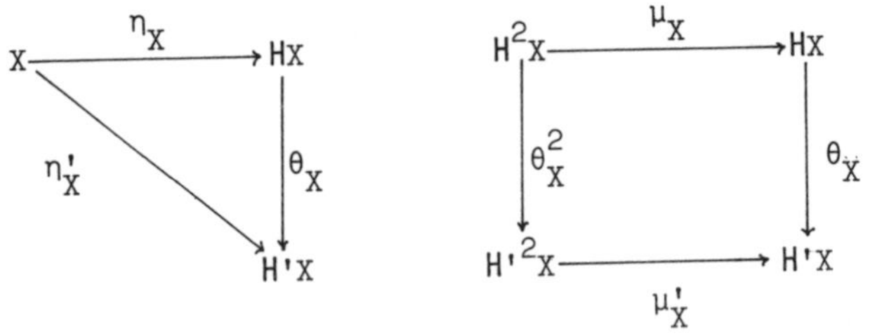

Here θ_X^2 is defined as the dotted arrow in the commutative diagram

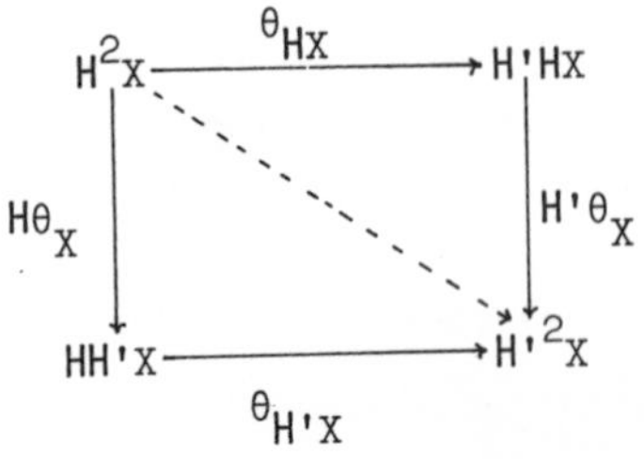

)1 This is Exercise 3 on p.138 in [ML].

If θ is such a morphism of monads from (H,η,μ) to (H',η',μ'), then commutativity of the diagrams

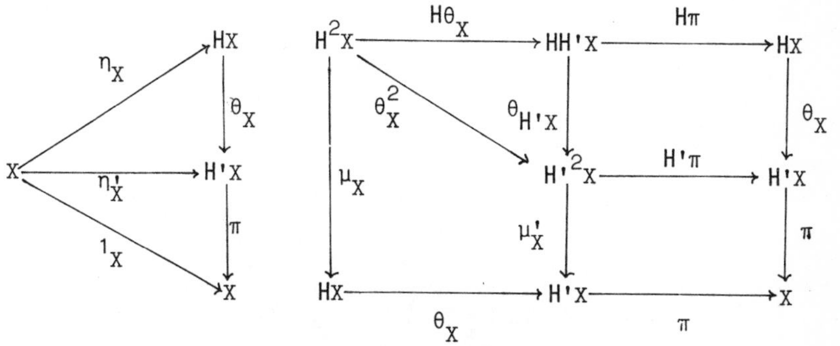

shows that for each H'-algebra (X,π) the morphism $\pi\theta_X$: $HX \to X$ in C is such that $(X,\pi\theta_X)$ is an H-algebra. Moreover, it is easily seen that for each morphism f: $(X,\pi) \to (Y,\sigma)$ of H'-algebras, f may also be interpreted as a morphism of H-algebras, namely, f: $(X,\pi\theta_X) \to (Y,\sigma\theta_Y)$. *So we have a functor* θ^*: $C^{H'} \to C^H$, *defined by the assignments*

$$\theta^*: \begin{cases} (X,\pi) \longmapsto (X,\pi\theta_X) & \text{on objects} \\ f \longmapsto f & \text{on morphisms.} \end{cases}$$

0.4.9. We shall briefly deal with the dual of 0.4.5 through 0.4.7. A *comonad* (H,δ,ε) in a category D consists of a functor H: $D \to D$, together with natural transformations

$$\delta: H \to I_D; \quad \varepsilon: H \to H^2$$

such that the following diagrams commute:

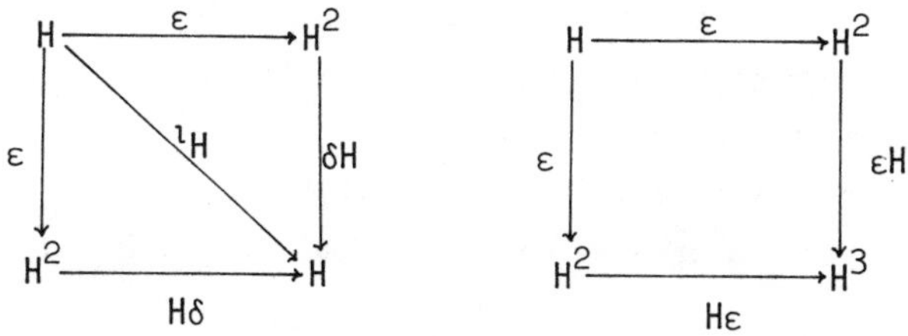

Suppose we are given a pair of functors F: $C \to D$, G: $D \to C$, where F is left adjoint to G with unit ξ: $I_C \to GF$ and counit δ: $FG \to I_D$. *Then* $(FG,\delta,F\xi G)$ *is a comonad in* D.

Furthermore, any comonad (H,δ,ε) in D arises in this way by considering the category D_H of H-*coalgebras*. An object of D_H is a pair (X,σ) with X an object in D and $\sigma\colon X \to HX$ a morphism in D such that the diagrams

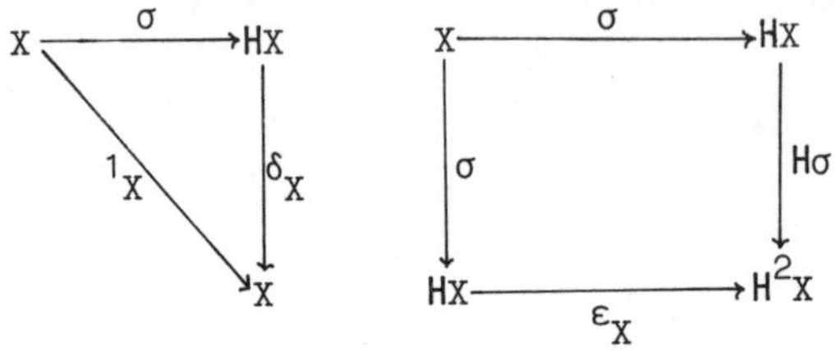

commute. Moreover, morphisms in D_H from (X,σ) to (Y,ζ) are morphisms $f\colon X \to Y$ in D such that

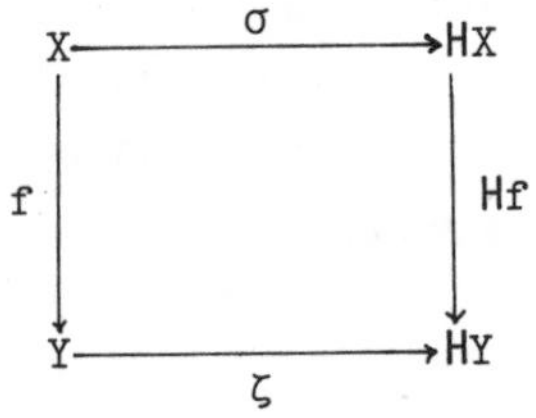

commutes. Next, one defines functors $F_H\colon D_H \to D$ and $G_H\colon D \to D_H$ by

$$F_H\colon \begin{cases} (X,\sigma) \longmapsto X \text{ on objects} \\ f \longmapsto f \text{ on morphisms} \end{cases} \qquad G_H\colon \begin{cases} X \longmapsto (HX,\varepsilon_X) \text{ on objects}^{)1} \\ f \longmapsto Hf \quad \text{on morphisms.} \end{cases}$$

Then we have natural transformations $\delta\colon F_H G_H = H \to I_D$ and $\beta\colon I_{D_H} \to G_H F_H$, where

$$\beta_{(X,\sigma)} := \sigma\colon (X,\sigma) \to (HX,\varepsilon_X)$$

for each H-coalgebra (X,σ). *Then* F_H *is left adjoint to* G_H *with unit* β *and counit* δ, *and the comonad* $(F_H G_H,\delta,F_H\beta G_H)$ *defined by this adjunction, just coincides with the original comonad* (H,δ,ε).

The functor F_H preserves colimits and epimorphisms, and, in addition, it reflects epimorphisms and creates colimits (dual of 0.4.7).

0.4.10. *Categorical notions in topology.* All proofs of the following statements can be found in [He] or else they are trivial. First, we describe

---

)1 (HX,ε_X) is called the *free coalgebra for* X.

some categorical notions in the category TOP. Basical is the observation that the forgetful functor TOP → SET has a left and a right adjoint (providing a set with the discrete and the indiscrete topology, respectively). Hence this forgetful functor preserves all limits, colimits, monomorphisms and epimorphisms. In addition, TOP *is complete and cocomplete*. Now the following descriptions can be given:

Product of $\{X_j : j \in J\}$ in TOP : cartesian productspace $\mathbb{P}_j X_j$ with projections $p_i : \mathbb{P}_j X_j \to X_i$ $(i \in J)$.

Coproduct of $\{X_j : j \in J\}$ in TOP : disjoint union $\Sigma_j X_j$ of the spaces X_j with the topological embeddings $r_i : X_i \to \Sigma_j X_j$ $(i \in J)$.

Monomorphisms in TOP : injective continuous functions.

Epimorphisms in TOP : surjective continuous functions.

Equalizer of $f_1, f_2 : X \to Y$: inclusion mapping $i: Z \to X$, with $Z := \{x \in X : f_1(x) = f_2(x)\}$.

Coequalizer of $f_1, f_2 : X \to Y$: quotient mapping $q: Y \to Y/R$ with R the smallest equivalence relation in Y containing all points $(f_1(x), f_2(x)) \in Y \times Y$ $(x \in X)$.

One particular colimit will be mentioned here: let A be a subset of a topological space X and let $i: A \to X$ be the inclusion mapping. The colimit of the diagram

$$X \xleftarrow{i} A \xrightarrow{i} X$$

in TOP shall be denoted $X \cup_A X$ with coprojections $f_1, f_2 : X \cup_A X$. Then f_1 and f_2 are topological embeddings of X into $X \cup_A X$. In fact, $X \cup_A X$ can be realized as $(X \times \{1,2\})/R$, where $\{1,2\}$ is a discrete two-point space (hence $X \times \{1,2\}$ is the disjoint union of two copies of X) and R is the equivalence relation $\{((x,1),(x,1)) : x \in X\} \cup \{((x,2),(x,2) : x \in X\} \cup \{((x,1),(x,2)) : x \in A\}$ on $X \times \{1,2\}$.

The most important facts about HAUS can be derived from the preceding ones, because *the inclusion functor* HAUS → TOP *creates, hence preserves, all limits and all coproducts (not coequalizers!)*. In particular, it preserves and reflects monomorphisms. Notice that the *epimorphisms* in HAUS are just all continuous mappings with dense ranges.

The inclusion functor COMP → HAUS *creates all limits, all finite coproducts and all coequalizers*. The epimorphisms in COMP are the surjections.

Finally, the inclusion functors COMP → HAUS and HAUS → TOP have left adjoints, i.e. COMP is (epi-)reflective in HAUS and HAUS is reflective in

TOP.)1 The reflection of an object $X \in$ TOP in HAUS is always a quotient mapping. The reflection of $X \in$ TOP in COMP will be denoted $\beta_X: X \to \beta X$; if X is a Tychonov space, it is a dense embedding, and then βX is called the *Stone-Čech compactification* of X; in all cases, the mapping β_X has a dense range in βX.

A description of the important category KR is postponed untill subsection 5.1.

0.4.11. *Categorical notions in topological groups.* The basical observation is, that the forgetful functor TOPGRP $\to$ GRP has both a left and a right adjoint (assigning to each group the discrete and the indiscrete topology, respectively). *So by* 0.4.4, *the forgetful functor* TOPGRP $\to$ GRP *preserves all limits, colimits, monomorphisms and epimorphisms. In addition, it can be shown that* TOPGRP *is complete and cocomplete.* Limits and colimits in TOPGRP can be formed by first computing the corresponding limits and colimits in GRP and then the resulting objects have to be provided with a suitable topology, in order to obtain the desired limits and colimits in TOPGRP. For limits, this suitable topology is easy to find. *In fact, the forgetful functor* TOPGRP $\to$ TOP *plainly creates all limits.* For colimits, the situation is more complicated. Cf. for instance S.A. MORRIS [1971] or E.T. ORDMAN [1974] and the references given there. Incidentally, it follows from the above remarks that *monomorphisms in* TOPGRP *are the injective morphisms and that epimorphisms in* TOPGRP *are the surjective morphisms* (indeed, in GRP this is well-known).

The full subcategory HAUSGRP *is reflective in* TOPGRP, for each object $G \in$ TOPGRP the reflection being the morphism $G \to G/\mathrm{cl}_G\{e\}$. So the last paragraphs in 0.4.4 provide the device to compute all limits and colimits in HAUSGRP. In fact, HAUSGRP is closed under the formation of all limits and coproducts (= free products) in TOPGRP (not under the formation of coequalizers)2); for limits this is obvious, for coproducts, cf. for example E.T. ORDMAN [1974] and the references given there.

)1 It follows that HAUS and COMP are complete and cocomplete (completeness follows also from the earlier remarks, but cocompleteness does not!).

)2 Consequently, we cannot characterize epimorphisms in HAUSGRP. It is an outstanding conjecture that it are the morphisms in HAUSGRP with dense ranges.

The category COMPGRP *is reflective in* HAUSGRP, *hence in* TOPGRP. The reflection $\alpha_G: G \to G^c$ of an object G of TOPGRP in COMPGRP is called the *Bohr compactification* of G. In contradistinction to the reflector of TOP to COMP, the reflector of TOPGRP to COMPGRP preserves all products (cf. P. HOLM [1964]).

The full subcategory of TOPGRP of all locally compact T_2-groups seems to be not yet systematically investigated, although a lot of information about it is known in the literature. For instance, coproducts in TOPGRP of locally compact Hausdorff groups may be not locally compact. The full subcategory of TOPGRP of all *abelian* locally compact T_2-groups behaves better, and a lot is known about it. Although, we shall not use this category, we refer the interested reader to D.W. ROEDER [1974] and the references given there for a categorical approach of the duality theorem.

1 - GENERALITIES ON TTGS

In this introductory section the basical concepts of this treatise are defined, and some simple properties are derived. First of all, the definition of a topological transformation group (a ttg) is given, and the relation with suitably topologized homeomorphism groups is investigated. Then, in subsection 1.3, more shape is given to the concept of a ttg by introducing orbits, the orbit space and the enveloping semigroup of a ttg. After this superficial glance at the internal structure of a ttg, the possibility of studying relations between ttgs is opened by defining morphisms of ttgs. This happens in subsection 1.4, where also some examples are provided, using the previously defined concepts. In order to facilitate subsequent constructions, this section will be closed by presenting some elementary constructions of new ttgs from given ones. In order to exclude trivialities, all phase spaces of ttgs in this section are supposed to be non-void.

1.1. Definitions and terminology

1.1.1. Let G be a topological group. For any topological space $X \neq \emptyset$, let $\eta_X^G: X \to G\times X$ and $\mu_X^G: G\times(G\times X) \to G\times X$ be defined by

$$(1) \qquad \eta_X^G(x) := (e,x); \qquad \mu_X^G(s,(t,x)) := (st,x)$$

($x \in X$ and $s,t \in G$). If G is understood we shall often write η_X and μ_X instead of η_X^G and μ_X^G.

An *action* of a topological group G on a non-void topological space X is a continuous function $\pi: G\times X \to X$ such that the following diagrams commute:

(2)

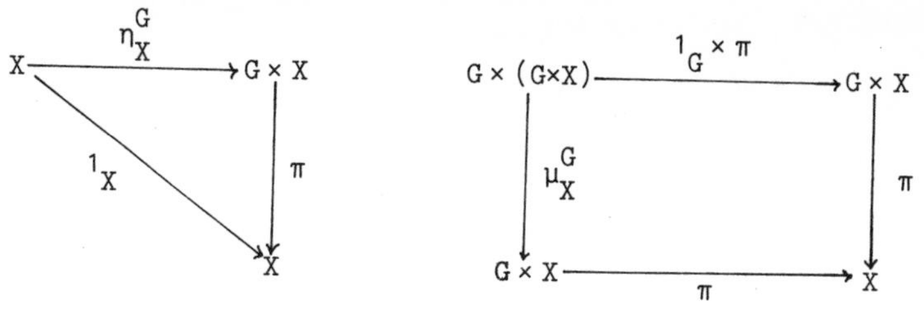

A *topological transformation group* (abbr.: a *ttg*, plural: *ttgs*) is a triple $\langle G,X,\pi\rangle$ with G a topological group, X a topological space, $X \neq \emptyset$, and π an action of G on X. Here G {X} is called the *phase group* {the *phase space*} of the ttg $\langle G,X,\pi\rangle$.

In accordance with our notational conventions, let

(3) $$\pi^t(x) := \pi(t,x) =: \pi_x(t)$$

($t \in G$, $x \in X$). Then the continuous mappings $\pi^t\colon X \to X$ {$\pi_x\colon G \to X$} are called the *transitions* {the *motions*} of the action π.

1.1.2. Let G be a topological group, X a topological space, and $\pi\colon G{\times}X \to X$ a continuous function. Then π is an action iff the following conditions are satisfied:

(i) $\pi^e = 1_X$.

(ii) $\pi^{st} = \pi^s\pi^t$ for all $s,t \in G$.

It is convenient to notice that for any ttg $\langle G,X,\pi\rangle$ the following diagrams commute for every $(t,x) \in G{\times}X$ (recall that $\lambda\colon G{\times}G \to G$ denotes the multiplication in G; in addition, tx stands for $\pi(t,x)$):

(4)

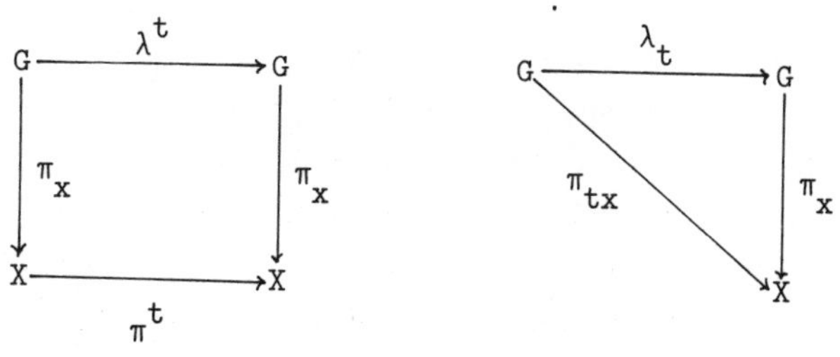

1.1.3. <u>PROPOSITION</u>. *If* $\langle G,X,\pi\rangle$ *is a ttg then each* π^t *is a homeomorphism of* X *onto itself* ($t \in G$). *In addition, the mapping* $\bar{\pi}\colon t \mapsto \pi^t$ *defines a morphism of groups from* G *into the full homeomorphism group* H(X,X) *of* X.

PROOF. Use (i) and (ii) of 1.1.2. □

1.1.4. The *transition mapping* of a ttg $\langle G,X,\pi\rangle$ is the mapping $\bar{\pi}\colon G \to X^X$, defined by the rule

$$(5) \qquad \bar{\pi}(t) := \pi^t$$

for $t \in G$.[1] Obviously, $\bar{\pi}[G]$ is a subgroup of the full homeomorphism group $H(X,X)$ of X. It is called the *transition group* of $\langle G,X,\pi\rangle$.

1.1.5. It follows immediately from 1.1.3 that for every ttg $\langle G,X,\pi\rangle$, π may also be considered as an action of the group G_d on the space X, where G_d denotes the group G with its discrete topology. Consequently, if $\langle G,X,\pi\rangle$ is a ttg, then we can speak about the ttg $\langle G_d,X,\pi\rangle$ as well.

1.1.6. We present now some elementary examples of ttgs. To this end, we fix a ttg G. Several ttgs $\langle G,X,\pi\rangle$ will be described by indicating X and π. Most proofs are left to the reader.

(i) The ttg $\langle G,G,\lambda\rangle$.
Here $\lambda(t,s) := ts$. The transitions are the left translations in G, and the motions are the right translations in G.

(ii) The ttg $\langle G,G\times X,\mu_X\rangle$, where X is any topological space.
Here $\mu_X := \mu_X^G : (s,(t,x)) \mapsto (st,x) : G\times(G\times X) \to G\times X$. If we take for X a one-point space, then we may identify $G\times X$ with G, and we obtain the ttg of example (i).

(iii) Suppose G is a subgroup of some topological group H. If $\pi\colon G\times H \to H$ is defined by $\pi(t,u) := tu$, then $\langle G,H,\pi\rangle$ is a ttg. The transitions are the left translations in H over elements of G. If $G = H$ then we obtain the ttg of example (i) above. If the quotient mapping $q\colon H \to H/G$ admits a *continuous cross-section*, then the ttg $\langle G,H,\pi\rangle$ may be identified with the ttg $\langle G,G\times(H/G),\mu_{H/G}\rangle$, defined according to example (ii). Here H/G denotes the space of all *right* cosets of G in H with its usual quotient topology. {Recall that a continuous cross-section of q is a continuous mapping $f\colon H/G \to H$ such that $qf = 1_{H/G}$. If it exists, then the mapping $u \mapsto (u\cdot(fqu)^{-1},qu)\colon H \to G\times(H/G)$ is a homeomorphism.

---

[1] *Warning:* we shall also use the symbol $\bar{\pi}$ for the corestriction of $\bar{\pi}$ to certain subsets of X^X containing $\bar{\pi}[G]$; if this occurs, such a corestriction shall also be called a transition mapping.

If we identify H with $G\times(H/G)$ via this homeomorphism, then the action π of G on H carries over to the action $\mu_{H/G}$ of G on $G\times(H/G)$.}

(iv) Let H be a subgroup of G and let the space $G\backslash H$ of *left* cosets of H in G be provided with its usual quotient topology. Then $\pi: G\times(G\backslash H)\to G\backslash H$ may unambiguously be defined by

$$\pi(t,q(s)) := q(ts)$$

for $t,s\in G$. Here $q: G\to G\backslash H$ is the quotient mapping. Then $\langle G,G\backslash H,\pi\rangle$ is a ttg (since q is open, continuity of π follows from 0.2.4(i)).

(v) Let S denote a semigroup with multiplication $(\xi,\eta)\mapsto\xi\eta : S\times S\to S$, not necessarily continuous. Let $\varphi: G\to S$ be a morphism of semigroups, and suppose that the topology on S is such that the mapping

$$\hat{\varphi}:(t,\xi)\mapsto\varphi(t)\xi : G\times S\to S$$

is continuous. If, in addition, $\varphi(e)$ is a *left unit* in S (i.e. $\varphi(e)\xi=\xi$ for every $\xi\in S$), then $\hat{\varphi}$ is a continuous action of G on S, so $\langle G,S,\hat{\varphi}\rangle$ is a ttg. In particular, if S is a topological group and if φ is a continuous morphism of groups, then we can define the ttg $\langle G,S,\hat{\varphi}\rangle$ in this way. In the general case, it is useful to notice that φ can be recovered from $\hat{\varphi}$ by means of the equality $\varphi=\hat{\varphi}_{\varphi(e)}$.

(vi) Let G be a locally compact Hausdorff group, and let $X := G\cup\{\infty\}$ denote its one-point compactification. Then $\pi: G\times X\to X$ may be defined by

$$\pi(t,x) := \begin{cases}\lambda(t,x) = tx & \text{if } x\in G\\ \infty & \text{if } x=\infty\end{cases}$$

for all $t\in G$. Plainly, π is continuous, and $\langle G,X,\pi\rangle$ is a ttg.

(vii) Let $X\neq\emptyset$ be any topological space. Then $\tau_X:(t,x)\mapsto x : G\times X\to X$ defines an action of G on X. The transition group of this action consists just of the one-element group $\{1_X\}$. This action τ_X will be referred to as the *trivial action* of G on X.

(viii) Let X be a topological space and let f be an autohomeomorphism of X. For $n\in\mathbb{N}$, let $f^n := f\circ\ldots\circ f$ (n times), let $f^0 := 1_X$ and $f^k := (f^{\leftarrow})^{-k}$ if $k\in\mathbb{Z}$, $k<0$. Finally, set $\pi(n,x) := f^n(x)$ for every $n\in\mathbb{Z}$ and $x\in X$. Then $\pi:\mathbb{Z}\times X\to X$ is continuous, and π is an action of $\mathbb{Z}$ on X. The ttg $\langle\mathbb{Z},X,\pi\rangle$ is called the *discrete ttg, generated by the homeomorphism* f. Notice, that $\pi^1=f$, and that, for all $n\in\mathbb{Z}$, $\pi^n=f^n=(\pi^1)^n$.

Observe that each action σ of $\mathbb{Z}$ on any space X is generated in this way by σ^1.

1.1.7. We shall now agree upon some informal terminology and notation. If $\langle G,X,\pi\rangle$ is a ttg, then $\pi(t,x)$ is denoted more concisely by $t\cdot x$ or tx when there is no risk for ambiguity. The statement "$\langle G,X,\pi\rangle$ is a ttg" may be rephrased as "G acts on X {by π}" or "X is a G-space {with action π}". We shall also use the description "the G-space $\langle G,X,\pi\rangle$".

If in a ttg $\langle G,X,\pi\rangle$ the action π has a certain property, then we may express this also by saying that $\langle G,X,\pi\rangle$ has that property, and vice versa. Alternatively, we say that G has the property *on* X, or that X has the property *under* G. Similarly, if $\langle G,X,\pi\rangle$ has a certain property at $x \in X$ then we say that G has the property *at* x, or that x has the property *under* G. In the same spirit we shall use in the sequel sometimes a more or less informal terminology which is not always defined explicitly but which is hoped to be clear from the context (and, of course, from previously given definitions).

1.1.8. In general, the transition mapping $\bar{\pi}$ for a ttg $\langle G,X,\pi\rangle$ is not injective (consider the trivial action of a non-trivial group G on any non-void space X). The action π in a ttg $\langle G,X,\pi\rangle$ is called *effective* (by 1.1.7, we may call $\langle G,X,\pi\rangle$ then an *effective ttg*) if $\bar{\pi}\colon G \to \mathcal{H}(X,X)$ is injective. Equivalently, $\langle G,X,\pi\rangle$ is effective iff

$$(6) \qquad \forall t \in G\ [t \neq e \Rightarrow \exists x \in X \ \vdots\ \pi(t,x) \neq x].$$

Stated more loosely, in any effective ttg the phase group may be identified with a topologized group of homeomorphisms of the phase space, namely with the transition group. We shall consider the topologies on such homeomorphism groups in more detail in section 1.2.

1.1.9. An action $\pi\colon G\times X \to X$ of the topological group G on the topological space X is *strongly effective* provided for every $x \in X$ the motion $\pi_x\colon G \to X$ is injective. Equivalently, π is strongly effective iff

$$(7) \qquad \forall t \in G\ [t \neq e \Rightarrow \forall x \in X : \pi(t,x) \neq x]$$

(compare this with (6) above). So a ttg $\langle G,X,\pi\rangle$ has a strongly effective action provided no transition π^t with $t \neq e$ has a fixed point ($t \in G$).

1.1.10. If G is a topological group then for any topological space X the ttg $\langle G, G\times X, \mu_X\rangle$ (cf. 1.1.6(ii)) is strongly effective. The ttgs of this form constitute a subclass of the class of all ttgs which plays a role similar to the class of free groups in the class of all groups. Cf. section 3.1. Therefore, we shall call the ttgs of this form *free ttgs*.

Warning: in a considerable part of the literature on ttgs a free ttg is what we have called a strongly effective ttg. For an example of a strongly effective ttg which is not free in our sense, see 1.3.8(iii) below.

1.1.11. Let $\langle G,X,\pi\rangle$ be a ttg. For each $x\in X$, the set $G_x := \overleftarrow{\pi}_x[x] = \{t\in G : \pi(t,x) = x\}$ is plainly a subgroup of G; it is called the *stability group*[1] *of* x. The stability groups are related to the transition mapping $\bar{\pi}$: $G \to \mathcal{H}(X,X)$ in the following way: if Ker $\bar{\pi}$ denotes the kernel of $\bar{\pi}$, i.e. Ker $\bar{\pi} := \{t\in G : \pi^t = 1_X\}$, then

$$\text{(8)} \qquad \text{Ker}\ \bar{\pi} = \bigcap\{G_x : x\in X\}.$$

Plainly, Ker $\bar{\pi}$ is a normal subgroup of G; it is called the *stability group*[1] *of* $\langle G,X,\pi\rangle$.

1.1.12. <u>PROPOSITION</u>. *If* $\langle G,X,\pi\rangle$ *is a ttg and* X *is a* T_0*-space, then each* G_x *is closed in* G. *In particular,* Ker $\bar{\pi}$ *is a closed normal subgroup of* G.

<u>PROOF</u>. In view of (8) it is sufficient to prove that each G_x is closed in G. Let $t\in \text{cl}\,G_x$. Then $\pi(t,x)\in \pi_x[\text{cl}\,G_x] \subseteq \text{cl}\,\pi_x[G_x] = \text{cl}\{x\}$. Since G_x is a subgroup of G, we have also $t^{-1}\in \text{cl}\,G_x$, and as before, $\pi(t^{-1},x)\in \text{cl}\{x\}$, whence $x\in \pi^t[\text{cl}\{x\}] = \text{cl}\{\pi^t x\}$. Now the T_0-separation property of X implies that $\pi^t x = x$, i.e. $t\in G_x$. □

1.1.13. The property of being effective or strongly effective can be expressed in terms of stability groups, as follows:

A ttg $\langle G,X,\pi\rangle$ *is effective iff* Ker $\bar{\pi} = \{e\}$, *and it is strongly effective iff* $G_x = \{e\}$ *for every* $x\in X$. This follows immediately from the definitions, and the proof is left to the reader.

1.1.14. To any ttg $\langle G,X,\pi\rangle$ there is related in an obvious way an effective ttg with X as a phase space and with the same transition group as the given ttg: take as the new phase group simply the transition group $\bar{\pi}[G]$ of $\langle G,X,\pi\rangle$ with its discrete topology. As the action of $\bar{\pi}[G]$ on X we choose the obvious action, viz. $\delta : (\xi,x) \mapsto \xi(x) : \pi[G]\times X \to X$.

---

[1] In [GH], the term "period" is used.

For certain purposes it is, however, undesirable that $\bar{\pi}: G \to \bar{\pi}[G]$ may be not continuous if $\bar{\pi}[G]$ has its discrete topology. However, if we provide $\bar{\pi}[G]$ with the finest topology making $\bar{\pi}: G \to \bar{\pi}[G]$ continuous, then plainly $\bar{\pi}[G]$ is homeomorphic with $G/\mathrm{Ker}\,\bar{\pi}$, and the homeomorphism which achieves this is, in addition, an isomorphism of groups. So by [HR], 5.2.6, $\bar{\pi}[G]$ is a topological group, and $\bar{\pi}: G \to \bar{\pi}[G]$ is an open mapping. It follows that $\bar{\pi}\times 1_X : G\times X \to \bar{\pi}[G]\times X$ is a quotient mapping. Since $\delta \circ (\bar{\pi}\times 1_X)$ is continuous (it just equals the continuous mapping $\pi: G\times X \to X$), we obtain that $\delta: \bar{\pi}[G]\times X \to X$ is continuous. Thus, $\bar{\pi}[G]$ acts on X by means of δ. Since δ is plainly an effective action, this proves

1.1.15. PROPOSITION. *Let* $\langle G,X,\pi\rangle$ *be a ttg and let* $\bar{\pi}[G]$ *be given the finest topology making* $\bar{\pi}: G \to \bar{\pi}[G]$ *continuous. Then* $\delta:(\xi,x) \mapsto \xi(x) : \bar{\pi}[G]\times X \to X$ *is continuous, and* $\langle \bar{\pi}[G],X,\delta\rangle$ *is an effective ttg.* □

1.1.16. *If* X *is a* T_0*-space then the topology on* $\bar{\pi}[G]$ *indicated in* 1.1.15 *is a Hausdorff topology.* Indeed, as mentioned before, $\bar{\pi}[G]$ is topologically isomorphic to $G/\mathrm{Ker}\,\bar{\pi}$, and if X is a T_0-space, then so is $G/\mathrm{Ker}\,\bar{\pi}$, by 1.1.12 and [HR], 5.2.6. Finally, recall that for topological groups, the T_0 and the T_2 separation axioms are equivalent.

1.1.17. Intuitively, in effective ttgs the connection between phase group and phase space is stronger than in non-effective ones. This is illustrated by the fact that most theorems relating properties of the phase group to properties of the phase space and of the action apply only to effective ttgs. As an example, we present a relation connecting the local weight of the phase group to the local weight of the phase space and the "measure of effectiveness". First, we have to introduce some terminology in order to be able to give a precise meaning to "measure of effectiveness".

1.1.18. A *stabilizing set* in an effective ttg $\langle G,X,\pi\rangle$ is a subset A of X such that $\pi^t|_A = \pi^e|_A$ implies $t = e$ $(t \in G)$. Equivalently, $A \subseteq X$ is a stabilizing set iff $\bigcap\{G_x : x\in A\} = \{e\}$. If $\langle G,X,\pi\rangle$ is an effective ttg, then the cardinal number

$$e\langle G,X,\pi\rangle := \min\{|A| : A\subseteq X \ \&\ A \text{ is stabilizing}\}$$

is in a certain sense a measure for the effectiveness of $\langle G,X,\pi\rangle$.

1.1.19. If $\langle G,X,\pi\rangle$ is an effective ttg, then X is a stabilizing set, hence $e\langle G,X,\pi\rangle \le |X|$. If, in addition, X is a T_2-space, then every dense subset of X is stabilizing, so $e\langle G,X,\pi\rangle \le d(X)$, the density of X. If $\langle G,X,\pi\rangle$ is strongly effective, then each $\{x\}$ is a stabilizing set $(x \in X)$, hence $e\langle G,X,\pi\rangle = 1$.

1.1.20. <u>LEMMA</u>. *Let* Y *be any topological space and suppose* $y \in Y$ *has a compact Hausdorff neighbourhood. Let* $\mathcal{B} \subseteq \mathcal{V}_y$ *and* $\bigcap \mathcal{B} = \{y\}$. *Then* $\ell w(Y,y) \le |\mathcal{B}|$.

<u>PROOF</u>. If $|\mathcal{B}|$ is finite, then y is isolated, and $\ell w(Y,y) = 1 \le |\mathcal{B}|$. Suppose $|\mathcal{B}| \ge \aleph_0$. Without restriction of generality we may suppose that each $B \in \mathcal{B}$ is compact and closed in Y. Let $\mathcal{B}^*$ denote the family of all intersections of finitely many members of $\mathcal{B}$. Then $|\mathcal{B}^*| = |\mathcal{B}|$ and $\mathcal{B}^*$ is easily seen to be a local base at y. Hence $\ell w(Y,y) \le |\mathcal{B}^*| = |\mathcal{B}|$. □

1.1.21. <u>PROPOSITION</u>. *Let* $\langle G,X,\pi\rangle$ *be an effective ttg. If* G *is a locally compact Hausdorff group and if* X *is a* T_1*-space, then*

(9) $$\ell w(G) \le e\langle G,X,\pi\rangle \cdot \ell w(X).$$

<u>PROOF</u>. Let A be a stabilizing set such that $|A| = e\langle G,X,\pi\rangle$. For each $a \in A$, let $\mathcal{B}_a$ denote a local base at a such that $|\mathcal{B}_a| = \ell w(X,a)$. Observe that $\overleftarrow{\pi}_a[V] \in \mathcal{V}_e$ for every $a \in A$ and $V \in \mathcal{B}_a$. Then

$$\bigcap_{a\in A}\ \bigcap_{V\in\mathcal{B}_a} \overleftarrow{\pi}_a[V] = \{e\},$$

by the T_1-separation property of X and the fact that A is stabilizing. Now apply 1.1.20. □

1.1.22. Actually, we proved a little bit more than has been expressed by the inequality (9), namely, that we have $\ell w(G) \le |A| \cdot \sup\{\ell w(X,a) : a\in A\}$ for any stabilizing set A in X. In particular, if $|A| = 1$, then $\ell w(G) \le \ell w(X,a)$, where a is the unique point in A.

1.1.23. <u>COROLLARY</u>. *Let* $\langle G,X,\pi\rangle$ *be a ttg with* G *a locally compact Hausdorff group and* X *a Hausdorff space. If the action* π *is effective, then* $\ell w(G) \le d(X) \cdot \ell w(X)$. *If* π *is strongly effective, then* $\ell w(G) \le \min\{\ell w(X,x) : x \in X\}$. *In particular, if* G *acts effectively {strongly effectively} on a separable first countable {a first countable} Hausdorff space, then* G *is metrizable.*

PROOF. Apply 1.1.21, 1.1.22 and [HR], 8.3, and recall from 1.1.19 that $e\langle G,X,\pi\rangle \leq d(X)$. □

1.1.24. NOTES. We shall not enter into the history and the development of the concept of a ttg. Nor shall we try to convince the reader of the importance of ttgs. For a flavour of it, the reader may read the prefaces to [MZ], [GH] and [El]. See also W.H. GOTTSCHALK [1958, 1964, 1968].

Usually, the definition of a ttg is given in the form of 1.1.2. The more "abstract" definition that we have presented in 1.1.1 has been motivated by the needs of §3.

In example 1.1.6(iii), the existence of a continuous cross-section $f: H/G \to H$ is equivalent to the existence of a *closed* subset S in H meeting each right coset of G in H in exactly one point, provided q is a closed mapping. In general, the best one can do is to prove the existence of *Borel* sets with this property: cf. G. MACKEY [1952], or J. FELDMAN & F.P. GREENLEAF [1968]. A sufficient condition for the existence of a continuous cross-section $f: H/G \to H$ can be found in E. MICHAEL [1959]: H is metrizable and G is a complete subgroup which is isomorphic to the additive topological group of a Banach space. Another result can be found in P.S. MOSTERT [1956]: if H is any locally compact Hausdorff group and G is a closed subgroup such that H/G is 0-dimensional, then q has a continuous cross-section. For related results, namely the local existence of continuous cross-sections, cf. P.S. MOSTERT [1953; 1956], [MZ], p.221 and [Ch.], p.109.

The question which additional conditions imply that a strongly effective ttg is free (of which the condition in 1.1.6(iii) is an instance) is related to the problem of *parallelizability of flows* (a *flow* is nothing but an action of the additive group $\mathbb{R}$). We shall return to this question in the notes to section 1.3.

The statements on the metrizability of G in 1.1.23 are well-known; see for instance [MZ], 2.11. The slight generalization of these statements formulated in 1.1.21 seems to be new, but as such it seems to be of limited interest. As an application we shall show in 2.3.15 that $w(G) = w(L^2(G))$ for every locally compact Hausdorff group G.

1.2. Topological homeomorphism groups

1.2.1. For any topological space X, the set X^X of all (not necessarily continuous) mappings of X into itself has a natural semigroup structure, the multiplication being defined by composition of mappings. Obviously,

$C(X,X)$ is a subsemigroup of X^X, and the set $H(X,X)$ of all homeomorphisms of X onto itself is a subgroup of $C(X,X)$. This group is called the *full homeomorphism group* of X. The identity element of $H(X,X)$ is 1_X, and the inverse of any ξ in the group $H(X,X)$ is $\xi^{\leftarrow}$. Thus, $\xi^{-1} = \xi^{\leftarrow}$.

A *homeomorphism group* of X (or: on X) is a subgroup of $H(X,X)$. A *topological homeomorphism group* on X is a subgroup T of $H(X,X)$ with a topology such that T is a topological group and the mapping $\delta:(h,x) \mapsto h(x): T\times X \to X$ is continuous.

1.2.2. *If* T *is a topological homeomorphism group on* X *and if* $\delta: T\times X \to X$ *is defined by* $\delta(h,x) := h(x)$, *then* δ *is an effective action of* T *on* X.

Conversely, if $\langle G,X,\pi\rangle$ is an effective ttg, then $T := \bar{\pi}[G]$, endowed with the unique topology making $\bar{\pi}: G \to T$ a homeomorphism, is a topological homeomorphism group on X. If we identify G with T by means of $\bar{\pi}$, then π corresponds to the mapping $(h,x) \mapsto h(x) : T\times X \to X$.

It follows from these remarks, that studying topological homeomorphism groups amounts to the same thing as studying effective ttgs. We shall collect now some facts about topologies on homeomorphism groups.

1.2.3. The following statements are well-known. The reader may find proofs e.g. in [Bo], Chapter X. As to the notation, see subsection 0.2.

(i) Let X be a *locally compact* topological Hausdorff space and let $T \subseteq C(X,X)$. Then the mappings

$$(\xi,\eta) \mapsto \xi\eta: T_c \times T_c \to C_c(X,X); \quad (\xi,x) \mapsto \xi(x): T_c \times X \to X$$

are continuous (cf. also 0.2.7).

(ii) Let X be a *uniform space*, and let $T \subseteq C(X,X)$. Then the mapping

$$(\xi,x) \mapsto \xi(x): T_u \times X \to X$$

is continuous.

(iii) Let X be a *uniform space* and let T be an *equicontinuous* subset of $C(X,X)$. Then the mappings

$$(\xi,\eta) \mapsto \xi\eta: T_p \times C_p(X,X) \to C_p(X,X); \quad (\xi,x) \mapsto \xi(x): T_p \times X \to X$$

are continuous.

Before going into details on the continuity of the mapping $\xi \mapsto \xi^{-1}$ on homeomorphism groups, we wish to stress the fact that the compact-open topology is in many cases the best candidate for a topology on a homeomorphism group to make it a topological homeomorphism group. In addition, it is important to observe the following: *if for a certain topology on a subset* T *of* $C(X,X)$ *the evaluation* δ: $(\xi,x) \mapsto \xi(x): T\times X \to X$ *is continuous, then this topology is finer than the compact-open topology* (this is an immediate consequence of the first statement in 0.2.7(iii)).

1.2.4. Let X be a topological space and let T be a subgroup of $H(X,X)$. The *bilateral compact-open topology* on T is the weakest topology making the mappings $\xi \mapsto \xi$ and $\xi \mapsto \xi^{-1}: T \to T_c$ continuous. If T is endowed with this topology we shall indicate this by writing T_{bc} instead of T.

1.2.5. <u>LEMMA</u>. *Let* T *be a homeomorphism group on the topological space* X. *Then the bilateral compact-open topology is the weakest topology for which the mapping* $\xi \mapsto \xi^{-1}: T \to T$ *is continuous and which is finer than the compact-open topology.*

<u>PROOF</u>. A straightforward consequence of the definition in 1.2.4 and the fundamental property of a weak topology (cf. 0.2.3). □

1.2.6. <u>COROLLARY 1</u>. *Suppose* T *is a topological homeomorphism group on the topological space* X. *Then the topology of* T *is finer than the bilateral compact-open topology on* T.

<u>PROOF</u>. The mapping $(\xi,x) \mapsto \xi(x): T\times X \to X$ is continuous, so the topology on T is finer than the compact-open topology on T. Now apply 1.2.5. □

1.2.7. <u>COROLLARY 2</u>. *Let* X *be a locally compact Hausdorff space. Then for any subgroup* T *of* $H(X,X)$, T_{bc} *is a topological homeomorphism group on* X. *In particular,* $H_{bc}(X,X)$ *is a topological homeomorphism group.*

<u>PROOF</u>. By 1.2.5, the mapping $\xi \mapsto \xi^{-1}: T_{bc} \to T_{bc}$ is continuous. Moreover, the mapping $(\xi,\eta) \mapsto \xi\eta: T_{bc}\times T_{bc} \to T_{bc}$ is continuous because its compositions with $\xi \mapsto \xi$ and $\xi \mapsto \xi^{-1}: T_{bc} \to T_c$ are (use 1.2.3(i)). □

1.2.8. Let T be a subgroup of $H(X,X)$. A subbase for the bilateral compact-open topology on T is formed by all sets $N(K,U) \cap T$, together with all sets of the type $\{\xi\in T : \xi^{\leftarrow} \in N(K,U) \cap T\}$ with K compact and U open in X. Since $\xi^{\leftarrow} \in T$ iff $\xi \in T$, sets of the latter type are equal to sets of the type $\{\xi\in T : \xi^{\leftarrow} \in N(K,U)\}$.

A similar description of a subbase for $H_{bc}(X,X)$ can be given. *In partic-*

ular, it follows that T_{bc} *has just the relative topology of* $H_{bc}(X,X)$.

1.2.9. <u>COROLLARY 3</u>. *For any ttg* $\langle G,X,\pi\rangle$ *the transition mapping* $\bar{\pi}: G\to H_{bc}(X,X)$ *is continuous. Consequently,* $\bar{\pi}: G\to H_c(X,X)$ *is continuous as well.*

<u>PROOF</u>. By the conclusion of 1.2.8, it is sufficient to show that $\bar{\pi}: G\to\bar{\pi}[G]_{bc}$ is continuous. If we give $\bar{\pi}[G]$ the finest topology making $\bar{\pi}$ continuous, then $\bar{\pi}[G]$ is a topological homeomorphism group (cf. 1.1.15). By 1.2.6, this topology is finer than the topology of $\bar{\pi}[G]_{bc}$. □

1.2.10. Let X be a *uniform* space with uniformity $\mathcal{U}$. In addition, let T be a homeomorphism group on X. We shall consider two situations in which T is a topological homeomorphism group in the compact-open topology.

(i) *Suppose* T *is equicontinuous. Then* $T_{bc} = T_c = T_p$, *and this is a topological homeomorphism group.*

{In view of 1.2.3(iii) and 1.2.6 it is sufficient to show that the mapping $\xi\mapsto\xi^{-1}: T_p\to T_p$ is continuous, i.e. that for each $x\in X$ the mapping $\xi\mapsto\xi^{-1}(x): T_p\to X$ is continuous. The proof is straightforward, and the reader may find the details in [Bo], Chap. X, §3.5.}

(ii) *If* X *is a compact Hausdorff space, then* T_u *is a topological homeomorphism group. In particular,* $H_u(X,X)$ *is a topological homeomorphism group.*

{Since T_u has the relative topology of $H_u(X,X)$, it is sufficient to prove the last statement. Observe, that $H_u(X,X) = H_c(X,X)$, so by 1.2.3(i), it is enough to show that the mapping $\xi\mapsto\xi^{-1}: H_u(X,X)\to H_u(X,X)$ is continuous. Again, the proof is straightforward, and we refer the reader to [Bo], Chap. X, §3.5.}

1.2.11. <u>PROPOSITION</u>. *Let* X *be a locally compact Hausdorff space,* T *a homeomorphism group on* X *and* S *the closure of* T *in* $C_c(X,X)$. *If* S_c *is compact, then* $S\subseteq H(X,X)$, $S_p = S_c = S_{bc}$, *and this is a compact topological homeomorphism group.*

<u>PROOF</u>. Since S_c is a compact space and S_p is a Hausdorff space, it follows that $S_c = S_p$. The proof of Theorem 4 in [Bo], Chap. X, §3.5, implies that $S\subseteq H(X,X)$ and that $\xi\mapsto\xi^{\leftarrow}: S\to H_c(X,X)$ is continuous. Using 1.2.3(i), it follows that S_c is a topological homeomorphism group. Therefore, $S_c = S_{bc}$ by the result of 1.2.6. □

1.2.12. <u>COROLLARY</u>. *Let* X *be a compact Hausdorff space,* T *an equicontinuous homeomorphism group on* X *and* S' *the closure of* T *in* X^X. *Then* $S' \subseteq H(X,X)$, *so that* S' *equals the closure of* T *in* $H_u(X,X)$. *Moreover,* $S_p = S_u$ *and this is a compact topological homeomorphism group.*

PROOF. Apply 0.2.8 and 1.2.11. □

1.2.13. NOTES. The results in this section are well-known. The definition of the bilateral compact-open topology occurs in [GH], 11.44 in a slightly different form, but it follows easily from 1.2.8 that our definition is equivalent to the one in [GH]. Our definition was motivated by [Bo], Chap. X, §3.5, Prop. 12. If X is a locally compact Hausdorff space then this topology is just the g-topology, introduced in R. AHRENS [1946a] (i.e. the relative topology of the given homeomorphism group in $C_u(X_\infty,X_\infty)$, where X_∞ is the one-point compactification of X).

There exists a notable generalization of proposition 1.2.11, namely, that *for a homeomorphism group* T *on a locally compact* T_2*-space the following conditions are equivalent:*

(i) *The closure of* T *in* $C_c(X,X)$ *is compact.*

(ii) *The closure of* T *in* $C_p(X,X)$ *is compact and this closure is a subgroup of* $H(X,X)$.

Of course, here (i) ⇒ (ii) is an immediate consequence of 1.2.11. Crucial in the proof of (ii) ⇒ (i) is that $\delta:(\xi,x) \mapsto \xi(x): S_p \times X \to X$ turns out to be continuous, where S denotes the closure of T in $C_p(X,X)$. This is an immediate consequence of the following famous theorem (cf. R. ELLIS [1957]):

Let X *be a locally compact* T_2*-space and let* T *be a homeomorphism group on* X. *Suppose* T *is given a locally compact topology which is finer than the point-open topology, such that multiplication is separately continuous. Then* T *is a topological homeomorphism group.*

It is an easy consequence of this theorem that a group with a locally compact T_2-topology such that multiplication is separately continuous is a *topological* group. An alternative proof of this statement for the compact case has been given in K. DE LEEUW & I. GLICKSBERG [1961] (cf. also [Bu], Theorem 1.28).

The following result of J. KEESLING [1971] is related to 1.2.11. In fact, it is an easy consequence of the above mentioned theorem of ELLIS and the fact that the product of a locally compact space and a k-space is again a k-space:

Let X *be a* T_2*-space and let* T *be a homeomorphism group on* X *such that* T_c *is locally compact. Then* T *is a topological group (hence* $T_c = T_{bc}$*). If, in addition,* X *is a* k*-space, then* T_c *is a topological homeomorphism group on* X.

For more results on topological homeomorphism groups, we refer the reader to R. ARENS [1946 a,b], or [GH], Chap. 11.

1.3. Orbit space and enveloping semigroup

1.3.1. In this section $\langle G,X,\pi\rangle$ always denotes a fixed ttg.

1.3.2. Let $H \subseteq G$ and $Y \subseteq X$. We say that Y is *invariant under* H whenever $\pi[H\times Y] \subseteq Y$, or equivalently, whenever $\pi^t Y \subseteq Y$ for all $t \in H$. In that case Y is said to be an H-*invariant subset of* X. If $x \in X$ and $\{x\}$ is H-invariant, then x is called an H-*invariant point of* X. The G-invariant subsets and points of X will simply be called *invariant* subsets and points of X (or of $\langle G,X,\pi\rangle$).

1.3.3. PROPOSITION. *Let* $H \subseteq G$*, and let* Y *be an* H*-invariant subset of* X. *Then* $\mathrm{int}_X Y$ *and* $\mathrm{cl}_X Y$ *are also* H*-invariant, and* $\mathrm{cl}_X Y$ *is even* $\mathrm{cl}_G H$*-invariant. If* $H = H^{-1}$*, then* $X \sim Y$ *is* H*-invariant.*

In addition, intersections and unions of arbitrary classes of H*-invariant subsets of* X *are* H*-invariant.*

PROOF. Everything except $\mathrm{cl}_G H$-invariance of $\mathrm{cl}_X Y$ follows trivially from the fact that each π^t is a homeomorphism of X ($t \in H$). That $\mathrm{cl}_X Y$ is invariant under $\mathrm{cl}_G H$ is a consequence of the inclusion $\pi[\mathrm{cl}_G H \times \mathrm{cl}_X Y] \subseteq \mathrm{cl}_X \pi[H\times Y]$. □

1.3.4. If H is a sub*group* of G and Y is a *non-void* H-invariant subset of X, then $\langle H,Y,\pi|_{H\times Y}\rangle$ is obviously a ttg. The following notational convention will often be employed in this situation: $\pi|_{H\times Y}$ will simply be denoted by π, so that we can speak and write about the ttg $\langle H,Y,\pi\rangle$.

1.3.5. If $x \in X$, then *the orbit* $C_\pi[x]$ *of* x *in* X (*under the action of* G *by* π) is the set

(1) $$C_\pi[x] := \pi_x[G] = \{\pi^t x : t \in G\}.$$

Plainly, $C_\pi[x]$ is the least invariant subspace of X containing the point x. More generally, if A is a subset of X then $C_\pi[A] := \bigcup\{C_\pi[x] : x \in A\} = \pi[G\times A]$ is the smallest invariant subset of X including A.

1.3.6. A subset Y of X is invariant iff $C_\pi[y] \subseteq Y$ for every $y \in Y$. In particular, if $x,y \in X$ then either $C_\pi[x] = C_\pi[y]$ or $C_\pi[x] \cap C_\pi(y) = \emptyset$. Consequently, *the orbits in* X *form a partition of* X. The corresponding equivalence relation in X will be denoted with C_π. In other words

$$(2) \qquad C_\pi = \{(x,y) \in X{\times}X : y \in C_\pi[x]\}.$$

1.3.7. The *orbit space* of the ttg $\langle G,X,\pi\rangle$ is the quotient space X/C_π, endowed with its quotient topology. The quotient mapping of X onto X/C_π shall consistently be denoted by c_π.

In discussions where the action π is understood we shall often write C and c instead of C_π and c_π.

1.3.8. EXAMPLES. We shall indicate here the orbit spaces for some of the ttgs defined in 1.1.6.

(i) The orbit space of $\langle G,G,\lambda\rangle$ consists of one point.

(ii) The orbit space of $\langle G,G{\times}X,\mu_X\rangle$ is homeomorphic to X. In fact, the projection $p:(t,x) \longmapsto x: G{\times}X \to X$ establishes a one-to-one correspondence between orbits in $G \times X$ and points of X, i.e. there is a bijection $f: (G{\times}X)/C \to X$ such that $fc = p$. This bijection is plainly a homeomorphism.

(iii) Let G be a subgroup of the topological group H, and let $\pi := \lambda(H)|_{G\times H}$ (cf. 1.1.6(iii)). Then the orbit space of $\langle G,H,\pi\rangle$ is just the space H/G of right cosets of G. It is obvious that the ttg $\langle G,H,\pi\rangle$ is strongly effective. If it were *free*, i.e. of the form $\langle G,G{\times}X,\mu_X\rangle$, then it would follow from example (ii) that (up to homeomorphism) $X = H/G$, hence $H = G \times (H/G)$. If we take $H = \mathbb{T}$ and $G = \{-1,1\}$ then this is impossible (otherwise $\mathbb{T}$ would be disconnected). So not each strongly effective ttg is free.

(iv) Let H be a subgroup of the topological group G, and consider the action π of G on the space $G\backslash H$ of left cosets of H in G defined in 1.1.6(iv). Then the orbit space of $\langle G,G\backslash H,\pi\rangle$ consists of one point only.

1.3.9. PROPOSITION. *The quotient mapping* $c_\pi: X \to X/C_\pi$ *is open.*

PROOF. Let U be an open subset of X. Then $\overleftarrow{c_\pi} c_\pi[U] = \bigcup\{\pi^t U : t \in G\}$, hence it is an open subset of X. Consequently, $c_\pi[U]$ is open in X/C_π. □

1.3.10. PROPOSITION. *The following statements are true:*

(i) X/C_π *is a* T_1*-space iff each orbit in* X *is closed.*

(ii) X/C_π *is a* T_2*-space iff* C_π *is a closed subset of* $X \times X$.

(iii) X/C_π *is a* T_3*-space iff each orbit in* X *is closed (i.e.* X/C_π *is* T_1*) and the following "regularity condition" is satisfied (i.e.* X/C_π *is regular): Every invariant neighbourhood of any point in* X *contains a closed invariant neighbourhood of that point.*

PROOF. (i) and (iii) are straightforward. For (ii), cf. [Du], Chap. VII, 1.6. Notice that here it is essential that c_π is open. □

1.3.11. For $x \in X$, the set $K_\pi[x] := \mathrm{cl}_X C_\pi[x]$ is called the *orbit-closure* of x. If π is understood, we write K[x] instead of $K_\pi[x]$.

1.3.12. For every $x \in X$, $K_\pi[x]$ is an invariant subset of X, by 1.3.3. Obviously, *it is the least closed invariant subset of* X *containing* x.

Consequently, a *closed* subset Y of X is invariant iff $K_\pi[y] \subseteq Y$ for all $y \in Y$. In general, the sets $K_\pi[x]$ for $x \in X$ do *not* form a partition of X. For example, in the ttg of 1.1.6(vi), $K_\pi[x] = X$ for each $x \in X \sim \{\infty\}$, and $K_\pi[\infty] = \{\infty\}$.

1.3.13. Let X^X be endowed with its usual topology of pointwise convergence. Define a mapping $\pi^*: G\times X^X \to X^X$ by

$$\pi^*(t,\xi) := \pi^t \circ \xi$$

for $t \in G$, $\xi \in X^X$. Since for any $x \in X$ the mapping $(t,\xi) \longmapsto \pi(t,\xi x): G\times X^X \to X$ is continuous, it follows that π^* is continuous. Moreover, π^* is easily seen to be an action, so we have a ttg $\langle G,X^X,\pi^*\rangle$.

Obviously, $1_X \in X^X$, and the orbit of the element 1_X in X^X under the action π^* of G is just the transition group $\bar{\pi}[G]$.

1.3.14. The *enveloping semigroup* $E_{\langle G,X,\pi\rangle}$ of the ttg $\langle G,X,\pi\rangle$ is the closure of the transition group $\bar{\pi}[G]$ in X^X. Instead of $E_{\langle G,X,\pi\rangle}$ we will often write E_X or even E. The *natural action* (sometimes called the *obvious* action) of G on E is the restriction to E of the action π^* of G on X^X (cf. 1.3.4). This action will also be denoted by π^*.

1.3.15. A few comments are in order about the terminology. The space X^X has a semigroup structure: if $\xi,\eta \in X^X$, then their composite $\xi\eta$ is in X^X, and

$(\xi,\eta) \mapsto \xi\eta : X^X \times X^X \to X^X$ is an associative multiplication. Notice, that 1_X is the identity of X^X with respect to this multiplication. We shall show that $E_{\langle G,X,\pi\rangle}$ is a subsemigroup of X^X.

1.3.16. LEMMA. *Let X be any topological space. Then the following statements are valid:*

(i) *For every* $\eta \in X^X$, *the mapping* $\xi \mapsto \xi\eta : X^X \to X^X$ *is continuous.*

(ii) *If* $\xi \in X^X$, *then the mapping* $\eta \mapsto \xi\eta : X^X \to X^X$ *is continuous iff* $\xi : X \to X$ *is continuous.*

PROOF.

(i): For any $x \in X$, the mapping $\xi \mapsto \xi(\eta x) : X^X \to X$ is continuous.

(ii): "If": for any $x \in X$, the mapping $\eta \mapsto \eta(x) : X^X \to X$ is continuous. Hence $\eta \mapsto \xi(\eta x)$ is continuous, provided ξ is continuous. So $\eta \mapsto \xi\eta$ is continuous in that case. "Only if": we leave this as an exercise for the reader. □

1.3.17. PROPOSITION. *The enveloping semigroup* $E_{\langle G,X,\pi\rangle}$ *of* $\langle G,X,\pi\rangle$ *is a subsemigroup of* X^X, *and the mapping* $\bar{\pi} : G \to E_{\langle G,X,\pi\rangle}$ *is a continuous morphism of semigroups. In addition, using the notation of* 1.1.6(v), *the natural action* π^* *of* G *on* $E_{\langle G,X,\pi\rangle}$ *is exactly the action* $(\bar{\pi})^\wedge$, *induced by the morphism* $\bar{\pi}$ *of semigroups.*

PROOF. The only non-trivial fact is that $E := E_{\langle G,X,\pi\rangle}$ is a subsemigroup of X^X. The proof is completely standard, but one has to start at the right point, as follows.

First notice that $\bar{\pi}[G]$ is a subgroup of X^X, consisting entirely of continuous elements of X^X. If $\xi \in \bar{\pi}[G]$, then the mapping $\eta \mapsto \xi\eta : X^X \to X^X$ sends $\bar{\pi}[G]$ into $\bar{\pi}[G]$. By 1.3.16(ii), this mapping is continuous, so it sends $\mathrm{cl}\,\bar{\pi}[G]$ into $\mathrm{cl}\,\bar{\pi}[G]$, i.e. its sends E into E. Thus $\xi\eta \in E$ for all $\xi \in \bar{\pi}[G]$ and $\eta \in E$. This means that the continuous mapping $\xi \mapsto \xi\eta : X^X \to X^X$ sends $\bar{\pi}[G]$ into E. Hence it sends E $(= \mathrm{cl}\,\bar{\pi}[G])$ into E $(= \mathrm{cl}\,E)$, that is, $\xi\eta \in E$ for all $\xi,\eta \in E$. □

1.3.18. PROPOSITION. *If* X *is a compact Hausdorff space and* $\langle G,X,\pi\rangle$ *is an equicontinuous ttg, i.e.* $\bar{\pi}[G]$ *is an equicontinuous subset of* X^X [)1], *then:*

(i) *The enveloping semigroup* E *of* $\langle G,X,\pi\rangle$ *is a group of continuous mappings of* X *into itself, and*

[)1] Recall that a compact Hausdorff space has a unique uniformity compatible with its topology.

(ii) $E_p = E_u$, *and this is a compact Hausdorff topological homeomorphism group.*

PROOF. Clearly, (ii) is a direct consequence of 1.2.12. The implication (ii) ⇒ (i) is trivial. □

1.3.19. REMARKS.

(i) The converse of 1.3.18 is also valid, i.e. if (i) of 1.3.18 holds, then $\bar{\pi}[G]$ is equicontinuous. The proof reads as follows: since E is compact and $E \subseteq C(X,X)$, E equals the closure of $\bar{\pi}[G]$ in $C_p(X,X)$. Therefore, by the implication (ii) ⇒ (i) in the theorem mentioned in the notes to section 1.2, the closure of $\bar{\pi}[G]$ in $C_u(X,X)$ is compact. Now a straightforward compactness argument, viz. 0.2.2(ii), shows that $\bar{\pi}[G]$ is equicontinuous (use 1.2.3(iii)).

(ii) The preceding proposition applies also to the ttg $\langle G_d, X, \pi\rangle$. This shows that the topology of G is irrelevant (this follows also from the proof).

1.3.20. NOTES. Orbit spaces are intensively explored in those parts of the theory of ttgs which have to do with bundle theory (in fact, a G-bundle is nothing but the triple $(X,c,X/C)$ for some G-space X (cf. [Hu], p.40)). One of the important questions concerning the orbit space of a ttg $\langle G,X,\pi\rangle$ is the existence of a *cross-section,* i.e. a *continuous* function $f: X/C \to X$ such that $c \circ f = 1_{X/C}$. Plainly, such a cross-section exists, whenever $\langle G,X,\pi\rangle$ is isomorphic to $\langle G, G\times(X/C), \mu_{X/C}\rangle$ as a G-space (for the precise definition of an isomorphism of G-spaces, cf. 1.4). So this problem is related to the following question: *when is a strongly effective ttg free?* (Cf. 1.1.10). For actions of the group $\mathbb{R}$, this problem is known as the question of when is a flow *parallelizable*? For some pertinent literature, cf. J. DUGUNDJI & H.A. ANTOSIEWICZ [1961] and O. HAJEK [1971]. The technique in these papers is to prove first the existence of *local* cross-sections and then "paste" them together to a global one (cf. also [St], Theorem 12.2 or [Br], Chap. II, 9.2). For the existence of local cross-sections, we have the classical WHITNEY-BEBUTOV theorem (cf. [Ha], Chap. VI, 2.13), or more generally, the existence theorem for so-called *slices* (e.g. R.S. PALAIS [1961]). For related results, cf. also Theorem 1.8 in App. II in [HM] and the paper P.S. MOSTERT [1956]. A related question is, which properties of the phase space of a ttg are inherited by the orbit space. We glanced at this subject already in 1.3.10. For more results in this direction and for some pertinent literature, we refer the reader to the notes in 4.1.11.

Concerning enveloping semigroups we can be brief here: they play an important role in certain parts of topological dynamics: cf. [El], from which 1.3.17 and 1.3.18 are taken.

1.4. Morphisms and comorphisms

1.4.1. Let $\langle G,X,\pi\rangle$ and $\langle H,Y,\sigma\rangle$ be ttgs. A *morphism of ttgs* from $\langle G,X,\pi\rangle$ to $\langle H,Y,\sigma\rangle$ is a pair $\langle\psi,f\rangle$ with ψ: $G\to H$ a continuous morphism of groups and f: $X\to Y$ a continuous function such that the following diagram commutes:

(1)

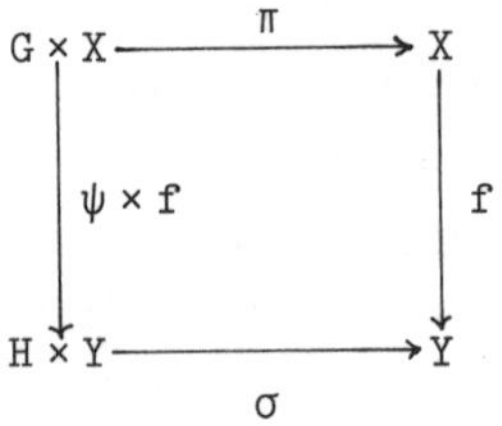

Notation: $\langle\psi,f\rangle$: $\langle G,X,\pi\rangle \to \langle H,Y,\sigma\rangle$. If $\langle\psi,f\rangle$ is a morphism of ttgs, then ψ and f are called its *group component* and its *space component*, respectively.

If G is a topological group, then a *morphism of G-spaces* from a G-space X with action π to a G-space Y with action σ is a morphism of ttgs of the form $\langle 1_G,f\rangle$: $\langle G,X,\pi\rangle \to \langle G,Y,\sigma\rangle$. In this case we shall also say that f: $X\to Y$ is a morphism of G-spaces.

A morphism $\langle\psi,f\rangle$: $\langle G,X,\pi\rangle \to \langle H,Y,\sigma\rangle$ of ttgs is said to be an *isomorphism of ttgs* whenever ψ is a topological isomorphism of G onto H and f is a homeomorphism of X onto Y. A morphism $\langle 1_G,f\rangle$: $\langle G,X,\pi\rangle \to \langle G,Y,\sigma\rangle$ of G-spaces is said to be an *isomorphism of G-spaces* whenever f is a homeomorphism of X onto Y (i.e. $\langle 1_G,f\rangle$ is an isomorphism of ttgs).

1.4.2. Let $\langle G,X,\pi\rangle$ and $\langle H,Y,\sigma\rangle$ be ttgs, ψ: $G\to H$ a continuous morphism of groups and f: $X\to Y$ a continuous function. Then $\langle\psi,f\rangle$ is a morphism of ttgs iff for all $(t,x)\in G\times X$ one of the following diagrams commutes:

(2)

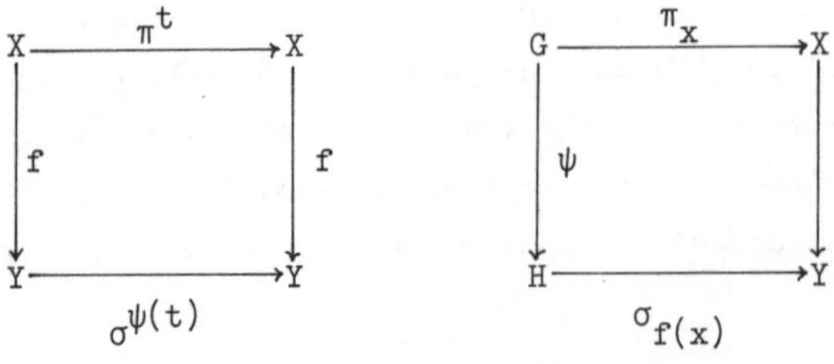

In that event, both diagrams commute for every $(t,x) \in G\times X$.

If $\langle G,X,\pi\rangle$ and $\langle G,Y,\tau\rangle$ are G-spaces, then f is a morphism of G-spaces iff for all $(t,x) \in G\times X$ one of the following diagrams commutes:

(3)

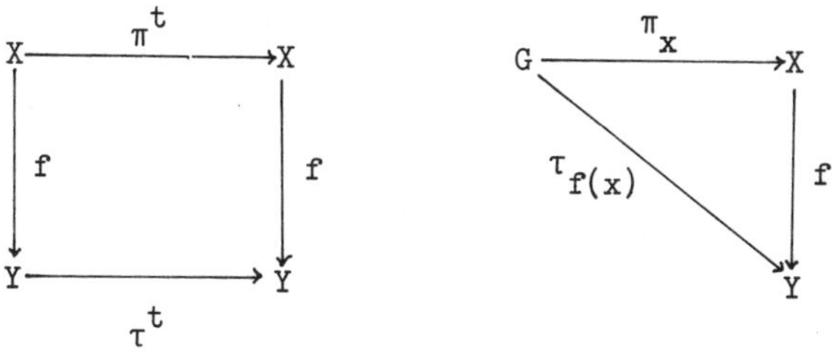

In that event, both diagrams commute for every $(t,x) \in G\times X$.

Sometimes it occurs that commutativity of the diagrams in (1) or (2) in a given situation has already been established before it is known that ψ and f are continuous. Then we say that f *is ψ-equivariant*. If (3) always commutes, then f is simply called *equivariant*. {Thus, $\langle\psi,f\rangle$ is a morphism of ttgs iff f is ψ-equivariant and both ψ and f are continuous. Similarly, f is a morphism of G-spaces iff f is equivariant and continuous.}

1.4.3. Let $\langle\psi,f\rangle : \langle G,X,\pi\rangle \to \langle H,Y,\sigma\rangle$ and $\langle\eta,g\rangle : \langle H,Y,\sigma\rangle \to \langle K,Z,\tau\rangle$ be morphisms of ttgs. Then clearly $\langle\eta\psi,gf\rangle : \langle G,X,\pi\rangle \to \langle K,Z,\tau\rangle$ is a morphism of ttgs. We call $\langle\eta\psi,gf\rangle$ the *composition* of the given morphisms $\langle\psi,f\rangle$ and $\langle\eta,g\rangle$. Notation:

$$\langle\eta,g\rangle \circ \langle\psi,f\rangle := \langle\eta\psi,gf\rangle.$$

In addition, if $\zeta := \eta\psi$ and $h := gf$, then we shall use diagrams like

(4)

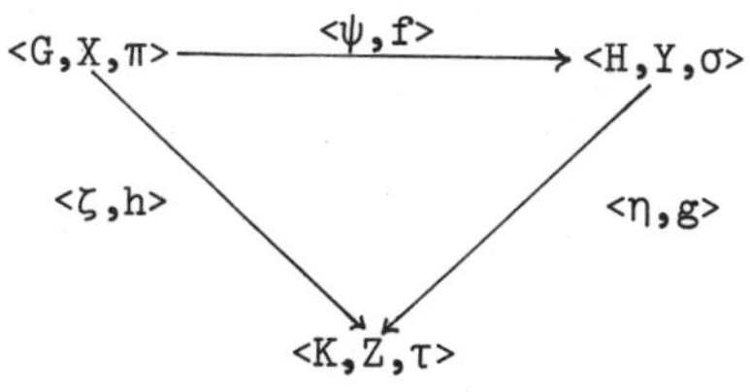

to illustrate the situation.

If in the above situation G = H = Z and $\psi = \eta = 1_G$, then, of course, $\zeta = 1_G$. In other words, *the composition of morphisms of* G*-spaces is again a morphism of* G*-spaces.*

1.4.4. <u>EXAMPLES</u>. Although we shall consider many examples of morphisms in the subsequent sections, we shall present here some simple examples.

(i) If $\langle G,X,\pi\rangle$ is any ttg, then for every $x \in X$, the motion $\pi_x\colon G \to X$ is a morphism of G-spaces from G (with action λ) to X (with action π). Cf. the diagrams (4) in 1.1.2 and (3) in 1.4.2.

(ii) If G and H are topological groups and $\psi\colon G \to H$ is a continuous morphism of groups, then $\langle\psi,\psi\rangle$ is a morphism of ttgs from $\langle G,G,\lambda(G)\rangle$ to $\langle H,H,\lambda(H)\rangle$ (recall that $\lambda(G)$ and $\lambda(H)$ are the actions of G and H on themselves by left translations; cf. 1.1.6(i)).

(iii) In the situation of (ii), $\psi\colon G \to H$ is a morphism of G-spaces from $\langle G,G,\lambda\rangle$ to $\langle G,H,\hat{\psi}\rangle$, where $\hat{\psi}\colon G\times H \to H$ is defined by $\hat{\psi}(t,u) = \psi(t)u$ for $(t,u) \in G\times H$ (cf. 1.1.6(v)).

(iv) Let H be a subgroup of the topological group G, $G\backslash H$ the space of all left cosets of H in G and $\langle G,G\backslash H,\pi\rangle$ the ttg which is described in 1.1.6(iv). Then the quotient mapping $q\colon G \to G\backslash H$ is a morphism of G-spaces from G (with action λ) onto $G\backslash H$ (with action π).

(v) Let $\langle G,X,\pi\rangle$ be a ttg and let $x \in X$. Let $G\backslash G_x$ denote the space of all left cosets of G_x in G and $q_x\colon G \to G\backslash G_x$ the quotient mapping. Since for all $s,t \in G$ we have $sx = tx$ iff $sG_x = tG_x$, there exists an injective function $\varphi_x\colon G\backslash G_x \to X$ such that $\pi_x = \varphi_x q_x$. It is easily seen that φ_x is continuous and that it is a morphism of G-spaces from $G\backslash G_x$ (cf. 1.1.6(iv)) into X. Observe, that $q_x\colon G \to G\backslash G_x$ and $\pi_x\colon G \to X$ are morphisms of G-spaces as well.

It is clear that φ_x maps $G\backslash G_x$ onto $C[x]$. So if ψ_x is the corestriction of φ_x to $C[x]$ and if j_x denotes the inclusion mapping of $C[x]$ into X then we have the following decomposition of π_x into morphisms of G-spaces (clearly, ψ_x and j_x are morphisms of G-spaces when G acts on $C[x]$ by π)

$$G \xrightarrow{\quad q_x \quad} G\backslash G_x \xrightarrow{\quad \psi_x \quad} C[x] \xrightarrow{\quad j_x \quad} X.$$

Topologically, q_x is a quotient mapping, ψ_x is a continuous bijection and j_x is a topological embedding.

In this context, the following observation is useful, namely, that *the statements*

(i) $\psi_x\colon G\backslash G_x \to C[x]$ *is a homeomorphism,*

(ii) $\pi_x\colon G \to C[x]$ *is open,*

(iii) $\pi_x\colon G \to C[x]$ *is open at* e,

are all equivalent (the proof is almost trivial).

(vi) Let $\langle G,X,\pi\rangle$ be a ttg, and consider the ttg $\langle G,E,\pi^*\rangle$, where E is the enveloping semigroup of $\langle G,X,\pi\rangle$, and π^* is the natural action of G on E (cf. 1.3.14). *Then* $\bar{\pi}:t\mapsto\pi^t : G\to E$ *is a morphism of* G*-spaces from* G *(with action* λ*) into* E *(with action* π^**).* See also (iii) above (notice that $\pi^* = \hat{\bar{\pi}}$).

For every $x\in X$, let $\delta_x: E\to X$ be defined by

$$\delta_x(\xi) := \xi(x)$$

($\xi\in E$). Obviously, δ_x is continuous. Moreover, $\delta_x(\pi^t) = \pi^t x = \pi_x t$, so that $\delta_x\bar{\pi}[G] = C_\pi[x]$. Since $\bar{\pi}[G]$ is dense in E, this implies that

$$\delta_x[E] \subseteq \mathrm{cl}\, C_\pi[x] =: K_\pi[x].$$

It is clear that we have equality here iff $\delta_x[E]$ is closed in X. In particular, if X is a *compact Hausdorff* space, then E is compact, hence $\delta_x[E]$ is closed in X, and $\delta_x[E] = K_\pi[x]$.

It is clear that, *for any ttg* $\langle G,X,\pi\rangle$ *and* $x\in X$, δ_x *is a morphism of* G*-spaces from* E *(with action* π^**) into* X *(with action* π*).* Indeed, if $t\in G$ and $\xi\in E$, then

$$\delta_x\pi^*(t,\xi) = \delta_x(\pi^t\circ\xi) = \pi^t\xi(x) = \pi(t,\delta_x\xi).$$

If $\langle G,X,\pi\rangle$ is *equicontinuous* and, in addition, X is a *compact Hausdorff* space, then E is a compact Hausdorff topological homeomorphism group; cf. 1.3.18. In that case, $\langle E,X,\delta\rangle$ is a ttg (here δ is defined by $\delta(\xi,x) := \xi(x)$, in accordance with the definition of δ_x above). In addition, $\langle\bar{\pi},1_X\rangle: \langle G,X,\pi\rangle \to \langle E,X,\delta\rangle$ is a morphism of ttgs.

1.4.5. Let $\langle\psi,f\rangle: \langle G,X,\pi\rangle \to \langle H,Y,\sigma\rangle$ be a morphism of ttgs. If $A\subseteq X$ is invariant under a subset S of G, then f[A] is invariant under the subset $\psi[S]$ of H. Hence $\mathrm{cl}_Y f[X]$ is invariant under $\mathrm{cl}_H\,\psi[S]$ (cf. 1.3.3). In addition, if $B\subseteq Y$ is invariant under a subset T of H, then $f^{\leftarrow}[B]$ is invariant under $\psi^{\leftarrow}[T]$. In particular, for each $x\in X$, $f^{\leftarrow}C_\sigma[f(x)]$ is an invariant subset of X. Since it contains x, it includes all of $C_\pi[x]$. Hence

(5) $$f[C_\pi[x]] \subseteq C_\sigma[f(x)].$$

If ψ is a surjection, then the inclusion in (5) is easily seen to be an equality. In fact, then the image under f of any invariant subset of X is an invariant subset of Y.

1.4.6. LEMMA. *Let* $\langle G,X,\pi\rangle$ *and* $\langle H,Y,\sigma\rangle$ *be ttgs and* $f: X\to Y$ *a continuous function. Then there exists a continuous function* $f': X/C_\pi \to Y/C_\sigma$ *such that* $f'c_\pi = c_\sigma f$ *iff for all* $x\in X$*, the inclusion* $f[C_\pi[x]] \subseteq C_\sigma[f(x)]$ *is valid.*

PROOF. Obvious. □

1.4.7. PROPOSITION. *If* $\langle\psi,f\rangle: \langle G,X,\pi\rangle \to \langle H,Y,\sigma\rangle$ *is a morphism of ttgs, then there exists a unique continuous function* $f': X/C_\pi \to Y/C_\sigma$ *with the property that* $f'c_\pi = c_\sigma f$.

PROOF. Use 1.4.5 and 1.4.6. □

1.4.8. If $\langle\psi,f\rangle: \langle G,X,\pi\rangle \to \langle H,Y,\sigma\rangle$ is a morphism of ttgs, then the function $f': X/C_\pi \to Y/C_\sigma$ for which $f'c_\pi = c_\sigma f$ will be called *the continuous mapping of orbit spaces, induced by* $\langle\psi,f\rangle$.

In general, f is not uniquely determined by f'. For example, all G-endomorphisms of a G-space which consists of one orbit induce the identity mapping of the (one-point) orbit space onto itself.

1.4.9. PROPOSITION. *Let* $\langle\psi,f\rangle: \langle G,X,\pi\rangle \to \langle H,Y,\sigma\rangle$ *be a morphism of ttgs. If* f *is an open mapping then* $f': X/C_\pi \to Y/C_\sigma$ *is open as well. If* f *is relatively open and, in addition,* ψ *is a surjection of* G *onto* H*, then* f' *is relatively open.*

PROOF. The first statement is almost trivial. In order to prove the second one, consider an open subset U of X/C_π. Then $f\overleftarrow{c_\pi}[U] = f[X]\cap V$ for some open subset V of Y. Since $f\overleftarrow{c_\pi}[U]$ and $f[X]$ are H-invariant subsets of Y, it follows easily that $f[X]\cap V = f[X]\cap\sigma[H\times V]$. Therefore, we may suppose that V is H-invariant. Hence, $f'[U] = f'[X/C_\pi]\cap c_\sigma[V]$ with $c_\sigma[V]$ open in Y/C_σ. □

1.4.10. COROLLARY. *If* A *is an invariant subset of the ttg* $\langle G,X,\pi\rangle$*, then the inclusion mapping* $i: A\to X$ *is a morphism of* G*-spaces from* A *(with action* π*) into* X *(with action* π*), and the mapping* $i': A/C_\pi \to X/C_\pi$ *induced by* i*, is a topological embedding. Consequently, if* Z *is any subset of* X/C_π*, then the orbit space of* $\langle G,\overleftarrow{c_\pi}[Z],\pi\rangle$ *may be identified with* Z *in the obvious way.* □

1.4.11. PROPOSITION. *Let* $\langle\psi,f\rangle: \langle G,X,\pi\rangle \to \langle H,Y,\sigma\rangle$ *be a morphism of ttgs, where* X *and* Y *are uniform Hausdorff spaces, and* f *is uniformly continuous. If* Y *is complete and if* f *is surjective, then there exists a unique continuous morphism of semigroups* $f'': E_X\to E_Y$ *such that the following diagram commutes for every* $x\in X$:

(6) 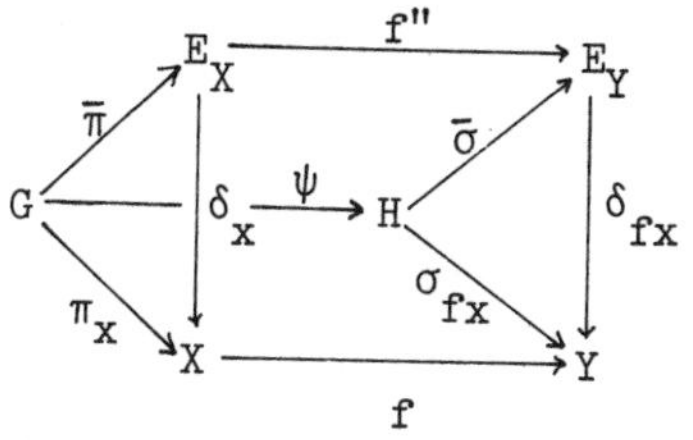

In particular, it follows that $\langle\psi, f''\rangle: \langle G, E_X, \pi^*\rangle \to \langle H, E_Y, \sigma^*\rangle$ *is a morphism of ttgs.*

<u>PROOF</u>. Let us first observe that the topologies of X^X, Y^Y and their subspaces are generated by the weakest uniformities making all evaluations on these spaces uniformly continuous. We shall first define $f^\wedge: \bar{\pi}[G] \to \bar{\sigma}[H] \subseteq Y^Y$ in such a way that $f^\wedge$ is easily seen to be uniformly continuous. Since Y^Y is a complete uniform space and $\bar{\pi}[G]$ is dense in E_X, $f^\wedge$ has a unique uniformly continuous extension denoted by f'', mapping E_X into $\mathrm{cl}\,\bar{\sigma}[H] = E_Y$ (cf. [Bo], Chap. II, §3.6, Theorem 2).

So let us define $f^\wedge$ on $\bar{\pi}[G]$ by $f^\wedge(\pi^t) := \sigma^{\psi(t)}$ $(t \in G)$. This definition is unambiguous, because $\pi^t = \pi^s$ implies $\sigma^{\psi(t)}f = \sigma^{\psi(s)}f$, whence $\sigma^{\psi(t)} = \sigma^{\psi(s)}$ (f is surjective!). Now $f^\wedge: \bar{\pi}[G] \to Y^Y$ is uniformly continuous, because $\delta_y \circ f^\wedge: \bar{\pi}[G] \to Y$ is uniformly continuous for every $y \in Y$. Indeed, if $y \in Y$, then $y = f(x)$ for some $x \in X$, and $\delta_{fx} \circ f^\wedge = f \circ \delta_x$ with δ_x and f uniformly continuous. So we can extend $f^\wedge$ to $f'': E_X \to E_Y$ in the way described above.

Finally, the requirements that f'' is a morphism of semigroups, that (6) commutes and that $\langle\psi, f''\rangle$ is a morphism of ttgs can be expressed as equations of continuous functions. These equations are easily seen to hold on dense subspaces of the spaces under consideration. Hence they hold everywhere. The details are left to the reader. □

1.4.12. The conclusions of the preceding proposition are in particular valid if X and Y are *compact Hausdorff* spaces and f is a continuous ψ-equivariant surjection: then f is uniformly continuous with respect to the (unique) uniformities for X and Y.

1.4.13. In this section we have obviously defined a category **TTG'** whose objects are ttgs, and whose morphisms are the ordered pairs $\langle\psi, f\rangle$ satisfying diagram (1) in 1.4.1. In addition, 1.4.7 shows that the assignment of the orbit space to a ttg is functorial on all of **TTG'**, and 1.4.11 shows that the same is true for enveloping semigroups on a suitable subcategory of TTG.

However, in considering invariant subsets of a ttg $\langle H,Y,\sigma\rangle$ another definition of a "morphism of ttgs" may come to one's mind. If X is an invariant subset of Y, set $G := \{\sigma^t|_X : t \in H\}$. Then G is a subgroup of $H(X,X)$, and $\psi: t \mapsto \sigma^t|_X: H \to G$ is a morphism of groups. If we give G the finest topology making ψ continuous, then $\delta: (\xi,y) \mapsto \xi(y): G \times X \to X$ is continuous, and $\langle G,X,\delta\rangle$ is a ttg (apply 1.1.15 to the ttg $\langle H,X,\sigma\rangle$). If $f: X \to Y$ denotes the inclusion mapping, then the following diagram commutes for all $t \in H$:

(11) 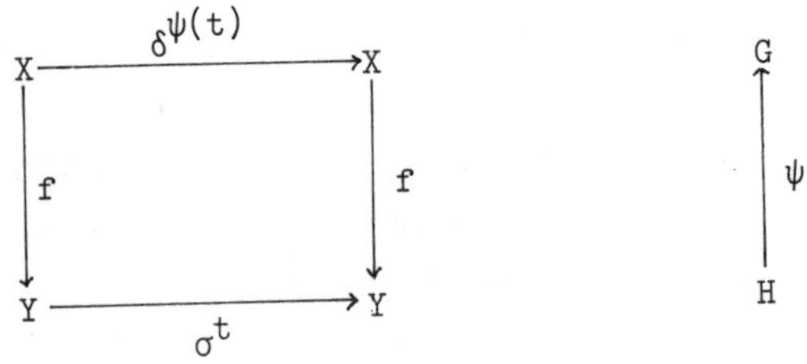

This motivates the following definition:

1.4.14. If $\langle G,X,\pi\rangle$ and $\langle H,Y,\sigma\rangle$ are ttgs, then a pair $\langle\psi^{op},f\rangle$ is called a *comorphism* of ttgs from $\langle G,X,\pi\rangle$ to $\langle H,Y,\sigma\rangle$, if $\psi: H \to G$ is a continuous morphism of groups)1, $f: X \to Y$ a continuous function, and for each $t \in H$ the diagram (11) commutes (with δ replaced by π).
Notation: $\langle\psi^{op},f\rangle: \langle G,X,\pi\rangle \to \langle H,Y,\sigma\rangle$. In this situation, ψ and f are called the *group component* and the *space component* of the comorphism, respectively.

1.4.15. Notice that the direction of a comorphism is the same as the direction of its space component. This choice is more or less arbitrary, but now we have the advantage that what we would like to call *a comorphism of G-spaces* (i.e. $H = G$ and $\psi = 1_G$ in definition 1.4.14) *is exactly the same as a morphism of G-spaces.*

1.4.16. If $\langle\psi^{op},f\rangle$ and $\langle\eta^{op},g\rangle$ are comorphisms of ttgs, and the codomain of $\langle\psi^{op},f\rangle$ equals the domain of $\langle\eta^{op},g\rangle$, then $\langle(\psi\eta)^{op},gf\rangle$ is a comorphism of ttgs.
Notation: $\langle(\psi\eta)^{op},gf\rangle =: \langle\eta^{op},g\rangle \circ \langle\psi^{op},f\rangle$.

)1 If $\psi: H \to G$ is a continuous morphism of groups, we shall express this some- times by writing $\psi^{op}: G \to H$. Cf. 6.1 for the proper context of this notati

Obviously, we have defined now another category, denoted TTG_*. Its objects are just all ordinary ttgs and its morphisms are the comorphisms, defined in 1.4.14. We shall have now a brief look at the behaviour of orbit spaces and enveloping semigroups with respect to comorphisms.

1.4.17. <u>PROPOSITION</u>. *Let* $\langle\psi^{op},f\rangle: \langle G,X,\pi\rangle \to \langle H,Y,\sigma\rangle$ *be a comorphism of ttgs. If* $\psi: H \to G$ *is surjective then there exists a unique continuous function* $f': X/C_\pi \to Y/C_\sigma$ *such that* $f'c_\pi = c_\sigma f$.

<u>PROOF</u>. Straightforward. □

1.4.18. <u>PROPOSITION</u>. *Let* $\langle\psi^{op},f\rangle: \langle G,X,\pi\rangle \to \langle H,Y,\sigma\rangle$ *be a comorphism of ttgs, where* Y *is a uniform Hausdorff space,* X *is a subspace of* Y *and* $f: X \to Y$ *is the inclusion mapping. If* X *is complete then there exists a unique continuous morphism of semigroups* $f'': E_Y \to E_X$ *such that the following diagram commutes for every* $x \in X$:

$$\begin{array}{ccc} E_X & \xleftarrow{\;f''\;} & E_Y \\ \downarrow{\scriptstyle \delta_x} & & \downarrow{\scriptstyle \delta_{fx}} \\ X & \xrightarrow{\;f\;} & Y \end{array}$$

Moreover, $\langle\psi^{op},f''\rangle: \langle H,E_Y,\sigma^*\rangle \to \langle G,E_X,\pi^*\rangle$ *is a morphism of ttgs.*

<u>PROOF</u>. Similar to 1.4.11. □

1.4.19. <u>NOTES</u>. There exist several other definitions of "morphisms of ttgs". Cf. O. HAJEK [1968]. The concept of a comorphism seems to be new, like propositions 1.4.17 and 1.4.18. However, 1.4.17 is an obvious adaptation of the well-known proposition 1.4.7. A similar remark holds with respect to 1.4.18 and 1.4.11. Here it may be noticed that 1.4.11 slightly generalizes [El] 3.8, where only the compact case has been treated.

1.5. <u>Operations on ttgs</u>

1.5.1. The operations we have in mind are the usual ones on topological groups and on topological spaces, but now combined in order to obtain operations on ttgs. Most of these operations are exactly what they are expected to be. These will not be treated here: we shall mention them here with a reference to the place where they are treated in more detail.

Subobjects: 1.3.4, 3.1.12(ii) and 3.2.6.

Products : 3.1.12(i) and 3.2.6.

Coproducts: 3.4.12 and 3.4.2.

In this section we shall consider only some questions related to the formation of quotients.

1.5.2. Let $\langle G,X,\pi\rangle$ be a ttg and let $H \subseteq G$. Then an equivalence relation R on X is said to be *invariant under* H *or* H-*invariant* whenever $(x,y) \in R$ implies $(tx,ty) \in R$ for all $t \in H$. If R is a G-invariant equivalence relation, then R will simply be called *invariant.*

1.5.3. Let $\langle G,X,\pi\rangle$ be a ttg and let R be an invariant equivalence relation on X, with quotient map $q: X \to X/R$. Since $q(x) = q(y)$ implies $q(tx) = q(ty)$ for all $t \in G$ $(x,y \in X)$, it follows that there exists a *unique* function $\tau: G \times (X/R) \to X/R$ such that the following diagram commutes:

(1)
$$\begin{array}{ccc} G \times X & \xrightarrow{\quad \pi \quad} & X \\ \downarrow{\scriptstyle 1_G \times q} & & \downarrow{\scriptstyle q} \\ G \times (X/R) & \xrightarrow[\quad \tau \quad]{} & X/R \end{array}$$

Equivalently, τ is the unique mapping such that

(2) $$\tau^t q(x) = q(\pi^t x)$$

for all $t \in G$ and $x \in X$ (uniqueness: q is surjective).

1.5.4. In the sequel, up to 1.5.10, we shall use the notation of 1.5.3. In particular, the symbols s,t will always denote elements of G, and x,y will denote elements of X. Notice that each point in X/R is of the form q(x), because q is a surjection.

1.5.5. *The function* $\tau: G \times (X/R) \to X/R$ *is separately continuous and, in addition, it is an action of* G_d *on* X/R. *It is the unique action of* G_d *on* X/R *making* q *a morphism of* G_d*-spaces, from* X *(with action* π*; cf.* 1.1.5*) onto* X/R.

Continuity of each $\tau_{q(x)}$ is obvious from the equality $\tau_{q(x)} = q\pi_x$, and continuity of any τ^t follows from the continuity of its composition with the quotient mapping q, which equals $q\pi^t$. The other statements are easily verified.

1.5.6. In 1.5.11 below we present an example which shows that τ may be not continuous. Notice that τ *is the only candidate for an action of* G *on* X/R *for which* q: $X \to X/R$ *is a morphism of* G*-spaces from* $\langle G,X,\pi\rangle$ *to* $\langle G,X/R,\tau\rangle$.

1.5.7. PROPOSITION. *If one of the following conditions is fulfilled, then* τ *is continuous, i.e. then* τ *is the unique action of* G *on* X/R *making* q *a morphism of* G*-spaces:*

(i) R *is an open equivalence relation, i.e.* q *is an open mapping.*

(ii) R *is a closed equivalence relation and each equivalence class* R[x] *is compact, i.e.* q *is a perfect mapping.*

(iii) G *is a locally compact Hausdorff group.*

(iv) $G \times (X/R)$ *is a k-space.*

PROOF. Apply 0.2.4. □

1.5.8. COROLLARY 1. *Suppose we are given another action on* X*, say* $\sigma: H \times X \to X$*, where* H *is any topological group, and suppose that* σ *commutes with* π*, i.e.*

(3) $$\sigma^t\pi^s = \pi^s\sigma^t \quad (s \in G,\ t \in H).$$

Then there exists a unique action τ *of* G *on* X/C_σ *such that* $c_\sigma: X \to X/C_\sigma$ *is a morphism of* G*-spaces (*X *with action* π *and* X/C_σ *with action* τ*).*

PROOF. Use 1.5.7(i) with $R = C_\sigma$, hence $q = c_\sigma$ (keep in mind that c_σ is an open mapping; cf. 1.3.9). □

1.5.9. In 1.5.8, (3) is used in order to prove that C_σ is an invariant equivalence relation in X. For this, however, it would be sufficient to require

(4) $$\forall (s,t) \in G \times H,\ \exists t' \in H : \sigma^{t'}\pi^s = \pi^s\sigma^t.$$

This condition will certainly be fulfilled if H is a normal subgroup of G and $\sigma = \pi|_{H\times X}$ (i.e. $\sigma^t = \pi^t$ for every $t \in H$). In this case, we obtain an action τ of G on X/C_σ, making c_σ a morphism of G-spaces. Obviously, $H \subseteq \operatorname{Ker}\bar{\tau}$, hence $\bar{\tau}: G \to \bar{\tau}[G]$ factorizes over the quotient mapping $\psi: G \to G/H$, as follows:

(5)
$$\begin{array}{ccc} G & \xrightarrow{\;\bar{\tau}\;} & \bar{\tau}[G] \\ {\scriptstyle\psi}\big\downarrow & \nearrow{\scriptstyle\alpha} & \\ G/H & & \end{array}$$

Now we can define $\tau'\colon (G/H)\times(X/C_\sigma) \to X/C_\sigma$ by the rule

(6) $$\tau'(u,z) := \alpha(u)(z)$$

for $u \in G/H$ and $z \in X/C_\sigma$. Since α is a morphism of groups (notice that H was assumed to be a *normal* subgroup of G), τ' is plainly an action of $(G/H)_d$ on X/C_σ. However, by (5) and (6), $\tau'(\psi(t),c_\sigma(x)) = \bar{\tau}(t)(c_\sigma x) = \tau(t,c_\sigma(x)) = c_\sigma(\pi(t,x))$, so the following diagram commutes:

(7)
$$\begin{array}{ccc} G\times X & \xrightarrow{\;\pi\;} & X \\ {\scriptstyle\psi\times c_\sigma}\big\downarrow & & \big\downarrow{\scriptstyle c_\sigma} \\ (G/H)\times(X/C_\sigma) & \xrightarrow[\;\tau'\;]{} & X/C_\sigma \end{array}$$

It follows, that the mapping $\tau'\circ(\psi\times c_\sigma)$ is continuous. Since ψ and c_σ are both open mappings, $\psi\times c_\sigma$ is a quotient mapping. Hence τ' is continuous. *So we have the ttg* $\langle G/H, X/C_\sigma, \tau'\rangle$ *and by* (7), $\langle\psi,c_\sigma\rangle$ *is a morphism of ttgs. Moreover,* τ' *is the unique action of* G/H *on* X/C_σ *making* $\langle\psi,c_\sigma\rangle$ *a morphism of ttgs.*

We shall see later, in 3.3.15, that the preceding construction is a special case of a more general one with nice functorial properties.

1.5.10. COROLLARY 2. *Let* $\langle G,Y,\sigma\rangle$ *be a ttg and let* A *be a closed invariant subset of* Y. *Then there exists a unique action* τ *of* G *on* $Y\cup_A Y$ *such that the canonical injections* $f_1,f_2\colon Y \to Y\cup_A Y$ *are morphisms of G-spaces.*

PROOF. Recall that the space $Y\cup_A Y$ is obtained in the following way: first, form $X := Y\times\{1,2\}$, the disjoint union of two copies of Y, then form the quotient space $Y\cup_A Y := X/R$, where R is the equivalence relation $\{(x,x) : x\in X\} \cup \{((a,1),(a,2)) : a\in A\}$ in X. Notice that we have canonical embeddings

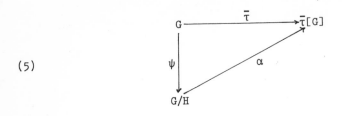

$r_i: y \longmapsto (y,i): Y \to X$, and that $f_i := qr_i$ $(i=1,2)$.

Define $\pi: G\times X \to X$ by $\pi^t(y,i) := (\sigma^t y,i)$ for $t \in G$, $y \in Y$ and $i = 1,2$. Then π is continuous, $\langle G,X,\pi\rangle$ is a ttg, and $r_1,r_2: Y \to X$ are morphisms of G-spaces. Now apply 1.5.7(ii) to the ttg $\langle G,X,\pi\rangle$ and the equivalence relation R in X, which is obviously invariant. Notice that R is a closed equivalence relation in X because A is closed in Y; each equivalence class R[x] is compact, since it consists of at most two points. □

1.5.11. EXAMPLE. In 0.2.5 we described a locally compact Hausdorff space X and an equivalence relation R on X such that on $\mathbb{Q} \times (X/R)$ the quotient topology induced by $1_{\mathbb{Q}}\times f: \mathbb{Q}\times X \to \mathbb{Q}\times(X/R)$ ($f: X\to X/R$ the quotient mapping) is strictly finer than the product topology on $\mathbb{Q} \times (X/R)$. If $\mathbb{Q} \times (X/R)$ is endowed with this quotient topology, we shall indicate this by writing $\mathbb{Q} \boxtimes (X/R)$ for this space.

Consider the ttg $\langle \mathbb{Q},\mathbb{Q}\times X,\mu_X\rangle$ (cf. 1.1.6(ii)). Let $D_{\mathbb{Q}} := \{(t,t) : t\in\mathbb{Q}\}$; then $D_{\mathbb{Q}}\times R$ is clearly an invariant equivalence relation in $\mathbb{Q} \times X$. Observe that the quotient mapping $q: \mathbb{Q}\times X \to (\mathbb{Q}\times X)/(D_{\mathbb{Q}}\times R)$ just equals $1_{\mathbb{Q}}\times f: \mathbb{Q}\times X \to \mathbb{Q} \boxtimes (X/R)$. The induced action τ of $\mathbb{Q}_d$ on $\mathbb{Q} \boxtimes (X/R)$ making $1_{\mathbb{Q}}\times f$ a morphism of $\mathbb{Q}_d$-spaces is given by $\tau(t,(s,f(x))) = (t+s,f(x))$. *We claim that* τ: $\mathbb{Q} \times (\mathbb{Q}\boxtimes(X/R)) \to \mathbb{Q} \boxtimes (X/R)$ *is not continuous.*

Suppose it were. Then in particular the mapping $(s,0,y) \longmapsto (s,y)$: $\mathbb{Q} \times A \to \mathbb{Q} \boxtimes (X/R)$ would be continuous, where $A := \{(0,y) : y \in X/R\} \subseteq \mathbb{Q} \boxtimes (X/R)$. Now A is a closed subspace of the quotient space $\mathbb{Q} \boxtimes (X/R)$, hence its topology equals the quotient topology when considered as a quotient space of $\{0\} \times X$; cf. [Du], Chap.VI, 4.2. So A may be identified with X/R, and the domain of the above mapping may be identified with $\mathbb{Q} \times (X/R)$ in its product topology. It would follow that this product topology is finer than the quotient topology, which is not true.

Remark. In the above example, $\mathbb{Q}$ is a k-space and X is a locally compact T_2-space, hence $\mathbb{Q} \times X$ is a k-space. Moreover, $\mathbb{Q} \boxtimes (X/R)$ with the quotient topology induced by $1_{\mathbb{Q}}\times f$ is a T_2-space, hence it is a k-space, by [Du], Chap. XI, Cor. 9.5.

If $\mathbb{Q} \times (\mathbb{Q}\boxtimes(X/R))$ were a k-space, then by 1.5.7(iv), the action τ of $\mathbb{Q}_d$ on $\mathbb{Q} \boxtimes (X/R)$ would be continuous on $\mathbb{Q} \times (\mathbb{Q} \boxtimes (X/R))$, which we just proved to be not true. Consequently, the product of the k-space $\mathbb{Q}$ and $\mathbb{Q} \boxtimes (X/R)$ is not a k-space (another example is given in [Du], Ex. 5 on p.132).

2 - ACTIONS OF GROUPS ON SPACES OF FUNCTIONS

Aim of this section is to provide some examples of ttgs which will be needed in the following chapters. In subsection 2.1 we study the action of a topological group G on the space $C_c(G,Y)$ by means of right translations, where Y is a topological space, fixed throughout the discussion. The most interesting applications are those with $Y = \mathbb{F}$; however, it will only rarely be assumed that $Y = \mathbb{F}$. In general, right translation in $C_c(G,Y)$ is only separately continuous; if G is locally compact T_2, then it is simultaneously continuous, and we have, indeed, an action of G on $C_c(G,Y)$. If G is not locally compact, but under the assumption that Y is a uniform space, right translation is at least simultaneously continuous on orbit closures of elements of RUC(G,Y). Moreover, these orbit closures are compact in the compact-open topology. In addition, we shall consider briefly the subspace $\{\pi_y : y\in Y\}$ of $C_c(G,Y)$ when π is an action of G on Y. This will turn out to be important for the considerations in §7.

If Y is a uniform space, right translations of G on $C_u(G,Y)$ are the context in which almost periodic functions are to be studied. We shall make some remarks about them in subsection 2.2. Here the original definition of H. BOHR is employed, and the difference between left and right almost periodicity (which does not occur if one uses the VON NEUMANN definition) is discussed.

Finally, we consider right translations in $L^p(G)$ and so-called weighted translations in $L^2(G)$, where G is a locally compact Hausdorff group. The results on weighted translations in $L^2(G)$ (subsection 2.4) will be needed in 8.2 for theorems on linearization of actions.

Most material in this section, except perhaps subsection 2.4, is well-known in one form or another, and can be omitted at first reading.

Notation. Throughout this section, the following notation will be used.

G: any topological group (which may be subjected to conditions like local compactness, etc.).

Y: any topological space (which may be specified to be $\mathbb{R}$ or $\mathbb{C}$, or which may otherwise be subjected to conditions of being a uniform space, etc.).

$\tilde{\rho}$: this is a short-hand notation for the mapping $\tilde{\rho}_Y^G\colon G\times Y^G \to Y^G$, defined by $[(\tilde{\rho}_Y^G)^t f](s) := f(st)$ for $f \in Y^G$ and $s,t \in G$ (*right translations* in Y^G).

We shall make an intensive use of the notational convention in 1.3.4: if $A \subseteq Y^G$ and $\tilde{\rho}[G\times A] \subseteq A$ (i.e. A is *right invariant*) then the restriction and corestriction of $\tilde{\rho}$ to the domain $G \times A$ and the codomain A will be denoted also by $\tilde{\rho}$.

2.1. Action of a group G on $C_c(G,Y)$

2.1.1. Obviously, $\tilde{\rho}$ is an action of G_d on the space Y^G with its discrete topology: in fact, it is easy to see that $\tilde{\rho}^e$ is the identity mapping on Y^G, and $\tilde{\rho}^s\tilde{\rho}^t = \tilde{\rho}^{st}$ for all $s,t \in G$. In addition, it is easy to see that $C(G,Y)$ is a right invariant subspace of Y^G.

2.1.2. PROPOSITION. *The mapping* $\tilde{\rho}\colon G\times C_c(G,Y) \to C_c(G,Y)$ *is separately continuous. Consequently,* $\langle G_d, C_c(G,Y), \tilde{\rho}\rangle$ *is a ttg.*

PROOF. If $K \subseteq G$ is compact and $U \subseteq Y$ is open, then for all $t \in G$ we have (cf. 0.2.6 for notation):

$$\tilde{\rho}^t N(Kt,U) = N(K,U). \tag{1}$$

This shows that $\tilde{\rho}^t\colon C_c(G,Y) \to C_c(G,Y)$ is continuous.

In addition, if $f \in N(K,U)$, then $K \subseteq \overleftarrow{f}[U]$, where $\overleftarrow{f}[U]$ is open in G. By compactness of K, there exists $V \in \mathcal{V}_e$ such that $KV \subseteq \overleftarrow{f}[U]$, hence $\tilde{\rho}^s f \in N(K,U)$ for all $s \in V$, that is, $\tilde{\rho}_f[V] \subseteq N(K,U)$. It follows that $\tilde{\rho}$ is continuous at e. By (1), it follows easily that $\tilde{\rho}_f$ is continuous at any point $t \in G$. □

2.1.3. THEOREM. *If* G *is a locally compact Hausdorff group, then* $\tilde{\rho}\colon G\times C_c(G,Y) \to C_c(G,Y)$ *is continuous, and, consequently,* $\langle G, C_c(G,Y), \tilde{\rho}\rangle$ *is a ttg.*

PROOF. By 2.1.2, each $\tilde{\rho}_f$: $G \to C_c(G,Y)$ is continuous ($f \in C_c(G,Y)$). So in view of 0.2.7(iii) it is sufficient to show that the mapping $f \mapsto \tilde{\rho}_f$: $C_c(G,Y) \to C_c(G,C_c(G,Y))$ is continuous. Now the codomain of this mapping may be identified with $C_c(G\times G,Y)$ according to 0.2.7(iii). In doing so, $\tilde{\rho}_f$ corresponds to $f \circ \rho$, where $\rho(s,t) = ts$ for $s,t \in G$. So we have to prove that the mapping $f \mapsto f \circ \rho$: $C_c(G,Y) \to C_c(G\times G,Y)$ is continuous. This is easy and well-known (cf. [Du], Chap. XII, 2.1). □

2.1.4. If G is not locally compact, then $\tilde{\rho}$ may be not continuous on $G \times C_c(G,Y)$. To see this, first observe *that continuity of* $\tilde{\rho}$: $G\times C_c(G,Y) \to C_c(G,Y)$ *implies continuity of the evaluation mapping* $\delta:(f,t) \mapsto f(t) = \tilde{\rho}^t f(e)$: $C_c(G,Y)\times G \to Y$. By the result of ARENS, mentioned in 0.2.7, this is impossible if G is not locally compact (e.g. $G = \mathbb{Q}$) and $Y = [0,1]$.

2.1.5. If G is not locally compact, there still are certain useful right invariant subspaces of $C_c(G,Y)$ on which G acts continuously by means of $\tilde{\rho}$. For simplicity, let us assume from now on up to 2.1.11 that Y *is a uniform Hausdorff space with uniformity* $\mathcal{U}$.

2.1.6. LEMMA. *The mapping* $\tilde{\rho}$: $G\times C_c(G,Y) \to C_c(G,Y)$ *is continuous on each set* $G\times A$ *with* $A \subseteq C(G,Y)$ *such that* A *is equicontinuous at each point of* G.

PROOF. By equicontinuity $A_c = A_p$ and in addition, the mapping $(f,t) \mapsto f(t)$: $A_p \times G \to Y$ is continuous (cf. 1.2.3(iii)). Therefore, the mapping $\Delta:(f,s,t) \mapsto f(ts)$: $(A_p \times G)\times G \to Y$ is continuous. So for any compact subset K of G, the set $\{\Delta_t : t\in K\}$ of functions from $A_p \times G$ to Y is equicontinuous (cf. 0.2.2(ii)).

Let $f \in A_p$, $s \in G$, and let $M(K,\alpha)$ be a typical element of the uniform base of $C_c(G,Y)$, where K is a compact subset of G and $\alpha \in \mathcal{U}$. By equicontinuity of $\{\Delta_t : t\in K\}$ on $A_p \times G$ at the point (f,s), there are neighbourhoods of f in A_p and of s in G, say U and V respectively, such that $(\Delta_t(g,v),\Delta_t(f,s)) \in \alpha$ for all $g \in U$ and $v \in V$, and all $t \in K$. That is, $(\tilde{\rho}^v g,\tilde{\rho}^s f) \in M(K,\alpha)$ for all $(v,g) \in V\times U$. This proves continuity of $\tilde{\rho}$ on $G \times A_p$ at the point (f,s). □

2.1.7. Recall that the orbit of $f \in C_c(G,Y)$ under the action $\tilde{\rho}$ of G_d on $C_c(G,Y)$ is denoted by $C_{\tilde{\rho}}[f]$. The orbit-closure of f, that is, the closure of $C_{\tilde{\rho}}[f]$ in $C_c(G,Y)$ is denoted by $K_{\tilde{\rho}}[f]$.

2.1.8. LEMMA. *For* $f \in C_c(G,Y)$ *the following conditions are equivalent:*
(i) $f \in \mathrm{RUC}(G,Y)$.
(ii) $C_{\tilde\rho}[f]$ *is equicontinuous on* G.
(iii) $K_{\tilde\rho}[f]$ *is equicontinuous on* G.
(iv) $K_{\tilde\rho}[f] \subseteq \mathrm{RUC}(G,Y)$.
If these conditions are fulfilled then $\tilde\rho$: $G \times K_{\tilde\rho}[f] \to K_{\tilde\rho}[f]$ *is continuous. If, in addition,* $f[G]$ *is relatively compact in* Y, *then* $K_{\tilde\rho}[f]$ *is a compact subspace of* $\mathrm{RUC}_c(G,Y)$. *In that case, as a set and as a topological space,* $K_{\tilde\rho}[f]$ *equals the closure of* $C_{\tilde\rho}[f]$ *in* Y^G.

PROOF.
(i) $\Leftrightarrow$ (ii) : An immediate consequence of the definitions.
(ii) $\Leftrightarrow$ (iii): Cf. 0.2.8(i).
(iii) $\Rightarrow$ (iv) : If $K_{\tilde\rho}[f]$ is equicontinuous on G, then for all $g \in K_{\tilde\rho}[f]$, $C_{\tilde\rho}[g] \subseteq K_{\tilde\rho}[f]$, hence $C_{\tilde\rho}[g]$ is equicontinuous on G, and $g \in \mathrm{RUC}(G,Y)$, by the implication (ii) $\Rightarrow$ (i) above.
(iv) $\Rightarrow$ (i) : Obvious.

The other statements follow easily from 0.2.8, using the obvious observation that for each $t \in G$, $(C_{\tilde\rho}[f])(t) = f[G]$. □

2.1.9. PROPOSITION. $\mathrm{RUC}^*(G,Y)$ *is an invariant subset of the ttg* $\langle G_d, C_c(G,Y), \tilde\rho\rangle$. *Moreover, for each* $f \in \mathrm{RUC}^*(G,Y)$, $K_{\tilde\rho}[f]$ *is a compact invariant subset of* $\mathrm{RUC}^*(G,Y)$, *and* $\tilde\rho$: $G \times K_{\tilde\rho}[f] \to K_{\tilde\rho}[f]$ *is continuous. Hence* $\langle G, K_{\tilde\rho}[f], \tilde\rho\rangle$ *is a ttg with a compact Hausdorff phase space.*)1

PROOF. Use 2.1.6 and 2.1.8. □

2.1.10. In general, $\tilde\rho$: $G \times \mathrm{RUC}^*_c(G,Y) \to \mathrm{RUC}^*_c(G,Y)$ is not continuous. In fact, if $Y = [0,1]$ (consequently, also if $Y = \mathbb{R}$ or $Y = \mathbb{C}$), then continuity of $\tilde\rho$ implies that G is locally compact. Cf. the remark preceding the final lemma in 0.2.7 and use the method of 2.1.4.

2.1.11. We have shown in 2.1.9 that each point of $\mathrm{RUC}^*(G,Y)$ has a compact orbit closure in $C_c(G,Y)$ under the action of G_d by $\tilde\rho$. It follows from 0.2.8 and the equivalence of (i) and (ii) in 2.1.8, that the converse is also true if G is a k-space. Thus, we obtain the following statement:

If G *is a k-space (in particular, if* G *is a locally compact* T_2*-space) then an element* $f \in C_c(G,Y)$ *has a compact orbit closure in the* G_d*-space* $C_c(G,Y)$ *(with action* $\tilde\rho$*) iff* $f \in \mathrm{RUC}^*(G,Y)$.

)1 If $f \in \mathrm{RUC}(G,Y)$, then $\langle G, K_{\tilde\rho}[f], \tilde\rho\rangle$ is a ttg as well, but if f is not bounded, then $K_{\tilde\rho}[f]$ is not compact.

2.1.12. In the remainder of this section, let <G,Y,π> be an arbitrary ttg. Then, for every $y \in Y$ and $t \in G$,

$$(3)\qquad \tilde{\rho}^t(\pi_y) = \pi_{ty}$$

(cf. the second diagram in 1.1.2). *Consequently, the mapping*

$$(4)\qquad \underline{\pi}: y \mapsto \pi_y : Y \to C_c(G,Y)$$

is equivariant with respect to the action π *of* G_d *on* Y *and the action* $\tilde{\rho}$ *of* G_d *on* $C_c(G,Y)$. In particular, it follows that $\underline{\pi}[Y]$ is a right invariant subset of $C(G,Y)$.

2.1.13. LEMMA. *The mapping* $\underline{\pi}: Y \to C_c(G,Y)$ *defined in* (4) *above is a topological embedding.*

PROOF. For $y,z \in Y$, $y \neq z$, we have $\pi_y(e) = y \neq z = \pi_z(e)$. Hence $\underline{\pi}$ is injective. Moreover, $\underline{\pi}$ is continuous, by 0.2.7(iii). In order to show that $\underline{\pi}$ is a topological embedding, it is sufficient to show that for each $y \in Y$ and for each $U \in \mathcal{V}_y$ there exist a compact subset K of G and an open subset V of Y such that

$$(5)\qquad \{z \in Y : \underline{\pi}(z) \in N(K,V)\} \subseteq U.$$

Obviously, (5) is fulfilled if we take $K = \{e\}$ and $V = \text{int}\, U$. □

2.1.14. PROPOSITION. *The mapping* $\tilde{\rho}: G \times \underline{\pi}[Y]_c \to \underline{\pi}[Y]_c$ *is continuous, so* $\langle G, \underline{\pi}[Y]_c, \tilde{\rho}\rangle$ *is a ttg. Moreover,* $\underline{\pi}: Y \to \underline{\pi}[Y]_c$ *is an isomorphism of* G*-spaces.*

PROOF. A trivial consequence of 2.1.12 and 2.1.13. □

2.1.15. NOTES. The reader may have had the feeling that the proof of 2.1.3 as we have given it is somewhat obscure. We have chosen this proof in view of its generalization in 6.2.3 and 6.2.8. {A straightforward formulation of the proof of 2.1.3 is as follows (it is, indeed, exactly the same proof): proceed as in the second half of the proof of 2.1.2; since G is locally compact T_2, V may be supposed to be compact, hence KV is compact, and now $KV \subseteq f^{\leftarrow}[U]$ means that N(KV,U) is a neighbourhood of f in $C_c(G,Y)$. By (1), however, $\tilde{\rho}[V \times N(KV,U)] \subseteq N(K,U)$, so $\tilde{\rho}$ is continuous at $(e,f) \in G \times C_c(G,Y)$. Using (1) again, it follows that $\tilde{\rho}$ is continuous on all of $G \times C_c(G,Y)$.}

Although 2.1.8 is well-known, the ttgs of the form $\langle G, K_{\tilde{\rho}}[f], \tilde{\rho}\rangle$ with

$f \in RUC^*(G,Y)$, Y a uniform space, are considered in the literature mainly under the (superfluous) assumption that G is locally compact T_2. In this context, the following references are worth to be mentioned: L. AUSLANDER & F. HAHN [1963], J. AUSLANDER & F. HAHN [1967], A.W. KNAPP [1964, 1966, 1967]. In these papers classes of functions on G are considered which have been defined by means of certain dynamical properties of $\langle G,K_{\tilde{\rho}}[f],\tilde{\rho}\rangle$, mainly for the case that $G = \mathbb{R}$. Cf. also J.F. KENT [1972], where arbitrary locally compact groups are considered. For related results, cf. J.D. BAUM [1953] and R. ELLIS [1959, 1961].

2.2. Action of a group G on $C_u(G,Y)$

2.2.1. Throughout this subsection we shall assume that Y is a uniform space with uniformity $\mathcal{U}$. Then $C(G,Y)$ is a right invariant subset of Y^G, and we shall consider this space with its topology of uniform convergence on G, i.e. we consider the space $C_u(G,Y)$. Since for every $t \in G$ obviously $G = \{st : s \in G\}$ it is clear that for $\alpha \in \mathcal{U}$ we have

(1) $$(\tilde{\rho}^t \times \tilde{\rho}^t)M(G,\alpha) = M(G,\alpha).$$

Consequently, $\langle G_d, C_u(G,Y),\tilde{\rho}\rangle$ *is a ttg, and its transition group* $\{\tilde{\rho}^t : t \in G\}$ *is equi-uniformly continuous.*

In general, $\tilde{\rho}: G \times C_u(G,Y) \to C_u(G,Y)$ is not continuous, not even in the case $Y = \mathbb{R}$ or $Y = \mathbb{C}$. This is an immediate consequence of:

2.2.2. PROPOSITION. *Let* $f \in C(G,Y)$. *The following conditions are mutually equivalent:*

(i) $\tilde{\rho}_f: G \to C_u(G,Y)$ *is continuous.*

(ii) *For every* $t \in G$, $\tilde{\rho}: G \times C_u(G,Y) \to C_u(G,Y)$ *is continuous at the point* (t,f).

(iii) $f \in LUC(G,Y)$.

PROOF. The straightforward proofs are left to the reader. □

2.2.3. The preceding proposition remains true if we replace $C(G,Y)$ by $C^*(G,Y)$ and $LUC(G,Y)$ by $LUC^*(G,Y)$. In particular, if $Y = \mathbb{F}$, then for any $f \in C^*(G)$, the mapping $\tilde{\rho}_f: G \to C^*_u(G)$ is continuous iff $f \in LUC^*(G)$.

2.2.4. PROPOSITION. *The set* $LUC(G,Y)$ *is right invariant and* $\tilde{\rho}: G \times LUC_u(G,Y) \to LUC_u(G,Y)$ *is continuous. Hence* $\langle G, LUC_u(G,Y),\tilde{\rho}\rangle$ *is a ttg.*

PROOF. In view of the preceding proposition it is sufficient to prove that $\tilde{\rho}^u f \in \mathrm{LUC}(G,Y)$ for each $f \in \mathrm{LUC}(G,Y)$ and $u \in G$. If such f and u are fixed, then for every $\alpha \in \mathcal{U}$ there exists $V \in \mathcal{V}_e$ such that $(f(t),f(s)) \in \alpha$ for all $s,t \in G$ with $t^{-1}s \in V$. Now there is $W \in \mathcal{V}_e$ with $u^{-1}Wu \subseteq V$. Consequently, if $t^{-1}s \in W$, then $(tu)^{-1}su \in V$, and $(\tilde{\rho}^u f(t),\tilde{\rho}^u f(s)) \in \alpha$. Therefore, $\tilde{\rho}^u f \in \mathrm{LUC}(G,Y)$. □

2.2.5. We shall characterize now the elements in $C_u(G,Y)$ having a compact orbit closure in $C_u(G,Y)$ under the action of G_d by $\tilde{\rho}$. To this end we introduce some new concepts. Although everything may be done for an arbitrary complete uniform space Y (completeness is essential in 2.2.13 below), we shall write down the proofs only for the case $Y = \mathbb{F}$.

2.2.6. A function $f \in C_u(G)$ is called *Von Neumann almost periodic* if $C_{\tilde{\rho}}[f]$ is a relatively compact subset of $C_u(G)$. The set of all Von Neumann almost periodic functions will be denoted by $\mathrm{AP}(G)$.

2.2.7. LEMMA. *Let* $f \in C(G)$. *The following conditions are equivalent:*

(i) $f \in \mathrm{AP}(G)$.

(ii) *There exist a compact topological Hausdorff group* H *and a continuous morphism of groups* $\psi: G \to H$ *such that* $f = f' \circ \psi$ *for some* $f' \in C(H)$.

PROOF. (i) ⇒ (ii): If $f \in \mathrm{AP}(G)$, then the closure of $C_{\tilde{\rho}}[f]$ in $C_u(G)$ is a compact Hausdorff space. Let this space be denoted by X. Observe that X is right invariant (indeed, each $\tilde{\rho}^t: C_u(G) \to C_u(G)$ is continuous and leaves $C_{\tilde{\rho}}[f]$ invariant); so we can consider the ttg $\langle G_d, X, \tilde{\rho}\rangle$. By 2.2.1, this ttg is equicontinuous, hence 1.3.18 implies that the enveloping semigroup E of $\langle G_d, X, \pi\rangle$ is a compact topological Hausdorff group. Obviously, $f': \xi \mapsto \xi(f)(e)$ $E \to \mathbb{F}$ is continuous, and $f = f' \circ \bar{\pi}$. Since $\bar{\pi}: G \to E$ is a continuous morphism of groups, this shows that (i) implies (ii).

(ii) ⇒ (i): Since H is compact, $\mathrm{RUC}(H) = \mathrm{LUC}(H) = C(H)$. So for any $g \in C_u(H)$, $\tilde{\rho}_g: H \to C_u(H)$ is continuous. In particular, $\tilde{\rho}_g[H]$ is a compact subset of $C_u(H)$. A straightforward calculation shows that the mapping $C(\psi): h \mapsto h \circ \psi$: $C_u(H) \to C_u(G)$ sends $\tilde{\rho}_g[\psi[G]]$ onto the orbit $C_{\tilde{\rho}}[g \circ \psi]$ of $g \circ \psi$ in $\langle G_d, C_u(G), \tilde{\rho}\rangle$. Hence $C_{\tilde{\rho}}[g \circ \psi]$ is included in the image of the compact set $\tilde{\rho}_g[H]$ under the continuous mapping $C(\psi)$. It follows that $g \circ \psi \in \mathrm{AP}(G)$. □

2.2.8. Instead of the action $\tilde{\rho}$ of G_d on $C_u(G)$ we can consider also the action $\tilde{\lambda}$, defined by $\tilde{\lambda}^t f(s) = f(t^{-1}s)$ for $f \in C(G)$ and $t,s \in G$. Then, similar to 2.2.7 it can be shown that the following conditions on $f \in C(G)$ are equivalent:

(i) $C_{\tilde{\lambda}}[f]$ is a relatively compact subset of $C_u(G)$.

(ii) There exist a compact topological Hausdorff group H and a continuous morphism $\psi: G \to H$ of groups such that $f = f' \circ \psi$ for some $f' \in C(H)$.

Combining this with 2.2.7 it follows that *the "left" and the "right" versions of Von Neumann almost periodicity coincide:* if $f \in C(G)$, then $f \in AP(G)$ iff $C_{\tilde{\rho}}[f]$ has a compact closure in $C_u(G)$, iff $C_{\tilde{\lambda}}[f]$ has a compact closure in $C_u(G)$. For a different proof, see [HR], 18.1.

2.2.9. THEOREM. *The set of Von Neumann almost periodic functions equals the range of the mapping* $C(\alpha_G): C(G^c) \to C(G)$, *where* $\alpha_G: G \to G^c$ *denotes the Bohr compactification of* G.

PROOF. A straightforward consequence of 2.2.7 and the universal property of the Bohr compactification. □

2.2.10. We shall present now another definition of almost periodicity which is, in general, not equivalent to the above defined concept, and for which the left and right versions can be different.

Call a subset A of G *relatively dense* in G provided there exists a compact subset of K of G such that G = KA. Equivalently, A is relatively dense in G provided there exists a compact subset K_1 of G such that for each $t \in G$, $A \cap K_1 t \neq \emptyset$ (in this case, K and K_1 are related by $K_1 = K^{-1}$). {In [GH] the term *right syndetic* is used.}

If $f \in C(G)$ and $\varepsilon > 0$, then the set of all *ε-almost periods* of f is defined as follows:

(2) $$A(f,\varepsilon) := \{t : t \in G \ \& \ \|\tilde{\rho}^t f - f\| < \varepsilon\}.$$

Notice, that $A(f,\varepsilon)$ is a symmetric subset of G, that is, $t \in A(f,\varepsilon)$ iff $t^{-1} \in A(f,\varepsilon)$. Stated otherwise, $A(f,\varepsilon)^{-1} = A(f,\varepsilon)$.

An element $f \in C(G)$ is said to be *right almost periodic* provided $A(f,\varepsilon)$ is relatively dense in G for every $\varepsilon > 0$. The set of all right almost periodic functions on G will be denoted RAP(G).

2.2.11. Let $f \in \mathsf{C}(G)$. Then $f \in \mathsf{RAP}(G)$ iff for every $\varepsilon > 0$ there exists a compact subset $K(f,\varepsilon)$ of G such that

$$(3) \qquad \forall t \in G, \exists k \in K(f,\varepsilon) : \|\tilde{\rho}^t f - \tilde{\rho}^k f\| < \varepsilon.$$

Indeed, if $f \in \mathsf{RAP}(G)$, then for every $\varepsilon > 0$ there is a compact set $K(f,\varepsilon) \subseteq G$ such that $G = K(f,\varepsilon)A(f,\varepsilon)$. For each $t \in G$, take $k \in K(f,\varepsilon)$ such that $t^{-1}k \in A(f,\varepsilon)^{-1} = A(f,\varepsilon)$. Then $\|\tilde{\rho}^{t^{-1}k} f - f\| < \varepsilon$; since $\tilde{\rho}^t$ is an isometry, this is equivalent to $\|\tilde{\rho}^k f - \tilde{\rho}^t f\| < \varepsilon$. The proof of the reversed statement is left to the reader.

2.2.12. <u>LEMMA</u>. $\mathsf{RAP}(G) \subseteq \mathsf{RUC}^*(G)$.

<u>PROOF</u>. Consider $f \in \mathsf{RAP}(G)$, and let $\varepsilon > 0$. Fix $K := K(f,\varepsilon)$ in accordance with (3). For all $t \in G$, (3) implies that $|f(t)| \le \|f\|_K + \varepsilon$, where $\|f\|_K < \infty$. It follows that f is bounded.

Next, apply 0.2.2(ii) to the continuous function $(u,v) \mapsto f(vu)$: $G \times G \to \mathbb{F}$. There exists $V \in \mathcal{V}_e$ such that $|f(u) - f(vu)| < \varepsilon$ for all $u \in K$ and $v \in V$. If we choose $k_t \in K$ for each $t \in G$ in accordance with (3), then we have

$$|f(vt)-f(t)| \le |f(vt)-f(vk_t)| + |f(vk_t)-f(k_t)| + |f(k_t)-f(t)| < 3\varepsilon$$

for every $v \in V$. It follows that $|f(s)-f(t)| < 3\varepsilon$ if $s,t \in G$, $st^{-1} \in V$. □

2.2.13. <u>LEMMA</u>. *Let* $f \in \mathsf{C}(G)$, *and consider the following statements:*
(i) *The closure of* $C_{\tilde{\rho}}[f]$ *in* $\mathsf{C}_u(G)$ *is compact, i.e.* $f \in \mathsf{AP}(G)$.
(ii) $f \in \mathsf{RAP}(G)$.
Then (i) *implies* (ii). *If* $f \in \mathsf{LUC}(G)$, *then also* (ii) *implies* (i).

<u>PROOF</u>. (i) ⇒ (ii): Condition (i) is equivalent with total boundedness of $C_{\tilde{\rho}}[f]$ in the complete uniform space $\mathsf{C}_u(G)$. This, in turn, is equivalent with the existence, for every $\varepsilon > 0$, of a *finite* set $K \subseteq G$ such that

$$\forall t \in G, \exists k \in K : \|\tilde{\rho}^t f - \tilde{\rho}^k f\| < \varepsilon.$$

Since finite sets are compact, this shows that (i) ⇒ (ii), by 2.2.7.

Conversely, let $f \in \mathsf{RAP}(G) \cap \mathsf{LUC}(G)$, and let $\varepsilon > 0$. Take $K := K(f,\varepsilon)$ such that (3) holds. By 2.2.2, $\tilde{\rho}_f[K]$ is a compact subset of $\mathsf{C}_u(G)$, hence it is totally bounded. So there is a finite subset K_1 of K such that

$$\forall k \in K, \exists l \in K_1 : \|\tilde{\rho}^k f - \tilde{\rho}^l f\| < \varepsilon.$$

In view of (3), it follows that

$$\forall t \in G, \exists l \in K_1 : \|\tilde{\rho}^t f - \tilde{\rho}^l f\| < 2\varepsilon.$$

Consequently, $C_{\tilde{\rho}}[f]$ is totally bounded. □

2.2.14. Instead of the action $\tilde{\rho}$ of G_d on $C_u(G)$ we may also consider the action $\tilde{\lambda}$, defined in 2.2.8. Then for $f \in C_u(G)$ and $\varepsilon > 0$, set

$$B(f,\varepsilon) := \{t : t \in G \;\&\; \|\tilde{\lambda}^t f - f\| < \varepsilon\}.$$

Then f is called *left almost periodic* if $B(f,\varepsilon)$ is relatively dense in G for every $\varepsilon > 0$. The set of all left almost periodic functions is denoted by $LAP(G)$.

2.2.15. By similar methods as before, it may be shown that
(i) $LAP(G) \subseteq LUC^*(G)$ (cf. 2.2.12).
(ii) For any $f \in C(G)$, relative compactness of $C_{\tilde{\lambda}}[f]$ implies that $f \in LAP(G)$. The converse implication is valid whenever $f \in RUC(G)$ (cf. 2.2.13).

2.2.16. <u>THEOREM</u>. *Let* $f \in C(G)$. *Then the following conditions are mutually equivalent:*
(i) $C_{\tilde{\rho}}[f]$ *is a relatively compact subset of* $C_u(G)$.
(i)' $C_{\tilde{\lambda}}[f]$ *is a relatively compact subset of* $C_u(G)$.
(ii) $f \in RAP(G) \cap LUC^*(G)$.
(ii)' $f \in LAP(G) \cap RUC^*(G)$.
(iii) $f \in LAP(G) \cap RAP(G)$.
In particular, it follows that $AP(G) = LAP(G) \cap RAP(G)$.

<u>PROOF</u>. For the equivalence of (i) and (i)', cf. 2.2.8 above.
(i) ⇒ (iii): Use 2.2.13 and 2.2.15(ii) and the equivalence of (i) and (i)'.
(iii) ⇒ (ii) and (iii) ⇒ (ii)': Use 2.2.12 and 2.2.15(i).
(ii) ⇒ (i) and (ii)' ⇒ (i)' : Use the converse implications in 2.2.13. and 2.2.15(ii). □

2.2.17. <u>COROLLARY</u>. *If the right and the left uniform structures on* G *coincide, then the concepts of left almost periodicity, right almost periodicity and Von Neumann almost periodicity are all equivalent.*

<u>PROOF</u>. Immediate from 2.2.12, 2.2.15(i) and 2.2.16, since now obviously $LUC^*(G) = RUC^*(G)$. □

2.2.18. It may occur that LAP(G) ≠ RAP(G). Notice that for any $f \in$ LAP(G) the function $t \longmapsto f(t^{-1})$ is in RAP(G), and vice versa. So in case of inequality we must have LAP(G) $\nsubseteq$ RAP(G) and RAP(G) $\nsubseteq$ LAP(G). In addition, in that case the set of Von Neumann almost periodic functions cannot coincide with LAP(G) nor with RAP(G). The following example is due to T.S. WU [1966].

2.2.19. Let G be the semidirect product of a compact normal subgroup K and a subgroup H. This means that $G = KH$ and $K \cap H = \{e\}$ (cf. [HR], 2.6 and 6.20). Then each $t \in G$ has a unique representation $t = k_t h_t$ with $k_t \in K$ and $h_t \in H$. We shall assume that the mapping $t \longmapsto (k_t, h_t)\colon G \to K \times H$ is continuous (hence it is a homeomorphism!).

If $f \in C(K)$, then define $f^\wedge\colon G \to \mathbb{F}$ by $f^\wedge(t) := f(k_t)$. By our assumptions, it is clear that $f^\wedge \in C(G)$. First we show that $f^\wedge \in$ RAP(G) for every $f \in C(K)$. To this end, observe that for every $\varepsilon > 0$, $h \in H$ and $t \in G$ the inequality

$$|\tilde{\rho}^h f^\wedge(t) - f(t)| = |f^\wedge(k_t h_t h) - f^\wedge(k_t h_t)| = 0 < \varepsilon$$

shows that $A(f^\wedge, \varepsilon) \supseteq H$. Hence $G = KA(f^\wedge, \varepsilon)$, i.e. $A(f^\wedge, \varepsilon)$ is relatively dense in G. So indeed $f^\wedge \in$ RAP(G).

Finally, let us assume that G,K and H satisfy the following condition:

(4) G is metrizable and there exist $k \in K$, $k \neq e$, and a sequence $\{h_n : n \in \mathbb{N}\}$ in H such that $\lim_{n\to\infty} h_n^{-1} k h_n = e$.

Now for any $f \in C(K)$ with $f(k) \neq f(e)$ we have

$$|f^\wedge(h_n h_n^{-1} k h_n) - f^\wedge(h_n)| = |f^\wedge(k h_n) - f^\wedge(h_n)| = |f(k) - f(e)| \neq 0,$$

hence $f^\wedge \notin$ LUC(G). So by 2.2.15, $f^\wedge \notin$ LAP(G).

The only thing that remains is to give an example of a group G which satisfies all conditions above. To do this, we proceed as follows:

As a topological space, let $G := \mathbb{T}^2 \times \mathbb{Z}$. Let ψ denote any continuous automorphism of $\mathbb{T}^2$, $\psi \neq 1_{\mathbb{T}^2}$, and define a multiplication in G by

$$(u,m)(v,n) = (u\psi^m(v), m+n).$$

Then G is a metrizable topological group, and G is the semidirect product of the compact normal subgroup $K := \mathbb{T}^2 \times \{0\}$ and the closed subgroup

$H := \{e'\} \times \mathbb{Z}$, where $e' = (1,1)$ is the unit of $\mathbb{T}^2$. Now G meets all requirements, except possibly (4).

We shall show now that we can choose ψ in such a way that $\lim_{i\to\infty} \psi^{n_i}(v) = e'$ for some $v \in \mathbb{T}^2$, $v \neq e'$, and some sequence $\{n_i : i\in\mathbb{N}\}$ in $\mathbb{Z}$. For then, setting $k := (v,0)$ and $h_i := (e',1)^{-n_i} = (e',-n_i)$, we obtain

$$h_i^{-1}kh_i = (e',n_i)(v,0)(e',-n_i) = (e',n_i)(v,-n_i) = (\psi^{n_i}(v),0)$$

and, consequently, $\lim_{i\to\infty} h_i^{-1}kh_i = (e',0)$, the identity of G. Thus, condition (4) is also satisfied.

Finally we show that ψ has the above mentioned property if we take $\psi(t_1,t_2) := (t_1^2t_2,t_1t_2)$ for $(t_1,t_2) \in \mathbb{T}^2$. Obviously, ψ is a continuous automorphism of $\mathbb{T}^2$. Then we can apply [GH], 10.28 to the effect that there exists $v \in \mathbb{T}^2$ and a sequence $\{n_i : i\in\mathbb{N}\}$ in $\mathbb{Z}$ such that $\lim_{i\to\infty} \psi^{n_i}(v) = e'$, as desired. {In order that this theorem can be applied, it must be checked that $e' \in \mathbb{T}^2$ is invariant under ψ, and that the neighbourhood $U := \{(t_1,t_2) \in \mathbb{T}^2 : t_1 = \exp(i\alpha)$ with $|\alpha| < \pi/3\}$ of e' satisfies the condition that none of its points, except e', has its orbit under ψ completely in U.}

2.2.20. <u>NOTES</u>. In view of proposition 2.2.2 it is natural to ask when it occurs that $\mathrm{LUC}(G,Y) = \mathrm{C}(G,Y)$. Of course, a sufficient condition is that G is compact. In the case $Y = \mathbb{F}$ more can be said: then for any topological group the conditions $\mathrm{LUC}(G) = \mathrm{C}(G)$ and $\mathrm{LUC}^*(G) = \mathrm{C}^*(G)$ are equivalent, and they imply that either G is pseudocompact (that is, $\mathrm{C}(G) = \mathrm{C}^*(G)$) or G is a P-space (that is, each countable intersection of open sets in G is open in G). Cf. W.W. COMFORT & K.A. ROSS [1966]. In that paper it has also been shown that pseudocompactness of G is equivalent with the property that $\mathrm{AP}(G) = \mathrm{C}(G)$. See also Appendix A.

The definition of almost periodic functions which we have employed in 2.2.10 is a straightforward generalization of the original definition in H. BOHR [1924]. We borrowed it from [GH], Chap. 4. Notice that 2.2.10 through 2.2.16 are adapted from [GH], 4.58-4.61. Theorem 2.2.16 is a generalization of a characterization of almost periodic functions for the case $G = \mathbb{R}$, due to S. BOCHNER [1926]. It was used by VON NEUMANN [1934] to define almost periodic functions on arbitrary topological groups. Since then, the literature on almost periodic functions has grown enormously. Cf. for instance E.M. ALFSEN & P. HOLM [1962], P. HOLM [1964], and for semigroups, K. DE LEEUW & I. GLICKSBERG [1961] and J.S. PYM [1963]. In this context, also W.F. EBERLEIN [1949] should be mentioned. For almost periodic functions on groups, cf. also [Ma]; [BH] and [Bu] deal with almost periodic functions on semigroups and the relation with compactifications of semigroups (i.e. generalizations of 2.2.9).

The proof of 2.2.9 as we have presented it follows roughly the lines of Theorem 16.2.1 in [Di] (cf. also [We], §§33-35). It can also be shown that a compactification $\psi: G \to H$ of G(i.e. H a compact T_2-group, ψ a continuous morphism of groups with dense range) such that $C(\psi)[C(H)] = AP(G)$ essentially equals the Bohr-compactification of G. Cf. the papers of ALFSEN and HOLM and of DE LEEUW and GLICKSBERG mentioned above, or the last chapter in [Lo]. For a very simple proof, applying both to the group and the semigroup case, cf. J. DE VRIES [1970]. {All these references deal with the Von Neumann definition of almost periodicity: one considers points with compact orbit closures in $\langle G_d, C(G), \tilde{\rho}\rangle$, where $C(G)$ is given some suitable topology.}

2.3. Action of a locally compact Hausdorff group G on $L^p(G)$ for $1 \leq p < \infty$

2.3.1. In this section, G is a locally compact Hausdorff group with a fixed right invariant Haar measure μ. If G happens to be compact, we take μ normalized, i.e. $\mu(G) = \int_G 1_G d\mu = 1$. If f is an extended real- or complex valued function on G, then we shall often write $\int_G f(t)dt$ instead of $\int_G f d\mu$ whenever this expression has a meaning.

Let $1 \leq p < \infty$, and let $\mathcal{L}^p(G)$ be the set of all extended real- or complex valued measurable functions f on G such that $\|f\|_p := (\int_G |f|^p \, d\mu)^{1/p}$ is finite.[1] It is well-known that, with the usual pointwise operations, $\mathcal{L}^p(G)$ is a linear space and that $\|.\|_p$ is a pseudo-norm on it. Given $f,g \in \mathcal{L}^p(G)$, we have $\|f-g\|_p = 0$ iff $f(t) = g(t)$ almost everywhere on G, iff $f(t) = g(t)$ locally almost everywhere on G. Let $N := \{f \in \mathcal{L}^p(G) : \|f\|_p = 0\}$. Then N is a linear subspace of $\mathcal{L}^p(G)$, and $L^p(G) := \mathcal{L}^p(G)/N$ is a Banach space with its usual quotient norm. As is usually done, the elements of $L^p(G)$ will be denoted by their representants in $\mathcal{L}^p(G)$. So we will frequently refer to a function $f \in L^p(G)$, and it will be clear from the context in every case whether we mean the fixed function f or the equivalence class $f + N$ containing f.

By right-invariance of μ and the fact that each right translation $s \mapsto$

[1] We do not include the case $p = \infty$, because lemma 2.3.2 below is false for $p = \infty$.

st: $G\to G$ is a homeomorphism, it follows that $L^p(G)$ is a right invariant subset of $\mathbb{F}^G$, and that $\|\tilde\rho^t f\|_p = \|f\|_p$ for each $f \in L^p(G)$. In particular, N is right-invariant, and it follows easily that $\tilde\rho^t[f+N] = \tilde\rho^t f + N$. Therefore, we can define $\tilde\rho^t f$ for $t \in G$ and $f \in L^p(G)$ in an obvious way (cf. also 1.5.3). Thus, we obtain for each $t \in G$ a linear isometry $\tilde\rho^t\colon L^p(G) \to L^p(G)$. It is clear that $\tilde\rho$ is an action of G_d on $L^p(G)$, i.e. $\langle G_d, L^p(G), \tilde\rho\rangle$ is a ttg.

2.3.2. LEMMA. *For each* $f \in L^p(G)$, *the mapping* $\tilde\rho_f\colon G \to L^p(G)$ *is continuous.*

PROOF. Continuity of each $\tilde\rho_f$ means that the mapping $t \mapsto \tilde\rho^t\colon G \to GL(L^p(G))$ is continuous when its codomain is given the strong operator topology (i.e. the topology of pointwise convergence). It is well-known that this mapping is continuous: cf. [HR], 20.4. □

2.3.3. PROPOSITION. *For each* $p \ge 1$, *the mapping* $\tilde\rho\colon G\times L^p(G) \to L^p(G)$ *is continuous, and* $\langle G, L^p(G), \tilde\rho\rangle$ *is an effective ttg.*

PROOF. The continuity of $\tilde\rho$ follows from the inequality

$$\|\tilde\rho(t,g)-\tilde\rho(s,f)\|_p \le \|\tilde\rho^t(g)-\tilde\rho^t(f)\|_p + \|\tilde\rho_f(t)-\tilde\rho_f(s)\|_p$$

for $s,t \in G$ and $f,g \in L^p(G)$. Indeed, each $\tilde\rho^t$ is an isometry and each $\tilde\rho_f$ is continuous.

In order to show that $\langle G, L^p(G), \tilde\rho\rangle$ is effective, observe that for every $t \in G$, $t \neq e$, there exists $U \in \mathcal{V}_e$ such that $t \notin UU^{-1}$. Since G is a locally compact T_2-space there is $f \in C_{00}(G)$, $f \neq 0$, such that $supp(f) \subseteq U$. Then

$$(1) \qquad \|\tilde\rho^t f - f\|_p^p = \int_G |f(st)-f(s)|^p ds = \int_{Ut^{-1}} |f(st)|^p ds + \int_U |f(s)|^p ds.$$

Therefore, $\tilde\rho^t f \neq f$, hence $\tilde\rho^t \neq \tilde\rho^e$. □

2.3.4. It is not difficult to construct examples showing that in general $\langle G, L^p(G), \tilde\rho\rangle$ is not strongly effective. On the other hand, *there are no* $\tilde\rho$-*invariant points* $\neq 0$ *in* $L^p(G)$ *unless* G *is compact.*

Indeed, if G is compact, then all constant functions are in $L^p(G)$, and constant functions are clearly invariant under the action $\tilde\rho$. If G is not compact, then no *constant* function $\neq 0$ is in $L^p(G)$, otherwise we would have $\mu(G) < \infty$, contradicting the non-compactness of G (cf. [HR], 15.9).

However, this does not prove our claim that 0 is the only $\tilde{\rho}$-*invariant* point in $L^p(G)$ for non-compact groups G.

The difficulty in proving this claim is the following one: the condition $\tilde{\rho}^t f = f$ for all $t \in G$ means in the context of $L^p(G)$ that for every $t \in G$ there is a local null set N_t such that $f(st) = f(s)$ for all $s \in G \sim N_t$. We would like to show that there exists $s \in \bigcap\{G{\sim}N_t : t \in G\}$; then $f(st) = f(s)$ for all $t \in G$, and f would be constant. Actually, a little bit less is needed, and that can be shown using FUBINI's theorem: if for some $f \in L^p(G)$ we have $\|\tilde{\rho}^t f - f\|_p = 0$ for all $t \in G$, then

$$\int_G \int_G |f(st)-f(s)|^p \, dt \, ds = \int_G \int_G |f(st)-f(s)|^p \, ds \, dt$$

$$= \int_G \|\tilde{\rho}^t f - f\|_p^p \, dt = 0.$$

It follows, that $\int_G |f(st)-f(s)|^p \, dt = 0$ for almost all $s \in G$. Fix such an $s \in G$: then $|f(st)-f(s)|^p = 0$ for almost all $t \in G$. Consequently, $f(u) = f(s)$ for almost all $u \in G$, and f may be assumed to be a constant function in $L^p(G)$. Hence $f = 0$ by the above remarks.

2.3.5. *Suppose* $\mathrm{GL}(L^p(G))$ *is given its strong operator topology. Then the mapping* $t \mapsto \tilde{\rho}^t : G \to \mathrm{GL}(L^p(G))$ *is a topological embedding. Consequently, the transition group* $\{\tilde{\rho}^t : t \in G\}$ *with its point-open topology is a topological group.*

Since the point-open topology on $\{\tilde{\rho}^t : t \in G\}$ is just the relative topology of this set in $\mathrm{GL}(L^p(G))$, it is sufficient to prove the first statement. Obviously, the mapping $t \mapsto \tilde{\rho}^t : G \to \mathrm{GL}(L^p(G))$ is continuous. To prove that it is relatively open, it is sufficient to show that for every $V \in \mathcal{V}_e$ there exist $\varepsilon > 0$ and a finite subset F in $L^2(G)$ such that

(2) $$\|\tilde{\rho}^t f - f\| < \varepsilon \quad \text{for all } f \in F \quad \Rightarrow \quad t \in V.$$

This is easy: take $U \in \mathcal{V}_e$ such that $UU^{-1} \subseteq V$, take $F = \{f\}$ with f as in the proof of 2.3.3, and take $\varepsilon = \|f\|_p$. Then for all $t \in G$, $t \notin V$, we have by formula (1) in 2.3.3:

$$\|\tilde{\rho}^t f - f\|_p^p = 2\int_U |f(s)|^p\, ds = 2\,\|f\|_p^p > \varepsilon.$$

Hence (2) is valid for our choice of ε and F.

2.3.6. For p = 1,2, the ttgs $\langle G, L^p(G), \tilde{\rho}\rangle$, or rather their transition mappings $\bar{\tilde{\rho}}$: $G \to GL(L^p(G))$, play an important role in representation theory of locally compact groups. Cf. [HR], Chap. V. We cannot go into details here, but we wish to make the following remarks.

For p = 1 (and if G is compact, also for p = 2), the space $L^p(G)$ has the additional structure of a Banach *algebra*. Multiplication is provided by *convolution:* if $f, g \in L^1(G)$, then $f * g$ is defined by

$$(3)\qquad f * g(s) := \int_G f(t)\, g(t^{-1}s)\, dt$$

(this expression has a meaning for almost every $s \in G$, and if we take $f * g(s) = 0$ for all other s[1], then $f * g \in L^1(G)$). The relation between convolution and right translation is as follows:

$$(4)\qquad \tilde{\rho}^t(f * g) = f * \tilde{\rho}^t g$$

for all $t \in G$. The straightforward proof of (4) is left to the reader.

For p = 2, the space $L^p(G)$ has the additional structure of a *Hilbert space*, its inner product being defined by

$$(5)\qquad (f|g) := \int_G f(t)\, \overline{g(t)}\, dt$$

for $f, g \in L^2(G)$ (the horizontal bar denotes complex conjugation). Here each $\tilde{\rho}^t$ is a unitary operator.

We shall present now two theorems, one for the Banach algebra $L^1(G)$ and one for the Hilbert space $L^2(G)$, which are both based on proposition 1.1.21.

2.3.7. Recall that an *approximate unit* in $L^1(G)$ is a set $\{f_\iota : \iota \in I\}$ in $L^1(G)$ such that $\lim_{\iota\in I} f * f_\iota = f$ for each $f \in L^1(G)$ (cf. [HR], 20.27).

The following is well-known and easily established by standard methods:

---

[1] If one allows representants of elements of $L^p(G)$ which are defined almost everywhere, then (3) suffices as a definition of $f * g$.

$L^1(G)$ has an approximate unit of the form $\{f_V : V \in \mathcal{B}\}$, where $\mathcal{B}$ is a local base for the neighbourhood system at e in G, and $f_V \in C_{00}(G)$ (in fact, $supp\, f_V \subseteq V$; cf. [HR], 20.2).

2.3.8. LEMMA. *If* $\{f_\iota : \iota \in I\}$ *is an approximate unit in* $L^1(G)$, *then the subset* $\{f_\iota : \iota \in I\}$ *of* $L^1(G)$ *is a stabilizing set in* $\langle G, L^1(G), \tilde{\rho}\rangle$.

PROOF. Suppose we have $t \in G$ such that $\tilde{\rho}^t f_\iota = f_\iota$ for every $\iota \in I$. Then for each $f \in L^1(G)$ we have

$$\tilde{\rho}^t f = \lim_{\iota \in I} \tilde{\rho}^t (f * f_\iota) = \lim_{\iota \in I} f * \tilde{\rho}^t f_\iota = \lim_{\iota \in I} f * f_\iota = f.$$

Since $\langle G, L^1(G), \tilde{\rho}\rangle$ is effective, it follows that $t = e$. □

2.3.9. PROPOSITION. *For any approximate unit* $\{f_\iota : \iota \in I\}$ *in* $L^1(G)$ *we have* $|I| \geq \ell w(G)$. *Consequently, the least cardinal number of a directed set for an approximate unit in* $L^1(G)$ *equals* $\ell w(G)$.

PROOF. Since $L^1(G)$ is metrizable, its local weight is $\aleph_0$. Moreover, if $\{f_\iota : \iota \in I\}$ is an approximate unit in $L^1(G)$, then $|I| \geq e\langle G, L^1(G), \tilde{\rho}\rangle$ by 2.3.8. Now 1.1.21 implies that $|I| \geq \ell w(G)$.

The final statement in the proposition is a straightforward consequence of the first one and the observation in 2.3.7. □

2.3.10. Recall that the *dimension* $\delta(L^2(G))$ of the Hilbert space $L^2(G)$ is the cardinal number of an orthonormal base for it.

Since all rational combinations of elements in an orthonormal base are dense in $L^2(G)$ and, conversely, the base elements form a discrete subset in $L^2(G)$, it is easy to see that

$$\aleph_0 \cdot \delta(L^2(G)) = d(L^2(G)) = w(L^2(G)).$$

Obviously, each $\tilde{\rho}^t : L^2(G) \to L^2(G)$, being continuous and linear is completely determined by its values at the elements of an orthogonal base. *Consequently, each orthonormal base of* $L^2(G)$ *is a stabilizing subset of* $\langle G, L^2(G), \tilde{\rho}\rangle$. *In particular,* $e\langle G, L^2(G), \tilde{\rho}\rangle \leq \delta(L^2(G))$.

Yet another well-known inequality regarding the dimension of $L^2(G)$ is: $\delta(L^2(G) \leq w(G)$. For a proof, we refer the reader to the *proof* of Theorem 24.15 in [HR], which gives the desired result with only minor modifications. For *compact* groups it is known that $\delta(L^2(G)) = w(G)$ (see [HR], 28.2). We shall prove this equality for an arbitrary locally compact Hausdorff group G.

2.3.11. LEMMA. $w(G) \leq \ell w(G) \cdot L(G)$.

PROOF. Let $\mathcal{B}$ denote a local base at e with $|\mathcal{B}| = \ell w(G)$. For each $V \in \mathcal{B}$, let F_V be a covering of G with $L(G)$ left translates of V. then $\cup\{F_V : V \in \mathcal{B}\}$ is a base for the topology of G, and the cardinality of this base is $|\mathcal{B}| \cdot L(G) = \ell w(G) \cdot L(G)$. This proves the lemma. □

2.3.12. LEMMA. $L(G) \leq \delta(L^2(G))$.

PROOF. If G is finite, then $L(G) = |G| = \delta(L^2(G))$. So we may assume that G is infinite. Then there exists a family $\mathcal{W}$ of pairwise disjoint, non-empty open subsets of G such that $|\mathcal{W}| \geq L(G)$. Indeed, if G is not sigma-compact, then take for $\mathcal{W}$ the family of all left cosets of an open, sigma-compact subgroup of G (more details can be found in the first part of the proof of lemma 7.2.2). And if G is sigma-compact, then let $\mathcal{W} := \{U_n \sim cl_G U_{n+1} : n \in \mathbb{N}\}$ for some suitable sequence of open subsets U_n in G.

For each $W \in \mathcal{W}$, let $f_W \in C_{00}(G)$, $0 \neq f_W \geq 0$, $supp(f_W) \subseteq W$. After suitable normalization, $\{f_W : W \in \mathcal{W}\}$ is an orthonormal subset of $L^2(G)$, hence $\delta(L^2(G)) \geq |\mathcal{W}| \geq L(G)$. □

2.3.13. COROLLARY 1. *$\delta(L^2(G))$ is finite iff G is finite.*

PROOF. If G is finite, then $\delta(L^2(G)) = |G| < \aleph_0$. Conversely, if $\delta(L^2(G) < \aleph_0$, then $L(G) < \aleph_0$, by 2.3.12. Now it is easy to see that G is finite iff $L(G) < \aleph_0$. □

2.3.14. COROLLARY 2. $\ell w(G) \leq \delta(L^2(G))$.

PROOF. If $\delta(L^2(G)) < \aleph_0$ then G is finite, by 2.3.13. Now $\ell w(G) = 1 \leq \delta(L^2(G))$. If $\delta(L^2(G)) \geq \aleph_0$, then 1.1.21 and 2.3.10 imply the desired inequality. □

2.3.15. THEOREM. *For any locally compact Hausdorff group G the equality $w(G) = \delta(L^2(G))$ is valid.*

PROOF. The inequality "≥" was known before (cf. 2.3.10), and "≤" follows from 2.3.11 through 2.3.14. □

2.3.16. NOTES. The first part of the proof of 2.3.3 is a special case of a much more general theorem, namely the following one: *if E is any Banach space and* π: $G\times E \to E$ *is separately continuous, where each* π^t *is a continuous linear operator on* E, *then the inequality* $\|\pi(t,x)-\pi(s,y)\| \leq \|\pi^t\|\|x-y\| + \|\pi_y t-\pi_y s\|$ *shows that* π *is continuous*. Indeed, each $s \in G$ has a compact neighbourhood U, so that $\{\pi^t z : t\in U\}$ is compact, hence bounded in E, for each $z \in E$. Since E is not a first category space, the principle of uniform boundedness (cf. [Sc], Chap.III, 4.2) implies that $\|\pi^t\| \leq k$ for all $t \in U$, where $k > 0$. Observe, that here local compactness of G is quite essential.

Even more is known. Again, let E be a Banach space, and let E_w denote E with its weak topology (i.e. the $\sigma(E,E')$-topology). By the principle of uniform boundedness it is easy to see that a linear mapping $t: E\to E$ is continuous with respect to the norm topology iff $t: E_w \to E_w$ is continuous. Now the following can be shown: *if* π: $G\times E_w \to E_w$ *is separately continuous and each* π^t: $E\to E$ *is linear, then* π: $G\times E \to E$ *is continuous*. By the preceding remarks, it is sufficient to prove that each π_x: $G\to E$ is continuous. This can be done, using a certain amount of integration theory; see K. DE LEEUW & I. GLICKSBERG [1965], Theorem 2.8. A proof is also contained in [BH], p.41.

Proposition 2.3.9 is well-known: cf. [HR], 28.70(b); our proof seems to be a little bit simpler then the one suggested there. The inequality in lemma 2.3.11 is a special case of [Ju], 2.27; there it has been shown that we even have equality in 2.3.11. Corollary 2.3.13 is well-known (cf. [HR], 28.1) but our proof differs from that in [HR]. Finally, theorem 2.3.15 for general locally compact groups seems to be new. With only minor modifications, the proof carries over to $L^p(G)$ for $1 \leq p < \infty$. In that case, $\delta(L^p(G))$ should be defined as the least cardinal number of a discrete subset of $L^p(G)$ spanning a dense subspace of $L^p(G)$.

2.4. Weighted translations in $L^2(G)$

2.4.1. According to an idea of P.C. BAAYEN (cf. [Ba], Chap.IV; see also P.C. BAAYEN & J. DE GROOT [1968]) we wish to modify the ttg $\langle G,L^2(G),\tilde{\rho}\rangle$ by using a "weighted" translation instead of the mapping $\tilde{\rho}$. Notation will be as in the previous section. In particular, G is a locally compact Hausdorff group.

2.4.2. A *weight function* on G is an element $w \in L^2(G)$ satisfying the following conditions:

(i) For all $t \in G$, $w(t) > 0$.

(ii) The function $t \mapsto 1/w(t): G \to \mathbb{R}$ is bounded on compact subsets of G.

(iii) For all $s,t \in G$, $w(st) \geq w(s)w(t)$.

2.4.3. For examples of weight functions and for a proof of the following lemma, we refer to Appendix B, in particular B.2 through B.7.

2.4.4. <u>LEMMA</u>. *There exists a weight function on* G *iff* G *is sigma-compact. In that case, we may assume the existence of a lower semicontinuous weight function* w *on* G *such that* $w(t^{-1}) = w(t) \leq 1$ *for all* $t \in G$. □

2.4.5. In the remainder of this section, G is a sigma-compact, locally compact Hausdorff group. Fix a weight function w on G. For every $t \in G$, let a mapping $\sigma^t: L^2(G) \to L^2(G)$ be defined by

$$(1) \qquad (\sigma^t f)(s) = \frac{w(s)}{w(st)} f(st)$$

if $s \in G$ and $f \in L^2(G)$. Observe that $\sigma^t f \in L^2(G)$ for every $t \in G$ and $f \in L^2(G)$. Indeed, $\sigma^t f$ is a measurable function, and it follows from the inequality

$$(2) \qquad |(\sigma^t f)(s)|^2 \leq \left(\frac{w(s)}{w(s)w(t)}\right)^2 |f(st)|^2 = \frac{|f(st)|^2}{w(t)^2}$$

that $|\sigma^t f|^2$ is dominated by the integrable function $s \mapsto w(t)^{-2}(\tilde{\rho}^t f(s))^2$.

2.4.6. <u>LEMMA</u>. *For each* $t \in G$, σ^t *is a bounded invertible linear operator on the Hilbert space* $L^2(G)$, *and for its operator norm the inequality* $\|\sigma^t\| \leq w(t)^{-1}$ *is valid. If* w *is lower semicontinuous, then*

$$(3) \qquad \frac{w(e)^2}{w(t)} \leq \|\sigma^t\| \leq \frac{1}{w(t)} .$$)1

<u>PROOF</u>. We know already that σ^t maps $L^2(G)$ into itself. Plainly, σ^t is linear, and since formula (2) implies that

$$\|\sigma^t f\|_2^2 \leq w(t)^{-2} \int_G |f(st)|^2 \, ds = w(t)^{-2} \|f\|_2^2,$$

)1 If, in addition, $w(e) = 1$, then $\|\sigma^t\| = w(t)^{-1}$. Notice that in this case w is continuous, by Appendix B.9.

it follows that σ^t is bounded and $\|\sigma^t\| \le w(t)^{-1}$.

Next, let U be a compact symmetric neighbourhood of e in G. In view of condition 2.4.2(ii), there exists a number $k(U) > 0$ such that

$$(4) \qquad \forall s \in U : w(s) \ge k(U).$$

Then $w(t) = w(s^{-1}st) \ge w(s^{-1})w(st)$, whence

$$(5) \qquad \forall s \in U : w(st) \le \frac{w(t)}{k(U)} .$$

Let $f \in C_{00}(G)$ with $\mathit{supp}(f) \subseteq Ut$ and $\|f\|_2 \ne 0$. Then we have by (4) and (5)

$$\|\sigma^t f\|_2^2 = \int_G \left(\frac{w(s)}{w(st)}\right)^2 |f(st)|^2 \, ds \ge \frac{k(U)^4}{w(t)^2} \|f\|_2^2,$$

and it follows that $\|\sigma^t\| \ge k(U)^2 w(t)^{-1}$. Observe, that this inequality is valid for each compact symmetric neighbourhood U of e in G. If w is lower semicontinuous at e, then for each $\varepsilon > 0$ we can choose U such that $k(U) \ge (1-\varepsilon)w(e)$. Then we obtain $\|\sigma^t\| \ge (1-\varepsilon)^2 w(e)^2 w(t)^{-1}$. This holds for every $\varepsilon > 0$, so that, indeed, $\|\sigma^t\| \ge w(e)^2 w(t)^{-1}$.

Finally, it is an easy calculation to show that σ^e is the identity operator on $L^2(G)$ and that, for all $s,t \in G$, the equality $\sigma^{st} = \sigma^s\sigma^t$ is valid. From this it follows that σ is an action of G_d on $L^2(G)$. In particular, it follows that each σ^t is invertible, and that $(\sigma^t)^{\leftarrow} = \sigma^{t^{-1}}$ is a bounded linear operator on $L^2(G)$ as well. □

2.4.7. <u>PROPOSITION</u>. *The mapping* $\bar{\sigma}: t \mapsto \sigma^t: G \to \mathbf{GL}(L^2(G))$ *is a morphism of groups and if* $\mathbf{GL}(L^2(G))$ *is given its strong operator topology, it is a topological embedding.*

<u>PROOF</u>. The fact that $\bar{\sigma}$ is a morphism of groups has been indicated at the end of the proof of 2.4.6. So we shall confine ourselves to the proof that $\bar{\sigma}$ is a topological embedding of G into $\mathbf{GL}(L^2(G))$.

In order to show that $\bar{\sigma}$ is relatively open, it is sufficient to show that for each neighbourhood U of e in G there exist a finite set $A \subset L^2(G)$ and a real number $\varepsilon > 0$ such that

$$(6) \qquad \forall t \in G: \|\sigma^t f - f\| < \varepsilon \text{ for all } f \in A \quad \Rightarrow \quad t \in U.$$

The proof is similar to 2.3.5: let V be a compact symmetric neighbourhood of e in G such that $V^2 \subseteq U$. There is $f \in C_{00}(G)$ with $supp(f) \subseteq V$ and $\|f\|_2 = 1$. Now for all $t \in G$, $t \notin U$ implies $V \cap Vt^{-1} = \emptyset$, hence

$$\|\sigma^t f - f\|_2^2 = \int_G \left|\frac{w(s)}{w(st)} f(st) - f(s)\right|^2 ds$$

$$= \int_{Vt^{-1}} \left|\frac{w(s)}{w(st)} f(st)\right|^2 ds + \int_V |f(s)|^2 ds$$

$$\geq \|f\|_2^2 = 1.$$

So we may take $A = \{f\}$ and $\varepsilon = 1$ in (6). This proves that $\bar{\sigma}$ is relatively open. Notice, that the above proof shows that $\sigma^t f \neq f$ for all $t \in G$, $t \notin U$. If we have *any* $t \in G$, $t \neq e$, then there exists $U \in \mathcal{V}_e$ such that $t \notin U$, whence $\sigma^t f \neq f$ for a suitable $f \in C_{00}(G) \subseteq L^2(G)$. Hence $\sigma^t \neq \sigma^e$. Therefore, $\bar{\sigma}$ is injective.

We proceed by proving that $\bar{\sigma}$ is continuous. It is obviously sufficient to show that the mapping $t \mapsto \sigma^t f: G \to L^2(G)$ is continuous at e for every $f \in L^2(G)$ (continuity of $\bar{\sigma}$ at e implies continuity of $\bar{\sigma}$ at each point of G). The proof is in two steps, similar to the proof of [HR], 20.4 (cf. also 2.3.2).

First, we show that for every $f \in C_{00}(G)$, $f \neq 0$, the mapping $t \mapsto \sigma^t f$: $G \to L^2(G)$ is continuous at e. So take $f \in C_{00}(G)$, $f \neq 0$, fix $\varepsilon > 0$, and set $K := supp(f)$. In addition, fix a compact neighbourhood U of e in G. Then $U \cup KU$ is compact, hence $k := \sup\{w(s)^{-2} : s \in U \cup KU\}$ is finite, by 2.4.2(ii). Consequently, for every $t \in U$ we obtain (use, that $|a+b|^2 \leq 2|a|^2 + 2|b|^2$ for all $a,b \in \mathbb{F}$):

$$\|\sigma^t f - f\|_2^2 \leq 2 \int_G \left(\frac{w(s)}{w(st)}\right)^2 |f(st) - f(s)|^2 ds +$$

$$+ 2 \int_G \left|\frac{w(s)}{w(st)} - 1\right|^2 |f(s)|^2 ds$$

$$\leq \frac{2}{w(t)^2}\int_G |f(st)-f(s)|^2\, ds +$$

$$+ 2\int_K \frac{|w(s)-w(st)|^2}{w(st)^2}\,|f(s)|^2\, ds$$

$$\leq 2k\left\{\int_G |f(st)-f(s)|^2\, ds + \int_G |w(s)-w(st)|^2 |f(s)|^2\, ds\right\}.$$

By 2.3.2 (for the case $p = 2$), there exists $V \in \mathcal{V}_e$ such that for all $t \in V$

$$\int_G |f(st)-f(s)|^2\, ds < \frac{\varepsilon^2}{4k}$$

and

$$\int_G |w(s)-w(st)|^2\, ds < \frac{\varepsilon^2}{4k\|f\|_G^2},$$

where $\|f\|_G := \sup\{|f(s)| : s\in G\}$ is finite and non-zero. Hence for all $t \in U\cap V$ we obtain

$$\|\sigma^t f-f\|_2^2 \leq 2k\left(\frac{\varepsilon^2}{4k} + \frac{\varepsilon^2}{4k\|f\|_G^2}\cdot\|f\|_G^2\right) = \varepsilon^2.$$

This shows, that $t \longmapsto \sigma^t f\colon G \to L^2(G)$ is continuous at e for each $f \in C_{00}(G)$.

In the general case, take $f \in L^2(G)$, and let $\varepsilon > 0$. Since $C_{00}(G)$ is dense in $L^2(G)$, there exists $g \in C_{00}(G)$ such that $\|f-g\|_2 < \varepsilon/(2m)$, where $m := 1 + \sup\{w(s)^{-1} : s\in U\}$ (as before, U is a fixed compact neighbourhood of e). Since for each $t \in G$ we have $\|\sigma^t\| \leq w(t)^{-1}$, it follows that for all $t \in U$

$$\|\sigma^t f-f\|_2 \leq \|\sigma^t\|\,\|f-g\|_2 + \|\sigma^t g-g\|_2 + \|f-g\|_2 \leq \tfrac{1}{2}\varepsilon + \|\sigma^t g-g\|_2.$$

By our previous result, there exists a neighbourhood W of e such that $\|\sigma^t g-g\|_2 < \frac{1}{2}\varepsilon$ for all $t \in W$. Consequently, $\|\sigma^t f-f\|_2 < \varepsilon$ for all $t \in U\cap W$. □

2.4.8. COROLLARY. *The mapping* $\sigma\colon G\times L^2(G)\to L^2(G)$ *is continuous, hence it is an action of* G *on* $L^2(G)$. *Moreover, the ttg* $\langle G, L^2(G), \sigma\rangle$ *is effective, and the transition mapping* $\bar{\sigma}\colon G\to\bar{\sigma}[G]$ *is a topological isomorphism if the transition group* $\bar{\sigma}[G]$ *is given its point-open topology.*

PROOF. The fact that $\bar{\sigma}$ is a topological mapping is equivalent to saying that $\bar{\sigma}$ is a topological embedding of G into $\mathbf{GL}(L^2(G))$ if the latter space has its strong operator topology. So by 2.4.7 it remains only to show that σ is continuous. To this end, consider for $f,g\in L^2(G)$ and $s,t\in G$ the inequality

$$\|\sigma(t,f)-\sigma(s,g)\|_2 \le \|\sigma^t\|\cdot\|f-g\|_2+\|\sigma^t g-\sigma^s g\|_2$$

$$\le w(t)^{-1}\ \|f-g\|_2+\|\sigma^t g-\sigma^s g\|_2 .$$

Since each $s\in G$ has a compact neighbourhood on which the function $t\mapsto w(t)^{-1}$ is bounded, it follows easily, that σ is continuous at each point $(s,g)\in G\times L^2(G)$. □

2.4.9. COROLLARY. *Any sigma-compact locally compact Hausdorff group* G *admits an embedding (as a group and as a topological space)* $\bar{\sigma}\colon G\to\mathbf{GL}(L^2(G))$ *in such a way that the function* $w_0\colon t\mapsto\|\bar{\sigma}(t)\|^{-1}$ *is an upper semicontinuous weight function on* G.

PROOF. Take any lower semicontinuous weight function w on G and construct $\bar{\sigma}\colon G\to\mathbf{GL}(L^2(G))$ as before. Then $\bar{\sigma}$ is the desired embedding.

Indeed, it follows from (3) in 2.4.6 that

$$(7)\qquad w(t)\le\frac{1}{\|\sigma^t\|}\le\frac{w(t)}{w(e)^2}\ .$$

It follows that the function $w_0\colon t\mapsto\|\sigma^t\|^{-1}$ on G satisfies the conditions (i) and (ii) of 2.4.2. In addition, for all $s,t\in G$ we have $\|\sigma^{st}\| = \|\sigma^s\sigma^t\|\le \|\sigma^s\|\|\sigma^t\|$, so w_0 satisfies 2.4.2(iii). It remains to show that $w_0\in L^2(G)$ (then w_0 is a weight function) and that w_0 is upper semicontinuous.

To begin with the latter, we shall show that $\|.\|$ is lower semicontinuous on $\mathbf{L}(L^2(G))$. Obviously this implies that w_0 is upper semicontinuous, because $t\mapsto\sigma^t$ is a topological embedding of G into $\mathbf{GL}(L^2(G))\subseteq\mathbf{L}(L^2(G))$ (of course, we consider the strong operator topology on $\mathbf{L}(L^2(G))$). If we write $\delta_f(\tau) := \tau(f)$ for any $\tau\in\mathbf{L}(L^2(G))$ and any $f\in L^2(G)$ with $\|f\|_2\le 1$, then, by the definition of the norm on $\mathbf{L}(L^2(G))$,

$$\|\tau\| = \sup\{\|\delta_f(\tau)\|_2 : f\in L^2(G) \ \& \ \|f\| \le 1\}.$$

Since each of the δ_f: $L(L^2(G)) \to L^2(G)$ is continuous, and a pointwise supremum of continuous functions is lower semicontinuous, it follows that $\|.\|$ is lower semicontinuous on $L(L^2(G))$.

Finally, note that semicontinuity of w_0 implies its measurability. As w_0 is dominated by a scalar multiple of $w \in L^2(G)$, it follows that $w_0 \in L^2(G)$.□

2.4.10. There is a useful connection between the ttg $<G,C_c^*(G),\tilde{\rho}>$ and the ttg $<G,L^2(G),\sigma>$. If w is the weight function on G, used in the definition of the action σ according to 2.4.5, let F: $C^*(G) \to L^2(G)$ be defined by

$$(8) \qquad F(f)(t) := w(t)f(t)$$

for all $f \in C^*(G)$ and $t \in G$. Observe that $\|F(f)\|_2 \le \|w\|_2\|f\|_G$ for all $f \in C^*(G)$.

A straightforward calculation shows *that* F *is equivariant*. Moreover, F *is injective*. For if f and g are in $C^*(G)$, $f \ne g$, then there is an open subset of G, i.e. a set with positive Haar measure, on which f and g differ from each other. Since $w(t) \ne 0$ for all $t \in G$, it follows that F(f) cannot equal F(g) almost everywhere, i.e. $F(f) \ne F(g)$.

Obviously, F is linear. Hence the inequality $\|F(f)\|_2 \le \|w\|_2\|f\|_G$ for all $f \in C^*(G)$ and the equality $\|F(f)\|_2 = \|w\|_2\|f\|_G$ for $f = 1_G$ show, that F: $C_u^*(G) \to L^2(G)$ is a continuous linear operator with operator norm $\|F\| = \|w\|_2$.

The following shows that F is not a topological embedding of $C_u^*(G)$ into $L^2(G)$[1]. In fact, F *doesn't even induce a topological embedding of* $C_{00}(G)$ *into* $L^2(G)$ *unless* G *is a finite group*. **For** suppose that $F^{\leftarrow}$: $F[C_{00}(G)] \to C_{00}(G)$ were a continuous linear operator. Then there would be a number $c > 0$ such that $\|F(f)\|_2 \ge c\|f\|_G$ for all $f \in C_{00}(G)$, that is,

$$(9) \qquad \int_G w(t)^2|f(t)|^2\,dt \ge c^2 \sup_{t\in G}|f(t)|^2.$$

Since G is sigma-compact, $G = \bigcup\{C_n : n\in\mathbb{N}\}$, where $C_1 \subseteq C_2 \subseteq \dots$ are compact subsets of G. It follows, that

$$(10) \qquad \int_G w(t)^2\,dt = \lim_{n\to\infty} \int_{C_n} w(t)^2\,dt.$$

[1] So by BANACH's homomorphism theorem (cf. [Sc], Chap.III, 2.1), F has not a closed range in $L^2(G)$.

Hence there is an index n such that

$$(11)\qquad \int_{G\sim C_n} w(t)^2\,dt < c^2.$$

If $G\sim C_n \neq \emptyset$, there exists $f \in C_{00}(G)$ such that $supp(f) \subseteq G\sim C_n$ and $f \neq 0$. Now (9) and (11) imply

$$c^2\sup_{t\in G}|f(t)|^2 \le \int_{G\sim C_n} w(t)^2|f(t)|^2\,dt < c^2\sup_{t\in G}|f(t)|^2,$$

a contradiction. Hence $G = C_n$, that is, G is compact.

Next, let us assume that G is not discrete. Then for each $m \in \mathbb{N}$ there is $U_m \in \mathcal{V}_e$ such that $\mu(U_m) < m^{-1}$. Indeed, by [HR] 19.21, $\mu(\{e\}) = 0$, hence $\inf\{\mu(U) \,\vdots\, U\in\mathcal{V}_e\} = 0$ by regularity of μ. Since $w(t) \le 1$ for all $t \in G$, we can choose m such that (11) is valid with $G\sim C_n$ replaced by U_m. As before, we obtain a contradiction. Thus, the assumption that F is a topological embedding implies that G is compact and discrete, hence finite. The converse is almost trivial, and its proof is omitted.

2.4.11. <u>LEMMA</u>. *If* A *is a uniformly bounded subset of* $C_c^*(G)$, *then* $F|_A\colon A_c \to L^2(G)$ *is continuous. In particular, if* A *is a compact, bounded subset of* $C_c^*(G)$, *then* $F|_A\colon A_c \to L^2(G)$ *is a topological embedding.*

<u>PROOF</u>. Suppose $\|f\|_G \le k$ for all $f \in A$. Fix $f \in A$, and let $\varepsilon > 0$. In view of formula (10) in 2.4.10, there exists a compact subset K of G such that

$$\int_{G\sim K} w(t)^2\,dt < \frac{\varepsilon^2}{8k^2}\,.$$

Now for every $g \in A\cap U_f(K,\delta)$ with $\delta := \frac{1}{2}\varepsilon\|w\|_2^{-1}$ we have

$$\|F(g)-F(f)\|_2^2 = \int_K w(t)^2|g(t)-f(t)|^2\,dt + \int_{G\sim K} w(t)^2|g(t)-f(t)|^2\,dt$$

$$< \frac{\varepsilon^2}{4\|w\|_2^2}\|w\|_2^2 + 4k^2\frac{\varepsilon^2}{8k^2} < \varepsilon^2.$$

This shows that $F|_A$ is continuous at f.

Since a continuous injection of a compact space into a Hausdorff space is a topological embedding, the last statement of the lemma is clear. □

2.4.12. If G is not compact, then compact subsets of $C_c^*(G)$ may be not uniformly bounded. The following example shows that $F|_A$ may be not continuous on A if A is required only to be compact in $C_c(G)$.

Let $G = \mathbb{R}$, and set $w(t) := \exp(-|t|)$ for $t \in \mathbb{R}$. Then w is a weight function on $\mathbb{R}$. Define $A := \{f_n : n\in\mathbb{N}\}$ in $C_c^*(\mathbb{R})$ as follows:

$$f_n(t) := \begin{cases} 0 & \text{if } t \le n \\ (t-n)\exp(2n) & \text{if } n \le t \le n+1 \\ \exp(2n) & \text{if } t \ge n+1 \end{cases}$$

Then $\{f_n : n\in\mathbb{N}\}$ is pointwise bounded and equicontinuous on $\mathbb{R}$. In fact, the sequence $\{f_n : n\in\mathbb{N}\}$ converges to 0 in $C_c^*(\mathbb{R})$, so $\{f_n : n\in\mathbb{N}\} \cup \{0\}$ is a compact subset of $C_c^*(\mathbb{R})$.

In this situation, $F(f)(t) = f(t)\exp(-|t|)$ for $t \in \mathbb{R}$ and $f \in C_c^*(\mathbb{R})$. In particular,

$$\|F(f_n)\|_2^2 = \int_{\mathbb{R}} \exp(-2|t|)\, f_n(t)^2\, dt$$

$$\ge \int_{[n+1,\infty[} \exp(-2|t|+4n)\, dt$$

$$= \tfrac{1}{2}\exp(2n-1).$$

Therefore, the sequence $\{F(f_n) : n\in\mathbb{N}\}$ does *not* converge to 0 in $L^2(G)$. Consequently, F is not continuous on the compact set $\{f_n : n\in\mathbb{N}\} \cup \{0\}$.

2.4.13. PROPOSITION. *If* A *is a uniformly bounded, invariant subset of the ttg* $\langle G, C_c^*(G), \tilde{\rho}\rangle$, *then* $F|_A : A_c \to L^2(G)$ *is an injective morphism of* G*-spaces from* A_c *(with action* $\tilde{\rho}$*) into* $L^2(G)$ *(with action* σ*). If, in addition,* A_c *is compact, then* F *is a topological embedding.*

PROOF. Apply 2.4.10 and 2.4.11. □

2.4.14. For our purposes in §8, the ttg $\langle G, L^2(G), \sigma\rangle$ is too small. Therefore, we shall consider now the "Hilbert sum" of copies of $\langle G, L^2(G), \sigma\rangle$. To this end, let κ be a cardinal number, A a set with $|A| = \kappa$, and let $H(\kappa)$ be the Hilbert sum of κ copies of $L^2(G)$. Recall, that the elements of $H(\kappa)$ are just all elements $\xi = (\xi_\alpha)_\alpha \in L^2(G)^A$ for which the expression

$$(12) \qquad \|\xi\| := \Big(\sum_{\alpha\in A} \|\xi_\alpha\|_2^2\Big)^{1/2}$$

is finite. Then (12) defines a norm on $H(\kappa)$, and this norm can be derived from an inner product on $H(\kappa)$ which makes $H(\kappa)$ a Hilbert space.

For each $t \in G$ we have the bounded linear operator σ^t on $L^2(G)$. Define $\sigma(\kappa)^t$: $H(\kappa) \to H(\kappa)$ by $\sigma(\kappa)^t\xi := (\sigma^t\xi_\alpha)_\alpha$ for $\xi = (\xi_\alpha)_\alpha \in H(\kappa)$. Then $\sigma(\kappa)^t$ is easily seen to be a bounded linear operator with operator norm $\|\sigma(\kappa)^t\| = \|\sigma^t\|$. In fact, $\overline{\sigma(\kappa)}$: $t \longmapsto \sigma(\kappa)^t$ is a morphism of groups from G into the group $\mathbf{GL}(H(\kappa))$.

2.4.15. <u>LEMMA</u>. *If $\mathbf{GL}(H(\kappa))$ is given its strong operator topology, then the mapping $\overline{\sigma(\kappa)}: t \longmapsto \sigma(\kappa)^t$: $G \to \mathbf{GL}(H(\kappa))$ is a topological embedding.*

<u>PROOF</u>. Straightforward (use, among others, 2.4.7). □

2.4.16. <u>COROLLARY</u>. *For any cardinal number κ, the mapping $\sigma(\kappa)$: $G \times H(\kappa) \to H(\kappa)$ is continuous, hence it is an action of G on the Hilbert space $H(\kappa)$. Moreover, the ttg $\langle G,H(\kappa),\sigma(\kappa)\rangle$ is effective, and the transition mapping $\bar{\sigma}$: $G \to \bar{\sigma}[G]$ is a topological isomorphism if the transition group $\bar{\sigma}[G]$ is given its point-open topology.*

<u>PROOF</u>. The proof is similar to the proof of 2.4.8, since we have, again, local boundedness of the mapping $t \longmapsto \|\sigma(\kappa)^t\|^{-1}$. □

2.4.17. In contradistinction to the ttg $\langle G,L^2(G),\tilde{\rho}\rangle$, the ttg $\langle G,L^2(G),\sigma\rangle$ and its "Hilbert sums" $\langle G,H(\kappa),\sigma(\kappa)\rangle$ do have invariant points $\neq 0$ (for the lack of non-trivial invariant points in $\langle G,L^2(G),\tilde{\rho}\rangle$, see 2.3.4). The proof is more or less similar to the proof in 2.3.4. Indeed, we have:

2.4.18. <u>PROPOSITION</u>. *The set of invariant points in $\langle G,H(\kappa),\sigma(\kappa)\rangle$ is homeomorphic to a Hilbert space of dimension κ. In fact $\xi = (\xi_\alpha)_\alpha$ is an invariant point iff $\xi_\alpha = \lambda_\alpha w$ for scalars $\lambda_\alpha \in \mathbb{F}$ such that $\Sigma\{|\lambda_\alpha|^2 : \alpha\in A\} < \infty$.*

<u>PROOF</u>. Obviously, it is sufficient to show that $f \in L^2(G)$ is invariant under the action σ of G iff $f = \lambda w$ with $\lambda \in \mathbb{F}$. Since a straightforward

calculation shows that $\sigma^t w = w$ for all $t \in G$, it suffices to show that the condition $\|\sigma^t f - f\|_2 = 0$ for all $t \in G$ implies that $t \mapsto f(t)w(t)^{-1}: G \to \mathbb{F}$ is almost everywhere constant on G. The proof is an easy application of FUBINI's theorem: if $\|\sigma^t f - f\|_2 = 0$ for (almost) all $t \in G$, then

$$\int_G w(s)^2 \int_G \left|\frac{f(st)}{w(st)} - \frac{f(s)}{w(s)}\right|^2 dt\, ds =$$

$$= \int_G \int_G \left|\frac{w(s)}{w(st)} f(st) - f(s)\right|^2 ds\, dt$$

$$= \int_G \|\sigma^t f - f\|_2^2\, dt = 0.$$

Consequently, for almost all $s \in G$ we obtain

$$\int_G \left|\frac{f(st)}{w(st)} - \frac{f(s)}{w(s)}\right|^2 dt = 0.$$

Fix such an $s \in G$. Then it follows that $f(st)w(st)^{-1} = f(s)w(s)^{-1}$ for almost all $t \in G$, i.e. there exists $c \in \mathbb{F}$ such that $f(u)w(u)^{-1} = c$ for almost all $u \in G$. □

2.4.19. By 2.3.15, the dimension of $L^2(G)$ is just $w(G)$, the weight of G. Consequently, for any cardinal number κ, the dimension of $H(\kappa)$ equals $\kappa \cdot w(G)$. *If G is infinite, then $w(G) \geq \aleph_0$, hence in this case the dimension of $H(\kappa)$ equals $\max\{\kappa, w(G)\}$*[)1].

2.4.20. <u>NOTES</u>. The contents of this subsection are needed in section 8. For comments on this material, we refer the reader to the notes in 8.2.17 Most of these results are also contained in J. DE VRIES [1972]. Corollary 2.4.9 forms a partial answer to a problem posed by P.C. BAAYEN in [Ba], p.144.

)1 This is equivalent with the statement which appears without proof at the bottom of p.372 in P.C. BAAYEN & J. DE GROOT [1968].

CHAPTER II
CATEGORIES OF TOPOLOGICAL TRANSFORMATION GROUPS

3 - THE CATEGORIES TTG AND TOP^G

In this section we investigate the category **TTG**. This category is obtained from the category **TTG'** (cf. 1.4.13) by taking into consideration also "actions" of groups on empty spaces. These additional objects of **TTG** shall be called ttgs too. In addition, we investigate the category $\mathbf{TOP}^G$ of all G-spaces for a fixed topological group G. These categories turn out to be isomorphic to categories of algebras over suitable monads. As a consequence, we find that **TTG** and $\mathbf{TOP}^G$ are complete categories. The limit of a diagram in **TTG** can be computed by computing the limit of the corresponding diagram of phase groups in **TOPGRP** and the limit of the corresponding diagram of phase spaces in **TOP**: then there exists a unique action of this "limit group" on this "limit space" producing the limit in **TTG** of the given diagram. The situation in $\mathbf{TOP}^G$ is similar. For colimits the situation is a little bit more complicated. In order to prove that **TTG** and $\mathbf{TOP}^G$ are cocomplete, we have first to consider "induced actions". This concerns a construction which generalizes the well-known construction of extending the action of a subgroup to an action of the whole group. It turns out that these induced actions have nice functorial and universal properties. Using this, it can be shown that **TTG** and $\mathbf{TOP}^G$ are cocomplete. However, the structure of colimits in **TTG** is rather complicated. In $\mathbf{TOP}^G$ the situation is a little bit simpler: modulo the topology, colimits can be computed in **TOP**; if G is locally compact, then even the right topology is obtained.

3.1. Limits in TTG

3.1.1. Recall that **TTG'** denotes the category with all ttgs as its objects and with morphisms as defined in 1.4.1. As composition the operation will be used that has been defined in 1.4.3. In this subsection, we would like to investigate limits of diagrams in the category **TTG'**; in particular, we shall consider the categories **TOPGRP** and **TOP** as "known", so we shall be satisfied if we are able to express the behaviour of diagrams in **TTG'** in terms of the behaviour of corresponding diagrams in **TOPGRP** and **TOP**. The following convention will be convenient.

We shall consider **TOPGRP** simply as a subcategory of **TOP**. Thus, if G is an object in **TOPGRP** and X is an object in **TOP**, then the topological (cartesian) product $G\times X$ is just the product of G and X in the category **TOP**. We can express this convention also by saying that we shall suppress the forgetful functor **TOPGRP** $\to$ **TOP**.

In order to avoid difficulties, we have to extend the object class of **TTG'** with all objects of the form $<G,\emptyset,\varphi^G>$ (G a topological group), where φ^G denotes the empty mapping from the empty set $G\times\emptyset$ to the empty set. For each ttg $<H,Y,\sigma>$ and each morphism $\psi\colon G\to H$ in **TOPGRP** we can consider the pair $<\psi,\varphi_Y>$ as a morphism from $<G,\emptyset,\varphi^G>$ to $<H,Y,\sigma>$; similarly, we have $<\psi,\varphi_\emptyset>\colon <G,\emptyset,\varphi^G> \to <H,\emptyset,\varphi^H>$ (here $\varphi_Y\colon \emptyset\to Y$ is the unique mapping of $\emptyset$ into Y). In this way we obtain a category which properly contains **TTG'**; it will be denoted by **TTG**. Notice, that there exist no morphisms in **TTG** from $<G,X,\pi>$ to any $<H,\emptyset,\varphi^H>$, unless $X=\emptyset$. In the sequel, all terminology and all notions from §1 and §2, as far as they are meaningful, will be applied to the objects and morphisms in the extended category **TTG**.

3.1.2. Let the covariant functors **G**: **TTG** $\to$ **TOPGRP** and **S**: **TTG** $\to$ **TOP** (*"forgetful" functors*) be defined in the following way:

$$\mathbf{G}\colon \begin{cases} <G,X,\pi> \longmapsto G & \text{on objects} \\ <\psi,f> \longmapsto \psi & \text{on morphisms,} \end{cases}$$

$$\mathbf{S}\colon \begin{cases} <G,X,\pi> \longmapsto X & \text{on objects} \\ <\psi,f> \longmapsto f & \text{on morphisms.} \end{cases}$$

As usual, let **TOPGRP** $\times$ **TOP** denote the following category: objects are all pairs (G,X) with G and X objects in **TOPGRP** and **TOP**, respectively; morphisms are the pairs (ψ,f) with ψ and f morphisms in **TOPGRP** and **TOP**, composition of morphisms being defined coordinate-wise. Let $\mathbf{G}_0$: **TOPGRP** $\times$ **TOP** $\to$ **TOPGRP** and $\mathbf{S}_0$: **TOPGRP** $\times$ **TOP** $\to$ **TOP** denote the canonical projection functors. Then there exists a unique covariant functor K: TTG → TOPGRP×TOP such that $G_0K = G$ and $S_0K = S$. Obviously, K is described by:

$$K: \begin{cases} \langle G,X,\pi\rangle \longmapsto (G,X) & \text{on objects} \\ \langle \psi,f\rangle \longmapsto (\psi,f) & \text{on morphisms.} \end{cases}$$

3.1.3. The program suggested in 3.1.1 will partly be carried out by investigation of preservation and reflection properties of the functor K. In this context, the following trivial observations are useful:

(i) A morphism (ψ,f) in **TOPGRP** × **TOP** is monic {epic} iff ψ is monic {epic} in **TOPGRP** and f is monic {epic} in **TOP**. Similar for isomorphisms.

(ii) A diagram D: J → **TOPGRP** × **TOP** has a limit iff the diagrams G_0D: J → **TOPGRP** and S_0D: J → **TOP** both have a limit. If so, then $\psi: G \to G_0D$ and $f: X \to S_0D$ are limiting cones in **TOPGRP** and **TOP**, respectively iff $(\psi,f): (G,X) \to D$ is a limiting cone in **TOPGRP** × **TOP**. Here, of course, $(\psi,f)_j := (\psi_j,f_j)$ for each object j in J.

In particular, it follows that **TOPGRP** × **TOP** is complete, since **TOPGRP** and **TOP** are complete. Similar statements hold with respect to colimits of diagrams, so that **TOPGRP** × **TOP** is cocomplete.

3.1.4. *Let* $\langle\psi,f\rangle$ *be a morphism in* **TTG**. *Then the following statements are true:*

(i) $\langle\psi,f\rangle$ *is an isomorphism in* **TTG** *iff* ψ *is an isomorphism in* **TOPGRP** *and* f *is an isomorphism in* **TOP**. *Thus, the isomorphisms of ttgs defined in* 1.4.1 *are isomorphisms in* **TTG**.

(ii) *If* ψ *and* f *are monic {epic} in* **TOPGRP** *and* **TOP**, *respectively, then* $\langle\psi,f\rangle$ *is monic {epic} in* **TTG**.

The proofs are easy: we leave them to the reader.

3.1.5. We shall see that the converse of 3.1.4 (ii) is also true: *the functor* K *preserves all monomorphisms and all epimorphisms*. Although we can give a direct proof for the case of a monomorphism, we prefer to obtain it as a corollary to 3.1.10 below, where we show that K has a left adjoint. However, see also 4.1.7 below. Since K cannot have a right adjoint (cf. 3.4.12 below), we have to proceed in a different way if we want to show that K preserves epimorphisms. This will be postponed to subsection 3.4, where we shall show first that G: **TTG** → **TOPGRP** × **TOP** has a right adjoint (cf. 3.4.9 and 3.4.10).

3.1.6. In the sequel, we shall denote the category $\mathbf{TOPGRP} \times \mathbf{TOP}$ simply by $\mathbf{C}$. We shall construct a *monad* in $\mathbf{C}$ such that the corresponding category of algebras is isomorphic to **TTG**. To this end, consider the functor $H\colon \mathbf{C} \to \mathbf{C}$, defined in the following way:

$$H\colon \begin{cases} (G,X) \mapsto (G,G\times X) & \text{on objects} \\ (\psi,f) \mapsto (\psi,\psi\times f) & \text{on morphisms.} \end{cases}$$

In addition, for each object (G,X) in $\mathbf{C}$, let the morphisms

$$\eta_{(G,X)} : (G,X) \to (G,G\times X)$$

and

$$\mu_{(G,X)} : (G,G\times(G\times X)) \to (G,G\times X)$$

in $\mathbf{C}$ be defined by

$$\eta_{(G,X)} := (1_G,\eta_X^G); \quad \mu_{(G,X)} := (1_G,\mu_X^G).$$

Here η_X^G and μ_X^G are the mappings, defined in 1.1.1.

3.1.7. PROPOSITION. *The morphisms* $\eta_{(G,X)}$ *and* $\mu_{(G,X)}$ *in* $\mathbf{C}$ *for all objects* (G,X) *in* $\mathbf{C}$ *form up two natural transformations,*

$$\eta\colon I_{\mathbf{C}} \to H \quad \textit{and} \quad \mu\colon H^2 \to H,$$

and (H,η,μ) *is a monad in* $\mathbf{C}$.

PROOF. The straightforward verifications that η and μ are natural transformations are left to the reader. The proof that (H,η,μ) is a monad now reduces to showing that for each object (G,X) in $\mathbf{C}$ the following diagrams commute:

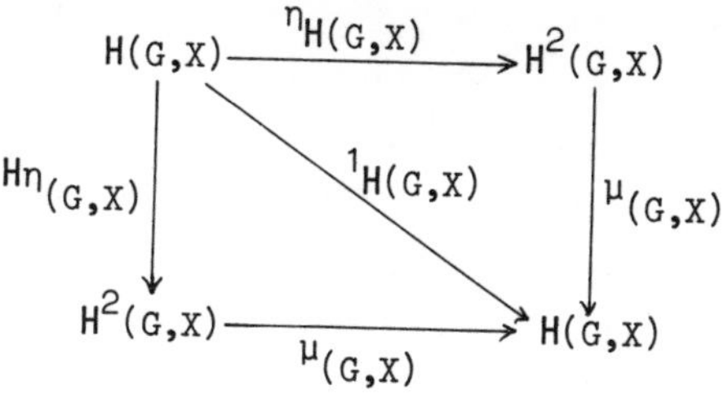

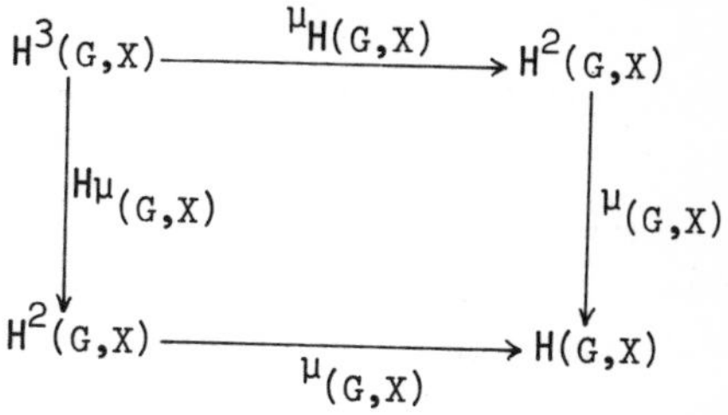

The images under G_0: $C \to$ TOPGRP of these diagrams commute trivially, because they contain only arrows $1_G: G \to G$. The images of these diagrams under the functor S_0: $C \to$ TOP are:

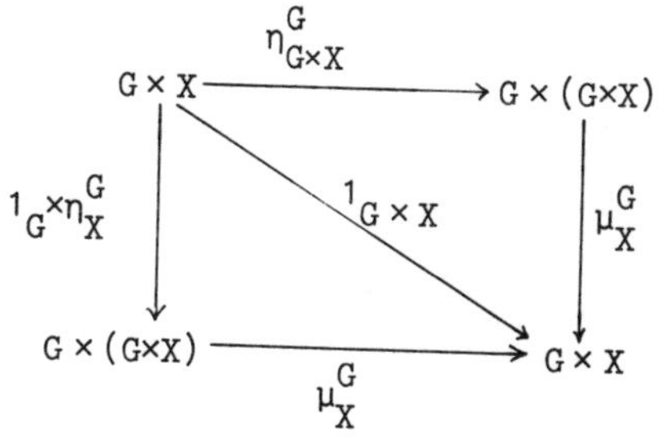

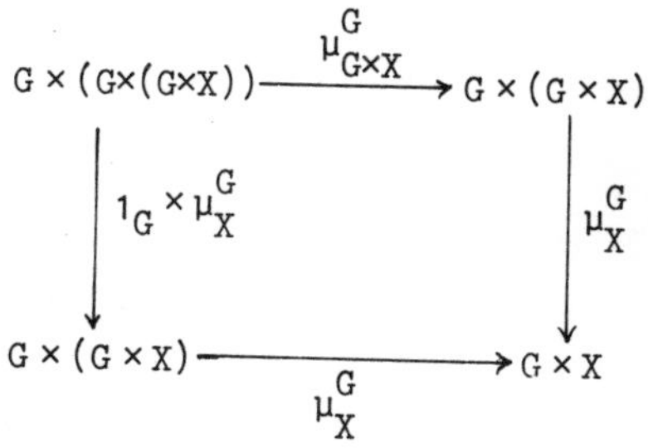

The first of these diagrams commutes because $es = s = se$ for all $s \in G$, and the second one commutes because $s(tu) = (st)u$ for all $s,t,u \in G$. [1] □

3.1.8. By definition, *an* H-*algebra* for the above defined monad (H,η,μ) is an ordered pair $((G,x),(\psi,\pi))$, consisting of an object (G,X) and a morphism $(\psi,\pi):(G,G\times X) = H(G,X) \to (G,X)$ in C such that the following diagrams commute:

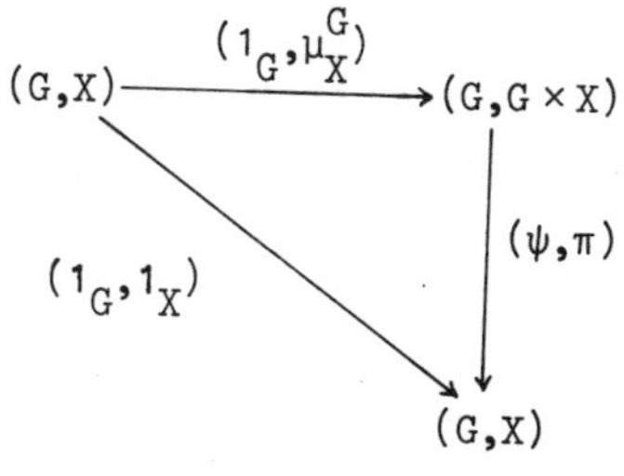

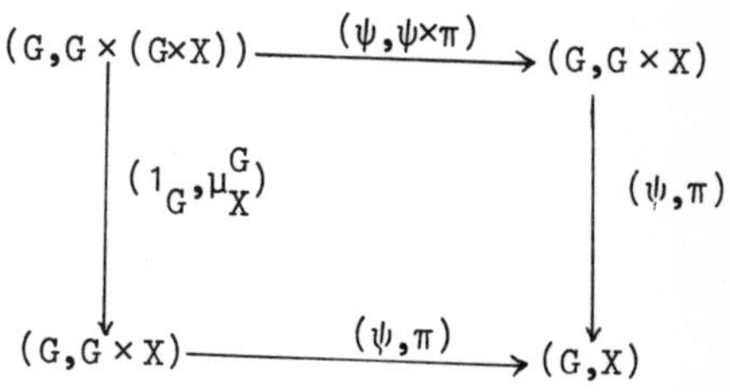

---

[1] So we need only that G is a semigroup with unit (i.e. G is a *monoid*).

The first of these diagrams requires that $\psi = 1_G$. Hence the condition that both diagrams commute is equivalent to the condition that the morphism $\pi: G\times X \to X$ in TOP is an action of G on X (cf. diagram (2) in 1.1.1). Stated otherwise: *the assignment* K_0: $\langle G,X,\pi\rangle \mapsto ((G,X),(1_G,\pi))$ *defines a bijection of the class of all objects in* TTG *onto the class of all* H*-algebras.*

A *morphism of* H*-algebras*, from $((G,X),(1_G,\pi))$ to $((H,Y),(1_H,\sigma))$ is by definition a morphism $(\psi,f): (G,X) \to (H,Y)$ in C such that the following diagram commutes:

$$\begin{array}{ccc} (G,G\times X) & \xrightarrow{(1_G,\pi)} & (G,X) \\ \Big\downarrow{\scriptstyle(\psi,\psi\times f)} & & \Big\downarrow{\scriptstyle(\psi,f)} \\ (H,H\times Y) & \xrightarrow{(1_H,\sigma)} & (H,Y) \end{array}$$

This is equivalent to saying that $\langle\psi,f\rangle: \langle G,X,\pi\rangle \to \langle H,Y,\sigma\rangle$ is a morphism in TTG. Stated otherwise: *the assignment* K_0: $\langle\psi,f\rangle \longmapsto (\psi,f)$ *defines a bijection of each morphism set* TTG$(\langle G,X,\pi\rangle,\langle H,Y,\sigma\rangle)$ *onto the corresponding set of all morphisms of* H*-algebras with domain* $K_0\langle G,X,\pi\rangle$ *and codomain* $K_0\langle H,Y,\sigma\rangle$.

Since K_0 is easily seen to preserve compositions of morphisms, this proves most of the following

3.1.9. <u>THEOREM</u>. *There exists an isomorphism* K_0 *of categories from* TTG *onto the category* C^H *of all* H*-algebras. If* $G^H: C^H \to C$ *denotes the usual forgetful functor, then the following diagram of functors commutes:*

$$\begin{array}{ccc} TTG & \xrightarrow{K_0} & C^H \\ & {\scriptstyle K}\searrow \quad \swarrow{\scriptstyle G^H} & \\ & C & \end{array}$$

<u>PROOF</u>. The first statement has been proved in 3.1.8. The second one is trivial, taking into account the definition of K_0. □

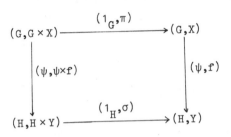

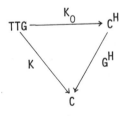

3.1.10. <u>COROLLARY 1</u>. *The functor* K: TTG → C *has a left adjoint. In addition, it creates all limits in* TTG.

<u>PROOF</u>. Apply 0.4.6 and 0.4.7, taking into account 3.1.9. □

3.1.11. <u>COROLLARY 2</u>. *The category* TTG *is complete and the functor* K: TTG → C *preserves all limits and all monomorphisms.*

<u>PROOF</u>. Completeness follows immediately from completeness of C (cf. 3.1.3) and the fact that K creates all limits in TTG. The preservation properties of K are a consequence of its having a left adjoint (cf. 0.4.4(ii)). □

3.1.12. It follows from 3.1.11 and 3.1.4(ii) that *a morphism* $\langle\psi,f\rangle$ *in* TTG *is monic iff* ψ *is monic in* TOPGRP *and* f *is monic in* TOP. We may summarize this by saying that "monomorphisms in TTG can be calculated in C".

Similarly, the behaviour of K with respect to limits may be expressed by saying that "limits in TTG can be calculated in C". That is)1, if D: J → TTG is a diagram, then its limiting cone $\langle\psi,f\rangle$: $\langle G,X,\pi\rangle \to D$ is obtained by taking ψ and G such that ψ: G → GD is the limiting cone of the diagram GD in TOPGRP; in addition, f: X → SD is the limiting cone of the diagram SD in TOP; finally, π is the *unique* action of G on X such that each $\langle\psi_j,f_j\rangle$: $\langle G,X,\pi\rangle \to$ Dj $(j\in J)$ is a morphism in TTG.

We shall present now a short description of products and equalizers in TTG, using the above characterization:

(i) *The product in* TTG *of a set* $\{\langle G_j,X_j,\pi_j\rangle : j\in J\}$ *of its objects* is the ttg $\langle \mathbb{P}_jG_j, \mathbb{P}_jX_j, \pi\rangle$, together with the projections $\langle\psi_i,f_i\rangle$: $\langle \mathbb{P}_jG_j, \mathbb{P}_jX_j, \pi\rangle \to \langle G_i,X_i,\pi_i\rangle$. Here $\mathbb{P}_jG_j$ and $\mathbb{P}_jX_j$ are the usual products in the categories TOPGRP and TOP, and ψ_i,f_i denote the usual projections. Moreover, π is defined by

$$\pi((t_j)_j,(x_j)_j) := (\pi_j(t_j,x_j))_j.$$

(ii) *The equalizer of a pair of morphisms* $\langle\psi_1,f_1\rangle,\langle\psi_2,f_2\rangle$: $\langle G,X,\pi\rangle \to \langle H,Y,\sigma\rangle$ *in* TTG is the morphism $\langle\psi,f\rangle$: $\langle K,Z,\pi|_{K\times Z}\rangle \to \langle G,X,\pi\rangle$ in TTG, where

$$K := \{t\in G : \psi_1(t)=\psi_2(t)\};\quad Z := \{x\in X : f_1(x)=f_2(x)\},$$

)1 We present here just a reformulation of "K creates all limits in TTG".

and ψ: $K \to G$, f: $Z \to X$ are inclusion maps (i.e. equalizers of ψ_1, ψ_2 in **TOPGRP** and of f_1, f_2 in **TOP**, respectively).

The straightforward justifications of (i) and (ii) are left to the reader.

3.1.13. As an application and extension of the preceding results, we prove the following well-known fact:

Let $\langle G,X,\pi\rangle$ *be a ttg and let* f': $Y \to X/C_\pi$ *be a continuous function. Then there exists a ttg* $\langle G,Z,\zeta\rangle$ *and a morphism of* G*-spaces* f: $Z \to X$ *such that*

(i) Y *is homeomorphic to* Z/C_ζ.

(ii) *If we identify* Y *with* Z/C_ζ *according to* (i), *then* $f'c_\zeta = c_\pi f$.

PROOF. Let σ and τ denote the trivial actions of G on Y, resp. X/C_π. Then we have the following diagram in **TTG** (solid arrows only):

$$\begin{array}{ccc} \langle G,Z,\zeta\rangle & \overset{\langle 1_G, f\rangle}{\dashrightarrow} & \langle G,X,\pi\rangle \\ {\scriptstyle \langle 1_G, g\rangle}\ \downarrow & & \downarrow\ {\scriptstyle \langle 1_G, c_\pi\rangle} \\ \langle G,Y,\sigma\rangle & \underset{\langle 1_G, f'\rangle}{\longrightarrow} & \langle G,X/C_\pi,\tau\rangle \end{array}$$

The limit of this diagram is the object $\langle G,Z,\zeta\rangle$, together with the dotted arrows in the above diagram. Here f: $Z \to X$ and g: $Z \to Y$ form the limiting cone of the diagram

$$Y \xrightarrow{\;f'\;} X/C_\pi \xleftarrow{\;c_\pi\;} X$$

in **TOP**. So we may take $Z := \{(x,y) \in X \times Y : c_\pi(x) = f'(y)\}$, and for f and g we may take the restrictions to Z of the projections of $X \times Y$ onto X and Y, respectively. The action ζ of G on Z is given by (still according to 3.1.12) $\zeta(t,(x,y)) := (\pi^t x, \sigma^t y) = (\pi^t x, y)$. Now some straightforward computations show that g: $Z \to Y$ is an open mapping, and that g induces a bijection of Z/C_ζ onto Y. Then (i) and (ii) follow readily (cf. also 1.4.9 and notice that $Y = Y/C_\sigma$). □

3.1.14. According to 0.4.6 and 3.1.9, the left adjoint F: $C \to$ **TTG** of the functor K: **TTG** $\to C$ is the functor $\overleftarrow{K_0}F^H$, where F^H is the left adjoint of G^H. To be concrete:

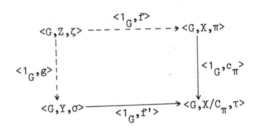

For any object $(G,X) \in \mathbf{C}$, the free H-algebra is $(\mathsf{H}(G,X),\mu_{(G,X)})$, which corresponds to the ttg $\langle G,G\times X,\mu_X^G\rangle$ (cf. 3.1.8, where K_0 is explicitly described). This ttg will be called *the free ttg for* G *and* X. Combining in a similar way the definitions of F^{H} and K_0 on morphisms, we obtain the following description of the left adjoint F of K:

$$\mathsf{F}: \begin{cases} (G,X) \mapsto \langle G,G\times X,\mu_X^G\rangle & \text{on objects} \\ (\psi,f) \mapsto \langle\psi,\psi\times f\rangle & \text{on morphisms.} \end{cases}$$

Translation of the remainder of 0.4.6 to the present situation gives the following results:

The *unit* of the adjunction of F to K is the natural transformation $\eta\colon I_{\mathbf{C}} \to \mathsf{KF} = \mathsf{H}$. So for each object (G,X) in $\mathbf{C}$ the arrow

$$(1_G,\eta_X^G)\colon (G,X) \longrightarrow (G,G\times X)$$

is universal from (G,X) to K.

The *counit* of the adjunction of F to K is the natural transformation $\xi\colon \mathsf{FK} \to I_{\mathbf{TTG}}$, defined by

$$\xi_{\langle G,X,\pi\rangle} := \langle 1_G,\pi\rangle\colon \langle G,G\times X,\mu_X^G\rangle \to \langle G,X,\pi\rangle$$

for each object $\langle G,X,\pi\rangle$ in $\mathbf{TTG}$.

{It may be comforting for a reader who doesn't like monads and algebras that it is easy to show directly that $(\mathsf{F},\mathsf{K},\eta,\xi)$ is an adjunction from $\mathbf{C}$ to $\mathbf{TTG}$; in addition, it can easily be shown that K creates limits (cf. also 4.1.3).}

3.1.15. According to 0.4.9, the adjunction of F and K, with unit η and counit ξ gives rise to the comonad $(\mathsf{FK},\xi,\mathsf{F}\eta\mathsf{K})$. The coalgebras for this comonad are the pairs $(\langle G,X,\pi\rangle,\langle\psi,f\rangle)$ with $\langle\psi,f\rangle\colon \langle G,X,\pi\rangle \to \mathsf{FK}\langle G,X,\pi\rangle = \langle G,G\times X,\mu_X^G\rangle$ a morphism in $\mathbf{TTG}$ such that the following diagrams commute:

(1)

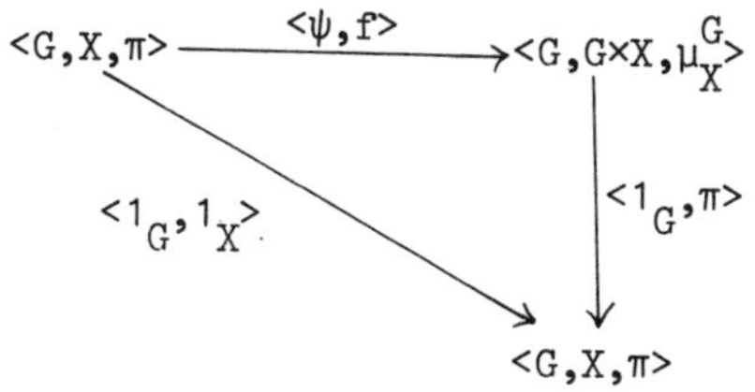

(2)
$$\begin{array}{ccc} \langle G,X,\pi\rangle & \xrightarrow{\langle\psi,f\rangle} & \langle G,G\times X,\mu_X^G\rangle \\ \Big\downarrow{\scriptstyle\langle\psi,f\rangle} & & \Big\downarrow{\scriptstyle\langle\psi,\psi\times f\rangle} \\ \langle G,G\times X,\mu_X^G\rangle & \xrightarrow{\langle 1_G,1_G\times\eta_X^G\rangle} & \langle G,G\times(G\times X),\mu_{G\times X}^G\rangle \end{array}$$

By (1), we obtain

(3) $\psi = 1_G;\quad \pi\circ f = 1_X,$

and then (2) implies, writing $f(x) =: (\gamma(x),g(x)) \in G\times X$ for $x\in X$,

(4) $\gamma(g(x)) = e;\quad g(g(x)) = g(x).$

In addition, the condition that $\langle 1_G,f\rangle\colon \langle G,X,\pi\rangle \to \langle G,G\times X,\mu_X^G\rangle$ is a morphism in **TTG** implies that

(5) $\gamma(\pi(t,x)) = t.\gamma(x);\quad g(\pi(t,x)) = g(x)$

for all $t\in G$, $x\in X$. If we set $S := g[X]$ and $\tau(x) := \gamma(x)^{-1}$, then (3), the first formula in (4) and the first formula in (5) imply that *for each* $x\in X$, $\tau(x)$ *is the unique element of* G *for which* $\pi(\tau(x),x)\in S$.

Conversely, if we are given an object $\langle G,X,\pi\rangle$ in **TTG**, a subset S of X, and a continuous function $\tau\colon X\to G$ such that for each $x\in X$, $\tau(x)$ is the unique element of G for which $\pi(\tau(x),x)\in S$, then we can define $\gamma(x) := \tau(x)^{-1}$, $g(x) := \pi(\tau(x),x)$ and $f(x) := (\gamma(x),g(x))$. If we do so, then (3), (4) and (5) can be derived (uniqueness of $\tau(x)$ is essential!), and $(\langle G,X,\pi\rangle,\langle 1_G,f\rangle)$ is an **FK**-coalgebra.

A pair (S,τ) as described above will be called *a continuous cross-section of the ttg* $\langle G,X,\pi\rangle$[1]. Now the first statement in the next proposition is just a reformulation of the preceding remarks:

3.1.16. PROPOSITION. *The coalgebras for the comonad* $(\mathsf{FK},\xi,\mathsf{F}\eta\mathsf{K})$ *in* **TTG** *are just the ttgs* $\langle G,X,\pi\rangle$ *admitting a continuous cross-section* (S,τ). *If* $\langle G,X,\pi\rangle$ *(with continuous cross-section* (S,τ)*) and* $\langle G',X',\pi'\rangle$ *(with continuous cross-section* (S',τ')*) are two such coalgebras, then a morphism* $\langle\psi,f\rangle\colon \langle G,X,\pi\rangle \to$

[1] Here terminology is a little bit confusing, because this concept of a cross-section is not the same as the one in 1.3.20. The latter concept is often called a *continuous selection*.

<G',X',π'> in TTG *is a morphism of coalgebras iff* $f[S] \subseteq S'$ *and, in addition, the following diagram commutes:*

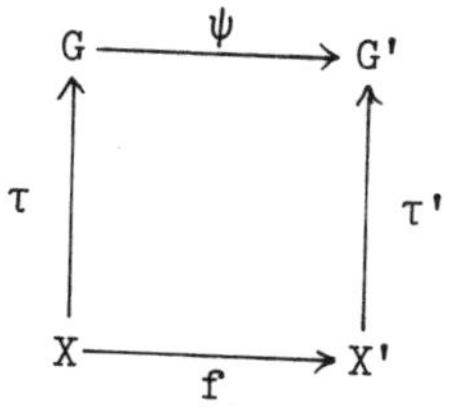

PROOF. The characterization of the morphisms of coalgebras follows by a straightforward argument from the definitions in 0.4.9 and the remarks, preceding our proposition. □

3.1.17. If $\langle G,X,\pi\rangle$ is a ttg with continuous cross-section (S,τ), then $x \mapsto (\tau(x)^{-1},\pi(\tau(x),x))$ is a homeomorphism of X onto $G \times S$; in fact, it defines an isomorphism in TTG of $\langle G,X,\pi\rangle$ onto $\langle G,G\times S,\mu_S^G\rangle$. In addition, it is easy to see that in this way *the category of all* FK*-coalgebras is isomorphic to the subcategory* F[C] *of* TTG[)1].

3.1.18. NOTES. It is well-known that group actions have a close connection with certain monads (H,η,μ) and that, in fact, G-spaces can be obtained as H-algebras. This is not surprising, since the abstract definition of H-algebras was constructed on the model of group actions. To be precise, one of the original examples which were of interest to GODEMENT when he introduced the concept of a "standard construction" (which is the same as a monad) in [Go] was the monad, generated in the category of abelian groups by tensoring with a *fixed* ring R. Moreover, in the paper of S. EILENBERG & J.C. MOORE [1965] where it was proved that each monad arises from a pair of adjoint functors, the construction of H-algebras was motivated by the example of the category of all Λ-modules. This is just the category of all H-algebras, where H is the functor in the category of modules over a commutative ring K, defined by tensoring with the fixed K-algebra Λ. Cf. also the motivation in [ML], p.137. Our functor H, defined in 3.1.6 is just similar to these examples, except that we do not restrict ourselves to a fixed group G; this is the only new point of view in this subsection. In addition, we were unable to find the observations of 3.1.16 in the literature. References to

---

)1 It can be shown that this is not a full subcategory of TTG.

the literature about continuous cross-sections in ttgs can be found in the notes to subsection 1.3.

3.2. Limits in TOP^G

3.2.1. In this subsection, the symbol G denotes always a given topological group. Then TOP^G denotes the subcategory of TTG defined by all objects having G as a phase group and all morphisms with 1_G as a group component. *Obviously, the morphisms in* TOP^G *are just the morphisms of* G-*spaces,* defined in 1.4.1.)1 For most groups G, TOP^G *is not a full subcategory of* TTG.

Let $S^G: \mathsf{TOP}^G \to \mathsf{TOP}$ be the restriction to TOP^G of the functor S, defined in 3.1.2. Thus,

$$(1) \qquad S^G: \begin{cases} \langle G,X,\pi\rangle \longmapsto X \text{ on objects} \\ \langle 1_G,f\rangle \longmapsto f \text{ on morphisms.} \end{cases}$$

3.2.2. *Let* $\langle 1_G,f\rangle$ *be a morphism in* TOP^G. *Then the following statements are true:*

(i) $\langle 1_G,f\rangle$ *is an isomorphism in* TOP^G *iff* f *is an isomorphism in* TOP. *Thus, the isomorphisms of* G-*spaces defined in* 1.4.1 *are isomorphisms in* TOP^G.

(ii) *If* f *is monic {epic} in* TOP, *then* $\langle 1_G,f\rangle$ *is monic {epic} in* TOP^G.

The easy proofs are left for the reader. We shall prove now first of all the converse of (ii) for epimorphisms.

3.2.3. PROPOSITION. *A morphism* $\langle 1_G,f\rangle$ *in* TOP^G *is epic iff* f *is epic in* TOP; *that is,* S^G *preserves and reflects epimorphisms.*

PROOF. Reflection: cf. 3.2.2(ii).
Preservation)2: Let $\langle 1_G,f\rangle: \langle G,X,\pi\rangle \to \langle G,Y,\sigma\rangle$ be an epimorphism in TOP^G. Then f[X] is an invariant subset of $\langle G,Y,\sigma\rangle$ (cf. 1.4.5). Consequently, R := $C_\sigma \cup (f[X]\times f[X])$ is an equivalence relation in Y, which is invariant under the action σ of G. Let Z := Y/R with its usual quotient topology, and let q: Y → Z be the quotient mapping. In addition, let q': Y → Z be the constant function with q'[Y] = q[f[X]]. Finally, let τ denote the trivial action of

)1 According to our agreement in 3.1.1, TOP^G contains also the object $\langle G,\emptyset,\varphi^G$ and, for every G-space $\langle G,Y,\sigma\rangle$, a morphism $\langle 1^G,\varphi_Y\rangle: \langle G,\emptyset,\varphi^G\rangle \to \langle G,Y,\sigma\rangle$.

)2 For alternative proofs, see 3.4.6 and 3.4.8 below.

G on Z[)1]. Then q and q' are morphisms of G-spaces, from Y with action σ to Z with action τ. Since $\langle 1_G,q\rangle\langle 1_G,f\rangle = \langle 1_G,q'\rangle\langle 1_G,f\rangle$, where $\langle 1_G,f\rangle$ is an epimorphism in $\mathbf{TOP}^G$, it follows that $q' = q$, whence $f[X] = Y$. Therefore, f is an epimorphism in **TOP**. □

3.2.4. THEOREM. *The functor* $S^G\colon \mathbf{TOP}^G \to \mathbf{TOP}$ *has a left adjoint. In addition, it creates all limits in* $\mathbf{TOP}^G$.

PROOF. Completely similar to the proof of 3.1.10, so we shall present only a brief outline of it. Define a functor $H^G\colon \mathbf{TOP} \to \mathbf{TOP}$ by

$$(2) \qquad H^G\colon \begin{cases} X \longmapsto G\times X & \text{on objects} \\ f \longmapsto 1_G\times f & \text{on morphisms.} \end{cases}$$

Then we have natural transformations $\eta^G\colon I_{\mathbf{TOP}} \to H^G$ and $\mu^G\colon (H^G)^2 \to H^G$, where for each object $X \in \mathbf{TOP}$, η^G_X and μ^G_X are as in 1.1.1 (compare also 3.1.6). Then similar to 3.1.7, one shows that (H^G,η^G,μ^G) is a monad. The category of all H^G-algebras may be identified with $\mathbf{TOP}^G$ in such a way that $S^G\colon \mathbf{TOP}^G \to \mathbf{TOP}$ corresponds to the forgetful functor from the category of H^G-algebras to **TOP**. Now the theorem follows from 0.4.6 and 0.4.7. □

3.2.5. COROLLARY. *The category* $\mathbf{TOP}^G$ *is complete, and all limits can be calculated in* **TOP**, *i.e.* S^G *creates and preserves all limits. In addition,* S^G *preserves and reflects all monomorphisms.* □

3.2.6. *The product in* $\mathbf{TOP}^G$ of a set $\{\langle G,X_j,\pi_j\rangle : j\in J\}$ of its objects is the G-space $\langle G,\mathbb{P}_jX_j,\pi\rangle$, where π is defined by $\pi(t,(x_j)_j) := (\pi_j(t,x_j))_j$. Moreover, *the equalizer in* $\mathbf{TOP}^G$ of a parallel pair of morphisms $\langle 1_G,f\rangle,\langle 1_G,g\rangle\colon \langle G,X,\pi\rangle \to \langle G,Y,\sigma\rangle$ is the morphism $\langle 1_G,h\rangle\colon\langle G,Z,\pi|_{G\times Z}\rangle \to \langle G,X,\pi\rangle$, where $Z := \{x\in X : f(x) = g(x)\}$, and $h\colon Z\to X$ is the inclusion mapping.

Notice, that it follows immediately from this description that *the inclusion functor of* $\mathbf{TOP}^G$ *in* **TTG** *does not preserve products, but that it creates and preserves all equalizers.*

3.2.7. For the description of the left adjoint F^G of the functor S^G and the unit and counit of adjunction we refer the reader to 3.1.14, where each morphism ψ in **TOPGRP** has to be replaced by 1_G.

[)1] Plainly, this proof fails if $X = \emptyset$. In that case, however, it is easy to see that $\langle 1_G,f\rangle$ is not an epimorphism if $Y \neq \emptyset$. So in that case, $Y = \emptyset$, and f is epic in **TOP**.

3.2.8. Now we consider another topological group H, and the corresponding monad (H^H, η^H, μ^H) in **TOP**. Again, the category of all H^H-algebras may be identified with the category $\mathbf{TOP}^H$. We shall investigate now the morphisms of monads from (H^H, η^H, μ^H) to (H^G, η^G, μ^G).

According to 0.4.8, a natural transformation $\theta\colon H^H \to H^G$ is a morphism of monads from (H^H, η^H, μ^H) to (H^G, η^G, μ^G) iff

(3) $$\theta \circ \eta^H = \eta^G; \quad \theta \circ \mu^H = \mu^G \circ \theta^2.$$

For each object $X \in$ **TOP**, θ_X is a continuous mapping,

(4) $$\theta_X\colon H \times X \to G \times X.$$

Identifying the H^G- and H^H-algebras with G- and H-spaces, the functor θ induces the functor $\theta^*\colon \mathbf{TOP}^G \to \mathbf{TOP}^H$ according to 0.4.8, as follows:

(5) $$\theta^*\colon \begin{cases} \langle G, X, \pi\rangle \longmapsto \langle H, X, \pi\theta_X\rangle & \text{on objects} \\ \langle 1_G, f\rangle \longmapsto \langle 1_H, f\rangle & \text{on morphisms.} \end{cases}$$

We shall describe now θ and θ^* in terms of morphisms in **TOPGRP** and in **TOP**.

3.2.9. <u>LEMMA</u>. *There exists a bijection* $\theta \mapsto \psi_\theta$ *from the set of all natural transformations* $\theta\colon H^H \to H^G$ *onto the set of all continuous functions* $\psi_\theta\colon H \to G$. *Here* θ *and* ψ_θ *are related by*

(6) $$\theta_X = \psi_\theta \times 1_X$$

for each object $X \in$ **TOP**.

<u>PROOF</u>. Let $(*)$ denote any one-point space. If $\theta\colon H^H \to H^G$ is a natural transformation then by (4) there is a continuous function $\psi_\theta\colon H \to G$ such that $\theta_{(*)} = \psi_\theta \times 1_{(*)}$. Next, fix any non-void object $X \in$ **TOP** and any point $x \in X$, and let $f\colon (*) \to X$ be defined by $f(*) := x$. Then f is a morphism in **TOP**, hence naturality of θ implies that $\theta_X \circ (1_H \times f) = (1_G \times f) \circ \theta_{(*)}$. It follows that $\theta_X(s,x) = (\psi_\theta(s), x)$ for all $s \in H$. Since $x \in X$ has been chosen arbitrarily, this proves (6) for each $X \neq \emptyset$. For $X = \emptyset$, (6) is obvious.

Conversely, if $\psi\colon H \to G$ is any morphism in **TOP**, then defining $\theta_X := \psi \times 1_X$ for every object $X \in$ **TOP**, we obtain a natural transformation $\theta\colon H^H \to H^G$ such that $\psi = \psi_\theta$. This completes the proof. □

3.2.10. LEMMA. *Let* θ *and* ψ_θ *be as in* 3.2.9. *Then* θ *satisfies the relations* (3) *iff* $\psi_\theta\colon H\to G$ *is a morphism in* **TOPGRP**.

PROOF. By a straightforward argument one shows that the natural transformation $\theta^2\colon (H^H)^2\to(H^G)^2$ is related with ψ_θ as follows: if X is an object in **TOP**, then $\theta^2_X\colon H\times(H\times X)\to G\times(G\times X)$ is given by $\theta^2_X = \psi_\theta\times\psi_\theta\times 1_X$. Therefore, the relations (3) are equivalent with

$$\psi_\theta(e_H) = e_G;\quad \psi_\theta(st) = \psi_\theta(s)\psi_\theta(t)$$

$(s,t\in H)$. This proves the lemma. □

3.2.11. THEOREM. *There exists a bijection* $\theta\mapsto\psi_\theta$ *from the set of all morphisms of monads* $\theta\colon (H^H,\eta^H,\mu^H)\to(H^G,\eta^G,\mu^G)$ *onto the set* **TOPGRP**(H,G). *Here* θ *and* ψ_θ *are related by* (6).

PROOF. Obvious from the preceding lemmas. □

3.2.12. If $\psi\colon H\to G$ is a morphism in **TOPGRP**, then let $R_\psi\colon \mathbf{TOP}^G\to\mathbf{TOP}^H$ be the functor, defined by $R_\psi := \theta^*$, where θ is the morphism of monads corresponding to ψ (i.e. $\psi=\psi_\theta$). Thus, by (5) and (6),

$$(7)\qquad R_\psi\colon\begin{cases}\langle G,X,\pi\rangle \mapsto \langle H,X,\pi\circ(\psi\times 1_X)\rangle & \text{on objects}\\ \langle 1_G,f\rangle \mapsto \langle 1_H,f\rangle & \text{on morphisms.}\end{cases}$$

3.2.13. NOTES. Most of the contents of this subsection are classical (cf. the notes in 3.1.18). Only 3.2.3 and 3.2.11 seem to be new.

Another approach to categories of G-spaces would be to consider G as a category. Then G is a small strict monoidal category, and as such one can define actions of the category G on the category **TOP**. For more details, cf. [ML], p.170, where also some references to pertinent literature are given.

3.3. Induced actions

3.3.1. In this subsection, let $\psi\colon H\to G$ be a fixed morphism in **TOPGRP**. For any G-space $\langle G,X,\pi\rangle$, let

$$(1)\qquad \pi^\psi := \pi\circ(\psi\times 1_X).$$

So the functor $R_\psi\colon \mathbf{TOP}^G\to\mathbf{TOP}^H$ defined in 3.2.12 can now be described as follows:

$$(2) \qquad R_\psi: \begin{cases} \langle G,X,\pi\rangle \mapsto \langle H,X,\pi^\psi\rangle & \text{on objects} \\ \langle 1_G,f\rangle \mapsto \langle 1_H,f\rangle & \text{on morphisms.} \end{cases}$$

For each G-space $\langle G,X,\pi\rangle$, we have the morphism

$$(3) \qquad \langle\psi,1_X\rangle: \langle H,X,\pi^\psi\rangle \to \langle G,X,\pi\rangle$$

in TTG. If $\langle 1_G,\bar{g}\rangle: \langle G,X,\pi\rangle \to \langle G,Z,\zeta\rangle$ is a morphism in TOP^G, then plainly the following diagram commutes:

$$(4) \qquad \begin{array}{ccc} \langle H,X,\pi^\psi\rangle & \xrightarrow{\langle\psi,1_X\rangle} & \langle G,X,\pi\rangle \\ \downarrow{\scriptstyle\langle 1_H,\bar{g}\rangle} & & \downarrow{\scriptstyle\langle 1_G,\bar{g}\rangle} \\ \langle H,Z,\zeta^\psi\rangle & \xrightarrow[\langle\psi,1_Z\rangle]{} & \langle G,Z,\zeta\rangle \end{array}$$

{So the morphisms $\langle\psi,1_X\rangle$ form a natural transformation from $E^H \circ R_\psi$ to E^G, where E^G and E^H denote the inclusion functors of TOP^G and TOP^H in TTG.}

3.3.2. <u>EXAMPLES</u>.

(i) Let H be a subgroup of G and let $\psi: H \to G$ be the inclusion mapping. Then the functor R_ψ assigns to each G-space the H-space which is obtained by restricting the action of G to H: $R_\psi\langle G,X,\pi\rangle = \langle H,X,\pi|_{H\times X}\rangle$.

(ii) Let $H = G_d$ and let $\psi: G_d \to G$ be the identical mapping. Then for each G-space $\langle G,X,\pi\rangle$, we have $R_\psi\langle G,X,\pi\rangle = \langle G_d,X,\pi\rangle$ (cf. also 1.1.5).

(iii) Let $G = \{e\}$ be a one-point group, and let $\psi: H \to G$ be the obvious surjection. Identify TOP^G in the obvious way with TOP. Then R_ψ assigns to each object $X \in$ TOP the H-space $\langle H,X,\tau_X^H\rangle$, where τ_X^H denotes the trivial action of H on X.

3.3.3. <u>PROPOSITION</u>. *Let* $\langle\psi,f\rangle: \langle H,Y,\sigma\rangle \to \langle G,X,\pi\rangle$ *be any morphism in* TTG. *Then* $\langle 1_H,f\rangle: \langle H,Y,\sigma\rangle \to \langle H,X,\pi^\psi\rangle$ *is the unique morphism of* H-*spaces for which the following diagram in* TTG *commutes:*

(5) $$\begin{array}{ccc} \langle H,X,\pi^{\psi}\rangle & \xrightarrow{\langle\psi,1_X\rangle} & \langle G,X,\pi\rangle \\ & {\scriptstyle\langle 1_H,f\rangle}\nwarrow \quad \nearrow{\scriptstyle\langle\psi,f\rangle} & \\ & \langle H,Y,\sigma\rangle & \end{array}$$

PROOF. Straightforward. □

3.3.4. We shall see in 3.3.12 below that this property of the arrow $\langle\psi,1_X\rangle$ is related to the fact that R_ψ has a left adjoint L_ψ. We shall prove this according to 0.4.2(i) by constructing for each H-space $\langle H,Y,\sigma\rangle$ a G-space $\langle G,X,\pi\rangle =: L_\psi\langle H,Y,\sigma\rangle$ and a universal arrow $\gamma_{\langle H,Y,\sigma\rangle}: \langle H,Y,\sigma\rangle \to \langle H,X,\pi^{\psi}\rangle = R_\psi L_\psi\langle H,Y,\sigma\rangle$ from $\langle H,Y,\sigma\rangle$ to R_ψ. We shall present first the construction of the object function of L_ψ.

3.3.5. Let $\langle H,Y,\sigma\rangle$ be an object in TOP^H. Define an action ρ of H on $G\times Y$ by the rule

(6) $$\rho^u(t,y) := (t\psi(u)^{-1},\sigma^u y)$$

$(u \in H,\ (t,y) \in G\times Y)$. Obviously, the action ρ of H on $G\times Y$ commutes with the action μ_Y^G of G on $G\times Y$, so by 1.5.8 there exists a unique action π of G on $X := (G\times Y)/C_\rho$ making $\langle 1_G,c_\rho\rangle: \langle G,G\times Y,\mu_Y^G\rangle \to \langle G,X,\pi\rangle$ a morphism of G-spaces. Now set $L_\psi\langle H,Y,\sigma\rangle := \langle G,X,\pi\rangle$.

3.3.6. With notation as in 3.3.5, set $f := c_\rho\circ\eta_Y^G$. Then $f: Y\to X$ is continuous, and using the fact that $c_\rho(\psi(u),y) = c_\rho(e,\sigma^u y)$ for all $(u,y) \in H\times Y$, it follows that $\langle\psi,f\rangle: \langle H,Y,\sigma\rangle \to \langle G,X,\pi\rangle$ is a morphism in TTG. Let

(7) $$\gamma_{\langle H,Y,\sigma\rangle} := \langle 1_H,f\rangle: \langle H,Y,\sigma\rangle \to \langle H,X,\pi^{\psi}\rangle.$$

Then, indeed, $\langle 1_H,f\rangle$ is a morphism of H-spaces (cf. 3.3.3). We shall show now that it is a universal arrow from $\langle H,Y,\sigma\rangle$ to R_ψ.

3.3.7. LEMMA. *Let $\langle H,Y,\sigma\rangle$ be an object in TOP^H and let $\langle G,X,\pi\rangle$ and $f: Y\to X$ be constructed as above. In addition, let $\langle G,Z,\zeta\rangle$ be any object in TOP^G, and let $\langle 1_H,g\rangle: \langle H,Y,\sigma\rangle \to \langle H,Z,\zeta^{\psi}\rangle$ be a morphism in TOP^H. Then there exists a unique morphism $\langle 1_G,\bar g\rangle: \langle G,X,\pi\rangle \to \langle G,Z,\zeta\rangle$ in TOP^G such that $g = \bar g f$, i.e.*

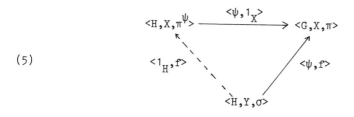

such that the following diagram commutes:

(8)

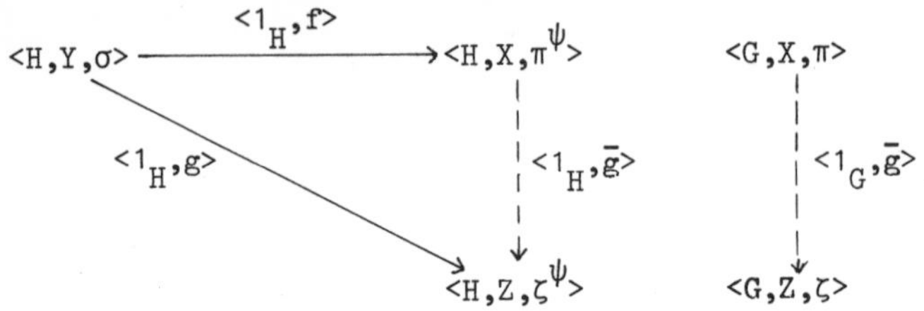

PROOF. Let notation be as in 3.3.5 and 3.3.6. Define a function $g'\colon G\times Y \to Z$ by $g'(t,y) := \zeta(t,g(y))$ for $(t,y) \in G\times Y$. Plainly, g' is continuous. In addition, for each $u \in H$ and each $(t,y) \in G\times Y$ we have

$$\begin{aligned} g'(t\psi(u)^{-1},\sigma^u y) &= \zeta(t\psi(u)^{-1}, g(\sigma^u y)) \\ &= \zeta(t\psi(u)^{-1}\psi(u), g(y)) \\ &= g'(t,y), \end{aligned}$$

that is, $g'\rho^u(t,y) = g'(t,y)$. Consequently, g' is constant on the orbits in $G\times Y$ under the action ρ of H. Hence there exists a unique continuous function $\bar{g}\colon X = G\times Y/C_\rho \to Z$ such that $g' = \bar{g}c_\rho$. By the definition of g', we have $g = g'\eta_Y^G$, hence $g = \bar{g}c_\rho\eta_Y^G = \bar{g}f$. Moreover, a straightforward calculation shows that $\langle 1_G, g'\rangle\colon \langle G, G\times Y, \mu_Y^G\rangle \to \langle G,Z,\zeta\rangle$ is a morphism of G-spaces. This implies that $\langle 1_G,\bar{g}\rangle\colon \langle G,X,\pi\rangle \to \langle G,Z,\zeta\rangle$ is a morphism of G-spaces as well.

Finally, suppose that $\langle 1_G,h\rangle\colon \langle G,X,\pi\rangle \to \langle G,Z,\zeta\rangle$ is another morphism of G-spaces such that $g = hf$. Then we have for all $(s,y) \in G\times Y$:

$$\begin{aligned} hc_\rho(s,y) &= hc_\rho\mu_Y^G(s,(e,y)) = \zeta(s,hc_\rho(e,y)) \\ &= \zeta(s,hf(y)) = \zeta(s,g(y)) = g'(s,y). \end{aligned}$$

Hence $hc_\rho = g' = \bar{g}c_\rho$. Since c_ρ is a surjection, it follows that $h = \bar{g}$. This proves uniqueness of $\bar{g}$. □

3.3.8. THEOREM. *Let* $\psi\colon H \to G$ *be a morphism in* TOPGRP. *Then the functor* $\mathsf{R}_\psi\colon \mathsf{TOP}^G \to \mathsf{TOP}^H$ *has a left adjoint* $\mathsf{L}_\psi\colon \mathsf{TOP}^H \to \mathsf{TOP}^G$.

PROOF. Use 3.3.5 through 3.3.7, and apply 0.4.2(i). □

3.3.9. The *unit* of the adjunction of L_ψ and R_ψ is the natural transformation $\gamma\colon I_{\mathsf{TOP}^H} \to \mathsf{R}_\psi\mathsf{L}_\psi$, indicated in 3.3.6 above (cf. (7)).

We shall describe now the *counit* γ': $L_\psi R_\psi \to I_{\mathsf{TOP}^G}$. To this end, consider an arbitrary object $\langle G,Z,\zeta\rangle$ in TOP^G. According to formula (5) in 0.4.2, $\gamma'_{\langle G,Z,\zeta\rangle}$ is obtainable as the morphism $\langle 1_G,\bar{g}\rangle$ in diagram (8) in 3.3.7 by taking there $\langle H,Y,\sigma\rangle := R_\psi\langle G,Z,\zeta\rangle = \langle H,Z,\zeta^\psi\rangle$ and $g = 1_Z$. If we do so, then the ttg $\langle G,X,\pi\rangle$ occurring in diagram (8) is $L_\psi R_\psi\langle G,Z,\zeta\rangle$, i.e. it is $L_\psi\langle G,Z,\zeta^\psi\rangle$. According to 3.3.5 and 3.3.6, the phase space of this ttg is the quotient space $(G\times Z)/C_\rho$, where ρ is defined according to (6) (of course, with $\sigma := \zeta^\psi$). Obviously, we have for $(t_1,z_1),(t_2,z_2) \in G\times Z$:

(9) $$c_\rho(t_1,z_1) = c_\rho(t_2,z_2) \iff \exists u\in H : t_2^{-1}t_1 = \psi(u) \;\&\; \zeta^{\psi(u)}z_1 = z_2$$
$$\iff t_2^{-1}t_1 \in \psi[H] \;\&\; \zeta(t_1,z_1) = \zeta(t_2,z_2).$$

Let the function k: $G\times Z \to (G\backslash\psi[H])\times Z$ be defined by

$$k(t,z) := (q(t),\zeta(t,z))$$

($(t,z) \in G\times Z$; here q: $G \to G\backslash\psi[H]$ is the usual quotient mapping). It is easy to see that k is a surjection. Furthermore, (9) implies that there exists a *bijection* h: $(G\times Z)/C_\rho \to (G\backslash\psi[H])\times Z$ making the following diagram commutative:

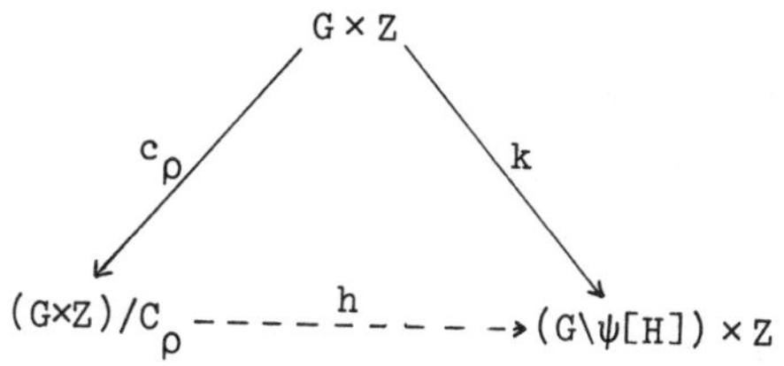

Therefore, *if we give* $(G\backslash\psi[H])\times Z$ *the quotient topology, induced by* k, then it may be identified with $(G\times Z)/C_\rho$, via h. In doing so, the action of G on $(G\times Z)/C_\rho$ turns out to correspond to the action ν of G on $(G\backslash\psi[H])\times Z$, defined by

$$\nu^t(q(s),z) := (q(ts),\zeta^t z).$$

If p: $(G\backslash\psi[H])\times Z \to Z$ is the projection, then $pk = \zeta$, hence p is continuous with respect to the quotient topology in $(G\backslash\psi[H])\times Z$, induced by k. In addition, p is equivariant with respect to the actions ν and ζ. A close examination of the proof of 3.3.7 shows, that under the above mentioned identification p corresponds to the mapping $\bar{g}$ in diagram (8), provided $g = 1_Z$.

Thus, up to isomorphism, we have

$$\gamma'_{\langle G,Z,\zeta\rangle} = \langle 1_G, p\rangle\colon \langle G,(G\backslash\psi[H])\times Z,\nu\rangle \to \langle G,Z,\zeta\rangle .$$

3.3.10. In diagram (8), we can insert arrows $\langle\psi,1_X\rangle$ and $\langle\psi,1_Z\rangle$. Then diagram (4) shows, that the resulting diagram is still commutative. Now lemma 3.3.7 can be reformulated as follows:

3.3.11. <u>COROLLARY</u>. *Let* $\langle H,Y,\sigma\rangle$ *be an object in* $\mathbf{TOP}^H$, *and let* $f\colon Y\to X$ *be as in* 3.3.6. *Then the arrow* $\langle\psi,f\rangle\colon \langle H,Y,\sigma\rangle \to \langle G,X,\pi\rangle$ *is "universal" in* **TTG** *for the class of all morphisms in* **TTG** *having group component* ψ *and domain* $\langle H,Y,\sigma\rangle$, *in the following modified sense: for any morphism* $\langle\psi,g\rangle\colon \langle H,Y,\sigma\rangle \to \langle G,Z,\zeta\rangle$ *in* **TTG** *there exists a unique morphism* $\langle 1_G,\bar{g}\rangle\colon \langle G,X,\pi\rangle \to \langle G,Z,\zeta\rangle$ *in* $\mathbf{TOP}^G$ [1] *making the following diagram commutative:*

$$\begin{array}{ccc}
\langle H,Y,\sigma\rangle & \xrightarrow{\ \langle\psi,f\rangle\ } & \langle G,X,\pi\rangle \ := \ L_\psi\langle H,Y,\sigma\rangle \\
 & \searrow^{\langle\psi,g\rangle} & \downarrow{\scriptstyle\langle 1_G,\bar{g}\rangle} \\
 & & \langle G,Z,\zeta\rangle
\end{array}$$

<u>PROOF</u>. By 3.3.3, any morphism $\langle\psi,g\rangle\colon \langle H,Y,\sigma\rangle \to \langle G,Z,\zeta\rangle$ in **TTG** factorizes as $\langle\psi,g\rangle = \langle\psi,1_Z\rangle\langle 1_H,g\rangle$. Taking into account the observation made in 3.3.10, the corrollary is an immediate consequence of 3.3.7. □

3.3.12. We mention without proof, that a similar reformulation of the universal property of the *counit* γ' of the adjunction of L_ψ and R_ψ shows: for any object $\langle G,Z,\zeta\rangle$ in $\mathbf{TOP}^G$ the arrow $\langle\psi,1_Z\rangle\colon \langle G,Z,\zeta^\psi\rangle \to \langle G,Z,\zeta\rangle$ is "universal" for all arrows in **TTG** with group component ψ and codomain $\langle G,Z,\zeta\rangle$ in the sense which has been described in 3.3.3.

3.3.13. <u>EXAMPLES</u>.

(i) Suppose H is a subgroup of G and $\psi\colon H\to G$ is the inclusion mapping. Then for each object $\langle H,Y,\sigma\rangle$ the universal arrow $\langle\psi,f\rangle\colon \langle H,Y,\sigma\rangle \to \langle G,X,\pi\rangle$ has the following additional properties. First, $f\colon Y\to X$ is *injective*. Indeed $c_\rho(e,y_1) = c_\rho(e,y_2)$ iff there exists $u\in H$ with $\psi(u) = e$ and $\sigma^u y_1 = y_2$, iff $y_1 = y_2$ [2] (notation: cf. 3.3.5 and 3.3.6).

[1] If there is *no* morphism $\alpha \neq 1_G$ in **TOPGRP** such that $\psi = \alpha\psi$, then $\langle 1_G,\bar{g}\rangle$ is unique in **TTG**.

[2] In fact, this argument shows that ψ injective $\Rightarrow$ f injective.

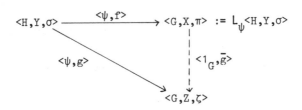

Second, $f[Y]$ *is an* H-*invariant subset of* $\langle G,X,\pi\rangle$ *and the smallest* G-*invariant set containing* $f[Y]$ *is just all of* X. Indeed, for all $(t,y) \in G\times Y$ we have $c_\rho(t,y) = c_\rho\mu_Y^G(t,(e,y)) = \pi^t c_\rho(e,y) = \pi^t f(y)$, whereas $c_\rho(t,y) \in f[Y]$ iff $t \in H$. Consequently, $\pi^t f(y) \in f[Y]$ iff $t \in H$. Notice that we proved just a little bit more: $\pi^t f[Y] \cap f[Y] = \emptyset$ iff $t \notin H$.)1

(ii) Let $H = G_d$ and let $\psi: G_d \to G$ be the identical mapping. Similar to the argument in 3.3.9 one shows that for each G_d-space $\langle G_d,Y,\sigma\rangle$ the universal arrow $\langle\psi,f\rangle: \langle G_d,Y,\sigma\rangle \to \langle G,X,\pi\rangle$ is as follows: $X = G\times Y/C_\rho$ may be identified with Y (as a set) in such a way that $c_\rho: G\times Y \to X$ corresponds to $\sigma: G\times Y \to Y$; furthermore, the action π of G on X corresponds (as a function $G\times X \to X$) with the function $\sigma: G\times Y \to Y$, and, finally, $f: Y \to X$ corresponds to the identical mapping of Y onto itself. The only differences between $\langle G,X,\pi\rangle$ and $\langle G_d,Y,\sigma\rangle$ are the topologies on G and X. *If T denotes the original topology on* Y, *then* $X = (Y,T')$ *where T' is the finest topology making* $\sigma: G\times(Y,T) \to (Y,T')$ *continuous.*)2 *Notice that always $T' \subseteq T$.*

(iii) Let $G = \{e'\}$ be a one point group, and let $\psi: H \to G$ be the obvious surjection. Identify $\mathbf{TOP}^G$ in the obvious way with $\mathbf{TOP}$ (by means of the functor S^G, which is now an isomorphism of categories). According to the construction in 3.3.5 and 3.3.6, for any object $\langle H,Y,\sigma\rangle$ in $\mathbf{TOP}^H$ we obtain for $f: Y \to X$ just the quotient mapping $c_\sigma: Y \to Y/C_\sigma$. So in identifying $\mathbf{TOP}^G$ with $\mathbf{TOP}$, the functor $L_\psi: \mathbf{TOP}^H \to \mathbf{TOP}^G$ carries over to the functor $S_1^H: \mathbf{TOP}^H \to \mathbf{TOP}$, defined as follows:

$$S_1^H: \begin{cases} \langle H,Y,\sigma\rangle \longmapsto Y/C_\sigma & \text{on objects} \\ \langle 1_H,g\rangle \longmapsto g' & \text{on morphisms,} \end{cases}$$

where for each morphism $\langle 1_H,g\rangle: \langle H,Y,\sigma\rangle \to \langle H,Z,\zeta\rangle$, $g': Y/C_\sigma \to Z/C_\zeta$ is the unique continuous function with $g'c_\sigma = c_\zeta g$ (cf. 1.4.7). By 3.3.8, the functor S_1^H has a right adjoint $R_1^H: \mathbf{TOP} \to \mathbf{TOP}_1^H$ where R_1^H is the functor, described in 3.3.2(iii). Moreover, the unit γ of adjunction

---

)1 In the general case, $\pi^t f[Y] = f[Y]$ iff $t \in \psi[H]$ and $\pi^t f[Y] \cap f[Y] = \emptyset$ iff $t \in G\setminus\psi[H]$.

)2 In this example we used only that $\psi: H \to G$ is bijective, i.e. G is just the group H with a weaker topology.

is given by

$$\gamma_{<H,Y,\sigma>} = <1_H, c_\sigma>: <H,Y,\sigma> \to <H, Y/C_\sigma, \tau^H_{Y/C_\sigma}>$$

where τ^H_{Y/C_σ} denotes the trivial action of H on Y/C_σ.

3.3.14. We close this subsection with some trivial, though useful remarks about the functors R_ψ and L_ψ. The easy proofs are left to the reader.

(i) *The functor* R_ψ *is always faithful. If* ψ *is surjective then* R_ψ *is full.*

(ii) If φ: $K \to H$ is a morphism in **TOPGRP**, then we have also functors R_φ: $\mathbf{TOP}^H \to \mathbf{TOP}^K$ and L_φ: $\mathbf{TOP}^K \to \mathbf{TOP}^H$, and L_φ is left adjoint to R_φ. *In addition,* $R_{\psi\varphi} = R_\varphi \circ R_\psi$, *hence* $L_{\psi\varphi} = L_\psi \circ L_\varphi$.

3.3.15. The reader is invited to calculate the universal arrow $<\psi,f>$: $<G,X,\pi> \to <G/N,Y,\sigma>$, where N is a normal subgroup of G and ψ: $G \to G/N$ is the quotient mapping. Cf. 1.5.9.

3.3.16. NOTES. The central facts in this subsection are the construction of the functor L_ψ and the proof that L_ψ is left adjoint to R_ψ. If ψ: $H \to G$ is an embedding (cf. 3.3.2(i) and 3.3.13(i)), then the construction is well-known, and has as its classical analog the famous FROBENIUS reciprocity theorem. The corresponding construction in ergodic theory can be found in K. LANGE, A. RAMSAY & G.-C. ROTA [1971].

It is interesting to know in example 3.3.13(i) when f: $Y \to X$ is a topological embedding. It is easy to see that this is so if G *is a discrete group*. A second situation in which f is a topological embedding occurs when G *is a Hausdorff group and* H *is a compact subgroup of* G: then η^G_Y: $Y \to G{\times}Y$ is a closed embedding and c_ρ: $G{\times}Y \to G{\times}Y/C_\rho$ is now a closed mapping (in any ttg with a compact phase group the projection of the phase space onto the orbit space is closed; this is an easy consequence of [GH], 1.18(5); cf. also [Br], Chap. I, Th. 3.1). This case is very important for the study of the structure of transformation groups with compact phase groups. Cf. for instance [Br], Chap. II. Finally, if Y *is a compact Hausdorff space and* H *is a closed subgroup of* G, then C_ρ turns out to be a closed subset of $(G{\times}Y) \times (G{\times}Y)$, so that $X = G{\times}Y/C_\rho$ is a Hausdorff space, by 1.3.10(ii). Since Y is compact and f: $Y \to X$ is injective, f is a topological embedding. See W.H. GOTTSCHALK [1973], p.123.

In all cases that H is a subgroup of G and f: $Y \to X$ is a topological embedding, the construction of $L_\psi\langle H,Y,\sigma\rangle$ can be described as an extension of the action of a subgroup to an action of the whole group by means of an extension of the phase space. Notice that the particular case of $H = \mathbb{Z}$, $G = \mathbb{R}$ fits in this situation with respect to compact spaces Y. It is an outstanding problem to give sufficient conditions for an action of $\mathbb{Z}$ on a compact T_2-space to be extendable to an action of $\mathbb{R}$ on *the same* phase space. That is, when can a single homeomorphism on a space Y be described as the transition π^1 for some ttg $\langle\mathbb{R},Y,\pi\rangle$? Cf. G.D. JONES [1972], also for further references to this subject and some remarks about its history. For certain spaces, this so-called *embedding problem* is equivalent to the HILBERT-SMITH conjecture for those spaces. (This conjecture reads as follows: if a compact Hausdorff group acts effectively on a connected manifold, then the group is a Lie group.) Cf. H. CHU [1973].

A close inspection of the construction of $f\colon Y \to X$ in 3.3.6 shows that $f = c_\rho \eta^G_Y$, where c_ρ is the coequalizer in **TOP** of the morphisms

$$G \times H \times Y \underset{(s,u,y)\ \longmapsto\ (s,\sigma^u y)}{\overset{(s,u,y)\ \longmapsto\ (s\psi(u),y)}{\rightrightarrows}} G \times Y.$$

Since c_ρ is an open mapping, it follows from the first remark in 3.4.4 below, that the functor S^G creates the corresponding coequalizer in $\mathbf{TOP}^G$, thus producing the action π of G on $G{\times}Y/C_\rho$. If we look at the construction from this point of view, we see that a basic point in the proof of theorem 3.3.8 is the existence of a certain coequalizer in $\mathbf{TOP}^G$. A similar statement, involving arbitrary morphisms of monads, may be found in Corollary 1 in F.E.J. LINTON [1969]. Although the idea of our proof of 3.3.8 is similar to that of LINTON's, our theorem turns out to be *not* a simple application of his result.

Finally, it is easy to see that 3.3.8 could have been proved by means of the FREYD adjoint functor theorem. Indeed, the solution set condition is obviously fulfilled, whereas R_ψ trivially preserves all limits (use 3.2.5). However, then it would be difficult to describe the functor L_ψ explicitly.

3.4. Colimits in TTG and $\mathbf{TOP}^G$

3.4.1. We are now in a position to prove that $\mathbf{TOP}^G$ and **TTG** are cocomplete categories. First we shall deal with $\mathbf{TOP}^G$. Here all coproducts turn out to be *created* by the functor S^G: $\mathbf{TOP}^G \to \mathbf{TOP}$, but S^G does not even *preserve* all coequalizers. However, if G is locally compact, then S^G creates all coequalizers, and $\mathbf{TOP}^G$ is cocomplete. The case of an arbitrary group G is then reduced to the locally compact case by considering G_d, using techniques from the previous subsection.

In **TTG** the situation is somewhat more complicated; fortunately, the functor G: $\mathbf{TTG} \to \mathbf{TOPGRP}$ preserves all colimits. Refinements of the arguments used for the proof of cocompleteness of $\mathbf{TOP}^G$ then show that TTG is cocomplete as well. The bad behaviour of the functor K: $\mathbf{TTG} \to \mathbf{C} := \mathbf{TOPGRP} \times \mathbf{TOP}$ with respect to colimits is caused by bad preservation properties of the functor S: $\mathbf{TTG} \to \mathbf{TOP}$. There are several "explanations" for this bad behaviour of S. First, S forgets all about actions of groups on spaces. Therefore, it seems quite natural that S has no reasonable preservation properties. However, S behaves nicely with respect to limits, so this explanation is quite unsatisfactory. No doubt, therefore, the difficulties are related to the fact that (unlike for limits) colimits in **TOPGRP** are not obtained by giving a suitable group structure to the corresponding colimit in **TOP**. On the contrary, colimits in **TOPGRP** are calculated in the category of (discrete) groups and afterwards they are provided with a suitable topology (cf. 0.4.11).

There is another functor, S_1: $\mathbf{TTG} \to \mathbf{TOP}$, which behaves better than S. It is defined as follows:

$$(1) \qquad S_1: \begin{cases} \langle G,X,\pi\rangle \longmapsto X/C_\pi & \text{on objects} \\ \langle \psi,f\rangle \longmapsto f' & \text{on morphisms} \end{cases}$$

where for each morphism $\langle\psi,f\rangle: \langle G,X,\pi\rangle \to \langle H,Y,\sigma\rangle$ in **TTG**, $S_1 f := f'$: $X/C_\pi \to Y/C_\sigma$ is the unique continuous function with $f'c_\pi = c_\sigma f$ (cf. 1.4.8). The restriction S_1^G of S_1 to $\mathbf{TOP}^G$ has already been defined in 3.3.13(iii). The functors S_1 and S_1^G will also be considered in this subsection.

All notation will be as in subsections 3.1, 3.2 and 3.3. In particular, G will always denote a topological group.

3.4.2. PROPOSITION. *The functor* S^G: $\mathbf{TOP}^G \to \mathbf{TOP}$ *creates all coproducts and, consequently,* S^G *preserves all coproducts.*

PROOF. It is sufficient to prove that S^G creates all coproducts: then by 0.4.4(iv) S^G preserves them, because **TOP** is cocomplete. The proof that S^G creates the coproduct for a given set $\{\langle G,X_j,\pi_j\rangle \,:\, j\in J\}$ of objects in $\mathbf{TOP}^G$

is straightforward. Representing the coproduct X of the set $\{X_j : j\in J\}$ in **TOP** as the disjoint union of the spaces X_j, the created coproduct of the given set in $\mathbf{TOP}^G$ is just what it is expected to be: the G-space $\langle G,X,\pi\rangle$ with $\pi^t|_{X_j} = \pi_j^t$ for each $t \in G$ and $j \in J$. Details are left to the reader. □

3.4.3. <u>THEOREM</u>. *Suppose* G *is a locally compact Hausdorff group. Then the functor* S^G: $\mathbf{TOP}^G \to \mathbf{TOP}$ *creates all colimits. Hence* $\mathbf{TOP}^G$ *is cocomplete, and* S^G *preserves all colimits.*

<u>PROOF</u>. Since **TOP** is cocomplete, it is sufficient to show that S^G creates all colimits. In view of 3.4.2, we can restrict ourselves to coequalizers (cf. [ML], p.109).

Suppose $\langle 1_G, f_i\rangle$: $\langle G,X,\pi\rangle \to \langle G,Y,\sigma\rangle$ $(i=1,2)$ are morphisms in $\mathbf{TOP}^G$. Let $g: Y\to Z$ denote the coequalizer of $f_1,f_2: X\to Y$ in **TOP**. Then for each $t \in G$, $g\sigma^t: Y\to Z$ is a morphism in **TOP**, and

$$g\sigma^t f_1 = gf_1\pi^t = gf_2\pi^t = g\sigma^t f_2.$$

By the coequalizer property of g, it follows that there exists a unique continuous mapping $\zeta^t: Z\to Z$ such that $g\sigma^t = \zeta^t g$. Stated otherwise, the quotient mapping $g: Y\to Z$ (cf. 0.4.10) is defined by an equivalence relation in Y which is invariant under the action σ of G. Then 1.5.7(iii) implies that ζ is a continuous action of G on Z. It is the unique action of G on Z making g a morphism of G-spaces (cf. 1.5.5). So the proof will be finished if $\langle 1_G, g\rangle$: $\langle G,Y,\sigma\rangle \to \langle G,Z,\zeta\rangle$ is shown to be the coequalizer of $\langle 1_G,f_1\rangle$ and $\langle 1_G,f_2\rangle$ in $\mathbf{TOP}^G$. This may be done by a straightforward argument which is left to the reader. □

3.4.4. If G is not locally compact, one shows as above that S^G creates coequalizers for those morphisms $\langle 1_G,f_1\rangle,\langle 1_G,f_2\rangle$: $\langle G,X,\pi\rangle \to \langle G,Y,\sigma\rangle$ in $\mathbf{TOP}^G$ for which the coequalizer $g: Y\to Z$ in **TOP** of $f_1,f_2: X\to Y$ is either an open mapping, or a perfect mapping, or for which $G\times Z$ is a k-space. Cf. 1.5.7.

The following example shows that some restriction has to be made in 3.4.3. Let $G = \mathbb{Q}$ and let Y be the locally compact Hausdorff space which admits an equivalence relation R such that on $\mathbb{Q}\times(Y/R)$ the quotient topology induced by $1_{\mathbb{Q}}\times f$ is strictly finer than the product topology (here $f: Y\to Y/R$ is the quotient mapping). Cf. 0.2.5. In 1.5.11 we pointed out that the equivalence relation $D_{\mathbb{Q}}\times R$ (with $D_{\mathbb{Q}} := \{(t,t) : t\in\mathbb{Q}\}$) is invariant in $\langle \mathbb{Q},\mathbb{Q}\times Y,\mu_Y^{\mathbb{Q}}\rangle$, but that *there exists no continuous action of* $\mathbb{Q}$ *on* $\mathbb{Q}\times Y/D_{\mathbb{Q}}\times R$

(= $\mathbb{Q} \times (Y/R)$ with its quotient topology) *for which the quotient mapping* $q\colon \mathbb{Q}\times Y \to \mathbb{Q}\times Y/D_{\mathbb{Q}}\times R$ *is equivariant*. Let $X := D_{\mathbb{Q}} \times R$, and observe that X is an invariant subset of the product in $\mathbf{TOP}^{\mathbb{Q}}$ of $\langle \mathbb{Q}, \mathbb{Q}\times Y, \mu_Y^{\mathbb{Q}}\rangle$ with itself. Let π denote the action of $\mathbb{Q}$ on X obtained by restriction of the action in this product to X. Then the restrictions f_1 and f_2 to X of the projections of $(\mathbb{Q}\times Y) \times (\mathbb{Q}\times Y)$ onto $\mathbb{Q} \times Y$ are equivariant, i.e. we have morphisms $\langle 1_{\mathbb{Q}}, f_i\rangle\colon \langle G, X, \pi\rangle \to \langle \mathbb{Q}, \mathbb{Q}\times Y, \mu_Y^{\mathbb{Q}}\rangle$ in $\mathbf{TOP}^{\mathbb{Q}}$. It is not difficult to show that the coequalizer in $\mathbf{TOP}$ of $f_1, f_2\colon X \to \mathbb{Q}\times Y$ is the quotient mapping $q\colon \mathbb{Q}\times Y \to \mathbb{Q}\times Y/D_{\mathbb{Q}}\times R$. By what we noticed above, it follows that $S^{\mathbb{Q}}$ *cannot create the coequalizer of* $\langle 1_{\mathbb{Q}}, f_1\rangle$ *and* $\langle 1_{\mathbb{Q}}, f_2\rangle$.

We shall see in 3.4.5 below, that the morphisms $\langle 1_{\mathbb{Q}}, f_1\rangle$ and $\langle 1_{\mathbb{Q}}, f_2\rangle$ do have a coequalizer in $\mathbf{TOP}^{\mathbb{Q}}$. So the above example shows, in addition, that *the functor* $S^{\mathbb{Q}}$ *does not preserve all colimits in* $\mathbf{TOP}^{\mathbb{Q}}$.

3.4.5. THEOREM. *For any topological group* G, *the category* $\mathbf{TOP}^G$ *is cocomplete, but in general the functor* $S^G\colon \mathbf{TOP}^G \to \mathbf{TOP}$ *does not preserve all colimits* [)1].

PROOF. The bad behaviour of S^G is already illustrated in 3.4.4. In order to prove that $\mathbf{TOP}^G$ is cocomplete, proceed as follows.

Let $H := G_d$ and let $\psi\colon H \to G$ be the identical mapping. Observe, that ψ is a bijection, so that the functor $R_\psi\colon \mathbf{TOP}^G \to \mathbf{TOP}^H$ is full and faithful (cf. 3.3.14(i)). Since H is a locally compact Hausdorff group, $\mathbf{TOP}^H$ is cocomplete by 3.4.3. Since R_ψ has a left adjoint L_ψ (cf. 3.3.8), an obvious application of 0.4.4(iii) shows that $\mathbf{TOP}^G$ is cocomplete. □

3.4.6. In the preceding proof we can replace the appeal to 0.4.4(iii) by the following argument (which is, in fact, a proof for 0.4.4(iii), adapted to the present situation): if $\mathbf{D}$ is a diagram in $\mathbf{TOP}^G$, then by 0.4.4(ii) the functor L_ψ preserves the colimit of the diagram $R_\psi \mathbf{D}$ in $\mathbf{TOP}^H$, thus giving rise to a colimit for the diagram $L_\psi R_\psi \mathbf{D}$. However, it follows immediately from the description of L_ψ for this particular case in 3.3.13(ii) or from the description of the counit of the adjunction of L_ψ and R_ψ in 3.3.9, that $L_\psi R_\psi$ may be identified with the identity functor on $\mathbf{TOP}^G$ (take into account that for any ttg $\langle G, Z, \zeta\rangle$ the finest topology $\mathcal{T}'$ on Z making $\zeta\colon G\times(Z,\mathcal{T}) \to (Z,\mathcal{T}')$ continuous just equals the original topology $\mathcal{T}$ on Z).

)1 Hence S^G cannot have a right adjoint, by 0.4.4(ii).

Thus, the image under L_ψ *of the colimit in* TOP^H *of* $R_\psi D$ *is just the colimit of* D *in* TOP^G.

We may rephrase this loosely by saying that it is only the topologies for which things go wrong. Indeed, colimits in TOP^H can be computed in TOP ($H = G_d$ is discrete; cf. 3.4.3), and application of L_ψ to these colimits means (according to 3.3.13(ii)) that the topologies of their phase spaces have to be altered. Stated otherwise: a colimit in TOP^G can be computed in TOP, but afterwards the topology in the phase space of an obtained "colimit" has to be suitably weakened in order to obtain the colimit in TOP^G.

It follows immediately from these remarks that the composition of S^G with the forgetful functor $P\colon \mathsf{TOP} \to \mathsf{SET}$ preserves all colimits (recall that P preserves colimits). In particular, PS^G preserves all epimorphisms. *Hence* S^G *preserves all epimorphisms* (P reflects them). This yields an alternative proof of 3.2.3.

We close our considerations about TOP^G by a brief inspection of the functor $S_1^G\colon \mathsf{TOP}^G \to \mathsf{TOP}$, defined in 3.3.13(iii).

3.4.7. PROPOSITION. *The functor* S_1^G *preserves all colimits and epimorphisms. In addition,* S_1^G *preserves all equalizers, but it does not preserve all finite products, unless* $G = \{e\}$.

PROOF. By 3.3.13(iii), S_1^G has a right adjoint. So 0.4.4(ii) implies that S_1^G preserves all colimits and all epimorphisms.

Next, consider morphisms $\langle 1_G, f_1\rangle, \langle 1_G, f_2\rangle\colon \langle G,X,\pi\rangle \to \langle G,Y,\sigma\rangle$ in TOP^G. Their equalizer in TOP^G is the morphism $\langle 1_G, g\rangle\colon \langle G,Z,\zeta\rangle \to \langle G,X,\pi\rangle$, where $Z := \{x \,\vdots\, x\in X \;\&\; f_1(x) = f_2(x)\}$ is a G-invariant subset of X, $g\colon Z \to X$ is the inclusion mapping, and $\zeta := \pi|_{G\times Z}$ (cf. 3.2.6). By 1.4.10, $S_1^G g$ is a topological embedding of $S_1^G\langle G,Z,\zeta\rangle = Z/C_\zeta$ into $S_1^G\langle G,X,\pi\rangle = X/C_\pi$, and its range is easily seen to be the subspace of X/C_π on which the mappings $S_1^G f_1$ and $S_1^G f_2$ coincide. This proves that S_1^G preserves all equalizers.

Finally, the following observations show that S_1^G does not always preserve finite products. Plainly, $S_1^G\langle G,G,\lambda\rangle$ is a one-point space. On the other hand, the product of $\langle G,G,\lambda\rangle$ with itself in TOP^G is $\langle G,G\times G,\pi\rangle$, where $\pi^t(u,v) := (tu,tv)$ $(t,u,v \in G)$. Hence $S_1^G\langle G,G\times G,\pi\rangle$ may be identified with G (and c_π then corresponds to the continuous and open mapping $(u,v) \mapsto u^{-1}v\colon G\times G \to G$). So if G is not a one-point group, S_1^G does not preserve the product of $\langle G,G,\lambda\rangle$ with itself. □

3.4.8. If $<1_G,f>: <G,X,\pi> \to <G,Y,\sigma>$ is an epimorphism in $\mathbf{TOP}^G$, then $f' := S_1^G f: X/C_\pi \to X/C_\sigma$ is epic in **TOP**, by 3.4.7, hence f' is a surjection. It follows that for every $y \in Y$ there exists $x \in X$ with $C_\sigma[y] = f'c_\pi x = C_\sigma[fx]$. Since $fC_\pi[x] = C_\sigma[fx]$, it follows that $f: X \to Y$ is a surjection. Consequently, we have proved, again, that S^G preserves all epimorphisms.

3.4.9. PROPOSITION. *The functor* G: $\mathsf{TTG} \to \mathsf{TOPGRP}$ *has a right adjoint. Consequently,* G *preserves all colimits and epimorphisms.*

PROOF. Fix a one-point space $(*)$. For any object $G \in \mathsf{TOPGRP}$, let τ^G denote the obvious action of G on $(*)$. Define the functor R: $\mathsf{TOPGRP} \to \mathsf{TTG}$ by

$$(2) \qquad \mathsf{R}: \begin{cases} G \mapsto <G,(*),\tau^G> & \text{on objects} \\ \psi \mapsto <\psi,1_{(*)}> & \text{on morphisms.} \end{cases}$$

Then the following diagram shows that R is right adjoint to G (apply 0.4.2(ii)):

(3)

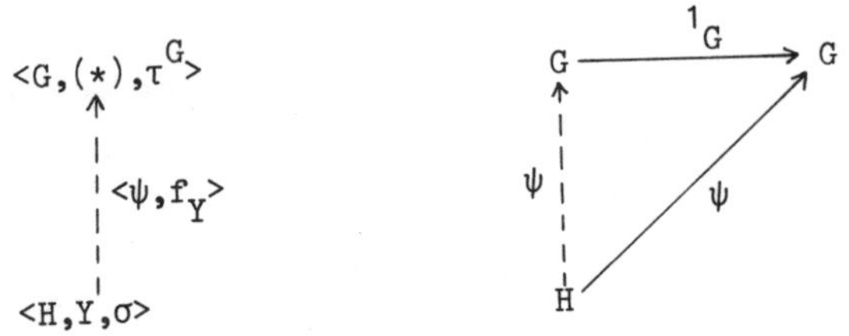

Here $f_Y: Y \to (*)$ is the unique surjection of the object Y onto $(*)$. □

3.4.10. COROLLARY. *The functor* K: $\mathsf{TTG} \to \mathsf{C}$[1] *preserves and reflects epimorphisms, i.e. a morphism* $<\psi,f>$ *in* TTG *is epic iff* ψ *is epic in* TOPGRP *and* f *is epic in* TOP.

PROOF. In view of 3.1.4(ii) we need only to prove that K preserves epimorphisms. So let $<\psi,f>: <G,X,\pi> \to <H,Y,\sigma>$ be an epimorphism in TTG. Then 3.4.9 implies that $\psi: G \to H$ is epic in TOPGRP, i.e. ψ is a surjection. Hence $f[X]$ is an invariant subset of $<H,Y,\sigma>$ (cf. 1.4.5). Therefore, the proof of 3.2.3 applies to the present case[2], showing that $f[X] = Y$. □

---

[1] Recall that $\mathsf{C} := \mathsf{TOPGRP}\times\mathsf{TOP}$.

[2] We have only to replace the trivial action of G on the space Z considered in 3.2.3 by the trivial action of H on Z.

3.4.11. We shall show now that **TTG** is cocomplete. The existence of coequalizers is shown by means of a more or less obvious modification of the proof of the existence of coequalizers in $\mathbf{TOP}^G$ (cf. 3.4.5). However, the construction of coproducts in **TTG** offers some difficulties. We shall show first that the object that might expected to be the colimit of a given set of ttgs is not the right one.

Let $\{\langle G_j, X_j, \pi_j\rangle : j\in J\}$ be a set of objects in **TTG**. If it has a coproduct, the phase group of the colimiting object has to be the coproduct of the set $\{G_j : j\in J\}$ in **TOPGRP**, and the group components of the coprojections in **TTG** have to be the coprojections $\beta_i\colon G_i \to G$ of the coproduct in **TOPGRP** (cf. 3.4.9). There exists an obvious action π of G on the disjoint union $\Sigma_j X_j$ of the spaces X_j (i.e. the coproduct of the set $\{X_j : j\in J\}$ in **TOP**) such that each $\langle\beta_i, r_i\rangle$ is a morphism in **TTG**; here $r_i\colon X_i \to \Sigma_j X_j$ is the canonical embedding (coprojection) of X_i into $\Sigma_j X_j$. In order to define this action π, first observe that each G_i admits a canonical embedding $\alpha_i\colon G_i \to \mathbb{P}_j G_j$. Since α_i is a morphism in **TOPGRP** for each $i \in J$, there exists a unique morphism $\alpha\colon G \to \mathbb{P}_j G_j$ in **TOPGRP** making the following diagram commutative for every $i \in J$:

(4)

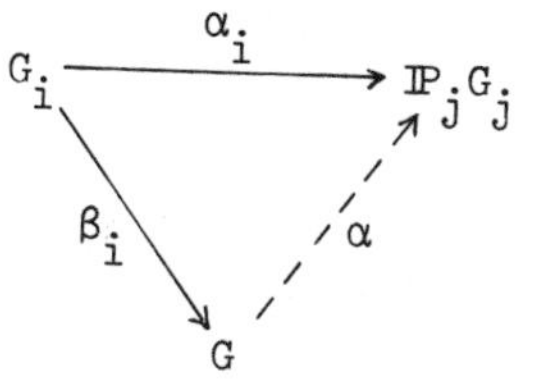

Furthermore, let $p_i\colon \mathbb{P}_j G_j \to G_i$ be the canonical projection. Then we can form the object $\langle G, X_i, \pi_i^{p_i\alpha}\rangle$ in **TTG**. Since $p_i\alpha_i = 1_{G_i}$, we have $p_i\alpha\beta_i = 1_{G_i}$, whence

(5) $$\langle\beta_i, 1_{X_i}\rangle\colon \langle G_i, X_i, \pi_i\rangle \to \langle G, X_i, \pi_i^{p_i\alpha}\rangle$$

is a morphism in **TTG**. Finally, form the coproduct $\langle G, \Sigma_j X_j, \pi\rangle$ of the set $\{\langle G, X_j, \pi_j^{p_j\alpha}\rangle : j\in J\}$ in $\mathbf{TOP}^G$ (cf. 3.4.2); the coprojections are the morphisms $\langle 1_G, r_i\rangle$, and using (5), we see that each $\langle\beta_i, r_i\rangle\colon \langle G_i, X_i, \pi_i\rangle \to \langle G, \Sigma_j X_j, \pi\rangle$ is a morphism in **TTG**. These morphisms form a cone in **TTG**, but we shall show now that it is not a colimiting cone for the given set of objects in **TTG**.

To this end, suppose we are given morphisms $\langle\psi_i, g_i\rangle\colon \langle G_i, X_i, \pi_i\rangle \to \langle H, Y, \sigma\rangle$ in **TTG**. Since $(G, \Sigma_j X_j)$ is the coproduct of the set $\{(G_j, X_j) : j\in J\}$ in **C** (where $\mathbf{C} = \mathbf{TOPGRP}\times\mathbf{TOP}$), there exists a unique morphism $(\psi, g)\colon (G, \Sigma_j X_j) \to (H, Y)$ in

C such that $(\psi_i, g_i) = (\psi, g)(\beta_i, r_i)$ for all $i \in J$. We shall show now that, *in general*, (ψ, g) *is not a morphism in* TTG *from* $\langle G, \Sigma_j X_j, \pi\rangle$ *to* $\langle H, Y, \sigma\rangle$. This shows that $\langle G, \Sigma_j X_j, \pi\rangle$ together with the morphisms $\langle \beta_i, f_i\rangle$ cannot form the desired coproduct in TTG. To this end, observe first that for $i, j \in J$, $i \neq j$ implies that $p_j \alpha_i t = e_j$, the unit of G_j, for each $t \in G_i$. Hence for $t \in G_i$ and $x \in X_j$, $\pi(\beta_i t, r_j x) = r_j \pi_j^{p_j \alpha}(\beta_i t, x) = r_j \pi_j(p_j \alpha_i t, x) = r_j(x)$. Consequently,

$$g\pi(\beta_i t, r_j x) = g r_j(x) = g_j(x),$$

whereas, on the other hand

$$\sigma(\psi \beta_i t, g r_j x) = \sigma(\psi_i t, g_j x).$$

Since there is no guarantee that $\sigma(\psi_i t, g_j x) = g_j(x)$ for all $i, j \in J$, $i \neq j$, $t \in G_i$ and $x \in X_j$, it follows that (ψ, g) need not be a morphism in TTG.

Observe, that the reason for this failure is, that the restriction of the action π^{β_i} of G_i to $r_j[X_j]$ is trivial if $i \neq j$.

3.4.12. <u>THEOREM</u>. *The category* TTG *is cocomplete. The functor* K: TTG $\rightarrow$ C *does not preserve all colimits*)1.

<u>PROOF</u>. We shall prove separately the existence of coproducts and of coequalizers in TTG. From the constructions it will be clear that K does not preserve all coproducts or all coequalizers.

I. Suppose $\{\langle G_j, X_j, \pi_j\rangle : j \in J\}$ is a set of objects in TTG. Let G and $\beta_i\colon G_i \rightarrow G$ be as in 3.4.11, and let for each $i \in J$,

$$\text{(6)} \qquad \langle \beta_i, h_i\rangle\colon \langle G_i, X_i, \pi_i\rangle \rightarrow L_{\beta_i}\langle G_i, X_i, \pi_i\rangle =: \langle G, Y_i, \sigma_i\rangle$$

be the morphism in TTG which is universal for the family of all morphisms in TTG with domain $\langle G_i, X_i, \pi_i\rangle$ and group component β_i (cf. 3.3.11). In addition, let $\langle G, \Sigma_j Y_j, \sigma\rangle$ denote the coproduct of the set $\{\langle G, Y_j, \sigma_j\rangle : j \in J\}$ in $\mathbf{TOP}^G$, with coprojections $\langle 1_G, f_i\rangle\colon \langle G, Y_i, \sigma_i\rangle \rightarrow \langle G, \Sigma_j Y_j, \sigma\rangle$ (cf. 3.4.2). We claim that $\langle G, \Sigma_j Y_j, \sigma\rangle$, together with the morphisms $\langle 1_G, f_i\rangle\langle \beta_i, h_i\rangle = \langle \beta_i, f_i h_i\rangle$, form the coproduct of the given set $\{\langle G_j, X_j, \pi_j\rangle : j \in J\}$ in TTG.

In order to prove this, suppose that we are given morphisms $\langle \psi_i, g_i\rangle\colon \langle G_i, X_i, \pi_i\rangle \rightarrow \langle H, Z, \zeta\rangle$ in TTG ($i \in J$). Then there exists a unique morphism

---

)1 In view of 3.4.9 this implies that S does not preserve all colimits. Hence S cannot have a right adjoint, no more than K can have.

$\psi\colon G\to H$ in **TOPGRP** such that $\psi_i = \psi\beta_i$ for every $i \in J$. Using 3.3.3, we see that each $\langle\psi_i,g_i\rangle$ factorizes as $\langle\psi,1_Z\rangle\langle\beta_i,g_i\rangle$ over the object $\langle G,Z,\zeta^\psi\rangle$ in **TTG**.

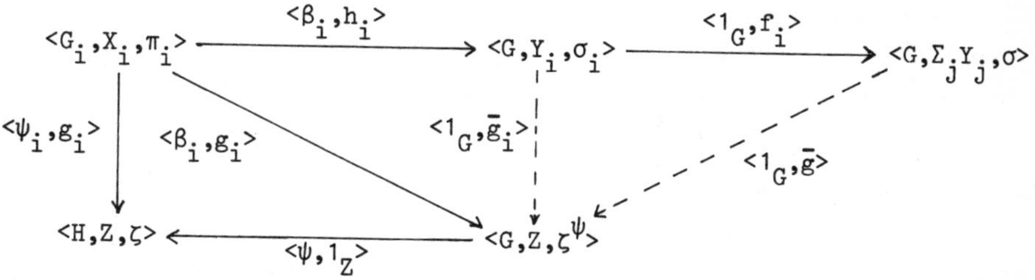

By the universal property of $\langle\beta_i,h_i\rangle$, there exists a morphism of G-spaces $\langle 1_G,\bar{g}_i\rangle\colon \langle G,Y_i,\sigma_i\rangle \to \langle G,Z,\zeta^\psi\rangle$ such that $g_i = \bar{g}_i h_i$, for every $i \in J$. Since $\langle G,\Sigma_j Y_j,\sigma\rangle$ is the coproduct of the G-spaces $\langle G,Y_i,\sigma_i\rangle$ in $\mathbf{TOP}^G$, this implies the existence of a unique morphism of G-spaces $\langle 1_G,\bar{g}\rangle\colon \langle G,\Sigma_j Y_j,\sigma\rangle \to \langle G,Z,\zeta^\psi\rangle$ such that $\bar{g}_i = \bar{g}f_i$ for every $i \in J$.

Thus, we have obtained a morphism $\langle\psi,\bar{g}\rangle\colon \langle G,\Sigma_j Y_j,\sigma\rangle \to \langle H,Z,\zeta\rangle$ in **TTG** such that $\langle\psi_i,g_i\rangle = \langle\psi,\bar{g}\rangle\langle\beta_i,f_i h_i\rangle$ for every $i \in J$. It is easy to see that this is the unique morphism in **TTG** with this property (use the fact that any morphism $\langle\psi,g'\rangle\colon \langle G,\Sigma_j Y_j,\sigma\rangle \to \langle H,Z,\zeta\rangle$ factorizes as $\langle\psi,1_Z\rangle\langle 1_G,g'\rangle$ over $\langle G,Z,\zeta^\psi\rangle$). This proves our claim.

{*Remark.* If α_i,p_i and α are as in 3.4.11, then set $\gamma_i := \beta_i p_i \alpha$. Observe that $\gamma_i\beta_i = \beta_i$. In 3.4.11, we considered the morphisms $\langle\beta_i,1_{X_i}\rangle\colon \langle G_i,X_i,\pi_i\rangle \to \langle G,X_i,\pi_i^{p_i\alpha}\rangle = R_{p_i\alpha}\langle G_i,X_i,\pi_i\rangle$. Let

(7) $$\langle\gamma_i,h_i^!\rangle\colon \langle G,X_i,\pi_i^{p_i\alpha}\rangle \to \langle G,Y_i^!,\sigma_i^!\rangle$$

be the universal arrow, according to 3.3.11. Here $\langle G,Y_i^!,\sigma_i^!\rangle := L_{\gamma_i}\langle G,Y_i,\pi_i^{p_i\alpha}\rangle = L_{\gamma_i}R_{p_i\alpha}\langle G_i,X_i,\pi_i\rangle = L_{\beta_i}(L_{p_i\alpha}R_{p_i\alpha}\langle G_i,X_i,\pi_i\rangle)$ (use 3.3.14(ii)). Since $p_i\alpha\colon G\to G_i$ is surjective, $R_{p_i\alpha}$ is full and faithful (cf. 3.3.14(i)), hence $L_{p_i\alpha}R_{p_i\alpha}\langle G_i,X_i,\pi_i\rangle$ may be replaced by $\langle G_i,X_i,\pi_i\rangle$, and $\langle G,Y_i^!,\sigma_i^!\rangle$ may by replaced by $L_{\beta_i}\langle G_i,X_i,\pi_i\rangle$, hence by $\langle G,Y_i,\sigma_i\rangle$. In addition, the morphism (6) is just the same (up to isomorphism) as $\langle\gamma_i,h_i^!\rangle\langle\beta_i,1_{X_i}\rangle = \langle\gamma_i\beta_i,h_i^!\rangle = \langle\beta_i,h_i^!\rangle\colon \langle G_i,X_i,\pi_i\rangle \to \langle G,Y_i^!,\sigma_i^!\rangle$. It follows that the construction in the present proof is just the construction of 3.4.11, except that we first apply L_{γ_i} to $\langle G,X_i,\pi_i^{p_i\alpha}\rangle$ for each $i \in J$.}

II. For $i=1,2$, let $\langle\psi_i,f_i\rangle: \langle G,X,\pi\rangle \to \langle H,Y,\sigma\rangle$ be a morphism in **TTG**. Let $\varphi: H\to K$ denote the coequalizer in **TOPGRP** of $\psi_1,\psi_2: G\to H$, and let g_0: $Y\to Z_0$ be the coequalizer in **TOP** of $f_1,f_2: X\to Y$. In general, the equivalence relation R_0 in Y defined by g_0 is not invariant under the action σ of H. Let R be the least invariant equivalence relation in Y with $R_0 \subseteq R$, i.e. R is the intersection of all invariant equivalence relations which include R_0. Let $Z_1 := Y/R$ and let ζ_1 be the action of H_d on Z_1 induced by σ. It follows easily, that the quotient mapping $q_1: Y\to Z_1$ is universal for all morphisms of H_d-spaces $g: Y\to Z$ with $gf_1 = gf_2$.

Next, let $\iota: H_d\to H$ denote the identical mapping, and let, according to 3.3.11,

$$\langle\iota,q_2\rangle: \langle H_d,Z_1,\zeta_1\rangle \to \langle H,Z_2,\zeta_2\rangle := \mathbf{L}_\iota\langle H_d,Z_1,\zeta_1\rangle$$

be the morphism in **TTG** which is universal for all morphisms $\langle\iota,h\rangle$ in **TTG** with domain $\langle H_d,Z_1,\zeta_1\rangle$. Then obviously

$$\langle 1_H,q_2q_1\rangle: \langle H,Y,\sigma\rangle \to \langle H,Z_2,\zeta_2\rangle$$

is a morphism in **TTG**, and this morphism is easily seen to be universal for all morphisms of H-spaces $\langle 1_H,g\rangle$ with domain $\langle H,Y,\sigma\rangle$ and satisfying the relation $f_1g = f_2g$.

Finally, let

$$\langle\varphi,q_3\rangle: \langle H,Z_2,\zeta_2\rangle \to \langle K,Z_3,\zeta_3\rangle := \mathbf{L}_\varphi\langle H,Z_2,\zeta_2\rangle$$

be the morphism in **TTG** which is universal for all morphisms $\langle\varphi,g'\rangle$ in **TTG** with domain $\langle H,Z_2,\zeta_2\rangle$. We claim that $\langle\varphi,q_3q_2q_1\rangle: \langle H,Y,\sigma\rangle \to \langle K,Z_3,\zeta_3\rangle$ is the coequalizer of $\langle\psi_1,f_1\rangle$ and $\langle\psi_2,f_2\rangle$ in **TTG**.

To this end, consider the following diagram, where $\langle\psi,g\rangle: \langle H,Y,\sigma\rangle \to \langle L,Z,\zeta\rangle$ is any morphism in **TTG** with $\langle\psi,g\rangle\langle\psi_1,f_1\rangle = \langle\psi,g\rangle\langle\psi_2,f_2\rangle$. Observe that there exists a unique morphism ψ' in **TOPGRP** such that $\psi = \psi'\varphi$. Now the trick is to factorize $\langle\psi,g\rangle$ a couple of times, using 3.3.3, and then to apply the above mentioned universality properties of $\langle 1_H,q_2q_1\rangle$ and $\langle\varphi,q_3\rangle$ in order to obtain the dotted arrows in the diagram.

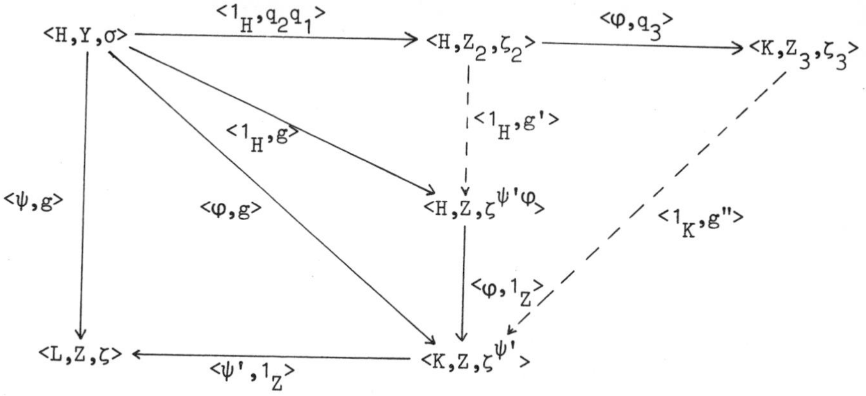

The proof that $\langle\psi',g''\rangle$ is the *unique* morphism in **TTG** with the property that $\langle\psi,g\rangle = \langle\psi',g''\rangle\langle\varphi,q_3q_2q_1\rangle$ is left as an exercise for the reader. □

3.4.13. In the first part of the preceding proof, each $\beta_i\colon G_i \to G$ is injective (indeed, $\alpha\beta_i = \alpha_i$ and α_i is injective). So 3.3.13(i) shows that $h_i\colon X_i \to Y_i$ is an injection (cf. (6)). We can show somewhat more, namely, *the functions* $h_i\colon X_i \to Y_i$ $(i\in J)$ *are topological embeddings, and there exist continuous surjections* $r_i^!\colon Y_i \to X_i$ *such that* $r_i^!h_i = 1_{X_i}$. *Thus, each* X_i *is a retract of* Y_i.

Indeed, for each $i \in J$ we have in the first part of the proof of 3.4.12 a morphism $f_ih_i\colon X_i \to \Sigma_jY_j$ in **TOP**. Hence there exists a unique morphism $k\colon \Sigma_jX_j \to \Sigma_jY_j$ in **TOP** such that $f_ih_i = kr_i$, where $r_i\colon X_i \to \Sigma_jX_j$ is the canonical embedding. On the other hand, in 3.4.11 we obtained morphisms $\langle\beta_i,r_i\rangle\colon \langle G_i,X_i,\pi_i\rangle \to \langle G,\Sigma_jX_j,\pi\rangle$ in **TTG**, and since $\langle\beta_i,f_ih_i\rangle\colon \langle G_i,X_i,\pi_i\rangle \to \langle G,\Sigma_jY_j,\sigma\rangle$ for $i \in J$ form the coproduct in **TTG** of the objects $\langle G_j,X_j,\pi_j\rangle$, it follows that there is a unique morphism $\langle\gamma,r\rangle\colon \langle G,\Sigma_jY_j,\sigma\rangle \to \langle G,\Sigma_jX_j,\pi\rangle$ in **TTG** such that $\langle\beta_i,r_i\rangle = \langle\gamma,r\rangle\langle\beta_i,f_ih_i\rangle$. Then clearly $\gamma = 1_G$ and $r_i = rf_ih_i$. In particular, the last equality together with the equality $f_ih_i = kr_i$ shows that $(rk)r_i = 1_{\Sigma_jX_j}r_i$, hence $rk = 1_{\Sigma_jX_j}$. Hence k is a topological embedding of Σ_jX_j into Σ_jY_j, mapping each $r_i[X_i]$ into $f_i[Y_i]$. So by the definition of k, each h_i is a topological embedding of X_i into Y_i. In addition, if $r_i^!$ is defined as the "restriction" and "corestriction" of r to the domain Y_i and the codomain X_i, then $r_i^!h_i = 1_{X_i}$.

3.4.14. Now we turn our attention to the functor $S_1\colon$ **TTG** → **TOP**, defined in 3.4.1. We start with a generalization of 3.3.13(iii), where it has been shown that the restriction of S_1 to $\mathbf{TOP}^G$ has a right adjoint.

3.4.15. PROPOSITION. *The functor* S_1: $\mathbf{TTG} \to \mathbf{TOP}$ *has a right adjoint. Hence* S_1 *preserves all colimits and all epimorphisms.*

PROOF. Fix a one-point topological group E, and define the functor R_1: $\mathbf{TOP} \to \mathbf{TTG}$ by

$$R_1: \begin{cases} X \longmapsto \langle E, X, \tau_X \rangle & \text{on objects} \\ f \longmapsto \langle 1_E, f \rangle & \text{on morphisms} \end{cases}$$

Here τ_X denotes the trivial action of E on the topological space X. Now S_1 is easily shown to be left adjoint to R_1, with unit $\bar{\gamma}$: $1_{\mathbf{TTG}} \to R_1 S_1$, given by

$$\bar{\gamma}_{\langle G,X,\pi \rangle} := \langle \psi^G, c_\pi \rangle : \langle G,X,\pi \rangle \to \langle E, X/C_\pi, \tau_{X/C_\pi} \rangle$$

for every object $\langle G,X,\pi \rangle \in \mathbf{TTG}$; here ψ^G: $G \to E$ is the obvious surjection. □

3.4.16. If $\langle \psi, f \rangle$: $\langle G,X,\pi \rangle \to \langle H,Y,\sigma \rangle$ is epic in $\mathbf{TTG}$, then ψ: $G \to H$ is surjective, by 3.4.9. Hence the arguments in 3.4.8 can be modified to the effect that we obtain a proof that f is surjective. Thus, we obtain an alternative proof of 3.4.10.

The following proposition should be compared with 3.4.7, where the behaviour of S_1^G with respect to products and equalizers is considered.

3.4.17. PROPOSITION. *The functor* S_1: $\mathbf{TTG} \to \mathbf{TOP}$ *preserves all products, but it does not preserve all equalizers.*

PROOF. Let $\{\langle G_j, X_j, \pi_j \rangle : j \in J\}$ be a set of ttgs. According to 3.1.12(i), their product in $\mathbf{TTG}$ is $\langle \mathbb{P}_j G_j, \mathbb{P}_j X_j, \pi \rangle$ with projections $\langle \psi_i, f_i \rangle$: $\langle \mathbb{P}_j G_j, \mathbb{P}_j X_j, \pi \rangle \to \langle G_i, X_i, \pi_i \rangle$. For each $(x_j)_j \in \mathbb{P}_j X_j$ we have plainly $C_\pi[(x_j)_j] = \mathbb{P}_j C_{\pi_j}[x_j]$. It follows that $C_\pi = \mathbb{P}_j C_{\pi_j}$ (cf. 0.2.4 for products of equivalence relations). Since each c_{π_j} is an open mapping there exists a homeomorphism g: $\mathbb{P}_j X_j/C_\pi \to \mathbb{P}_j (X_j/C_{\pi_j})$ such that $g \circ c_\pi = \mathbb{P}_j c_{\pi_j}$. If we identify $\mathbb{P}_j X_j/C_\pi$ with $\mathbb{P}_j (X_j/C_{\pi_j})$ via g, then $S_1\langle \psi_i, f_i \rangle$ is easily seen to correspond to the projection p_i: $\mathbb{P}_j (X_j/C_{\pi_j}) \to X_i/C_{\pi_i}$ in $\mathbf{TOP}$. This proves that the functor S_1 preserves all products.

The following example shows that S_1 does not preserve equalizers. Let G be any topological group with at least two points, and define actions π and σ of $G \times G$ on $G \times G$ and on G by

$$\pi((s,t),(x,y)) := (sx,ty); \quad \sigma((s,t),x) := sx$$

for $(s,t),(x,y) \in G \times G$. Furthermore, let $f\colon G\times G \to G$ be the projection (in **TOP**) of $G \times G$ onto its first coordinate, and let $\psi_1,\psi_2\colon G\times G \to G\times G$ in **TOPGRP** be defined by

$$\psi_1(s,t) := (s,t); \quad \psi_2(s,t) := (s,e)$$

for $(s,t) \in G\times G$. The equalizer of the morphisms $<\psi_1,f>,<\psi_2,f>\colon <G\times G,G\times G,\pi> \to <G\times G,G,\sigma>$ in **TTG** is, by 3.1.12(ii), the morphism $<\psi,1_{G\times G}>\colon <G\times\{e\},G\times G,\pi^{\psi}> \to <G\times G,G\times G,\pi>$, where $\psi\colon G\times\{e\} \to G\times G$ is the inclusion mapping. Then $S_1<\psi,1_{G\times G}>$ may be seen as the obvious mapping of G onto a one-point space, whereas $S_1<\psi_1,f>$ and $S_1<\psi_2,f>$ both are mappings of this one-point space onto another one. Since G has at least two points, $S_1<\psi,1_{G\times G}>$ is not the coequalizer of $S_1<\psi_1,f>$ and $S_2<\psi_2,f>$ in **TOP**. □

3.4.18. <u>NOTES</u>. Most results in this subsection seem to be new. However, it is not unlikely that some of them are straightforward modifications of known facts from category theory concerning categories of algebras over a monad (or, more specifically, of known theorems about the category of Λ-modules, say, where Λ is some K-algebra, K a commutative ring; cf. the notes in 3.1.18). The only result in this direction of which the present author is aware is a theorem in F.E.J. LINTON [1969], stating that the existence of coproducts in an algebra over a monad follows from the existence of certain coequalizers. Although our methods are quite different from LINTON's, the following similarity is quite striking. As a by-product, LINTON shows that the existence of certain coequalizers in a category **A** implies that the induced functor of algebras $\theta^*\colon \mathbf{A}^{H'} \to \mathbf{A}^{H}$ has a left adjoint, where $\theta\colon H \to H'$ is a morphism of monads. The analogue of this is our theorem 3.3.8, which played an essential role in the considerations of this subsection.

The attentive reader will have noticed that it is suggested by 1.4.11 that there is a functor from a suitable subcategory of **TTG** to the category of semigroups. Although this "enveloping semigroup functor" plays an important role in topological dynamics (cf. for instance the monograph [El]) it falls outside the scope of the present treatise. We return to it briefly in subsection 4.4.

4 - SUBCATEGORIES OF TTG

First, in subsection 4.1, we shall analyse the proofs of some of the reflection and preservation properties of the functor K: TTG → TOPGRP×TOP, given in §3. In addition, some generalizations will be given. We restrict ourselves here to limits, monomorphisms and epimorphisms. This is mainly due to the fact that we are interested in the applicability of the theorem in 0.4.3 to certain subcategories of TTG in order to prove that they are reflective. This will be done in subsection 4.3. We shall consider here only subcategories of TTG of the form $K^{\leftarrow}[A\times B]$, where A is a subcategory of TOPGRP and B is a subcategory of TOP. Consequently, we shall not consider subcategories of TTG which arise by imposing also conditions on the *actions* of their objects. Nevertheless, some results in subsection 4.4 are related to such subcategories, namely, the full subcategories of TTG, defined by all equicontinuous ttgs or by all ttgs on compact spaces having a dense orbit. There we investigate what the reflection of an object of TOP^G in $COMP^G$ looks like. This provides us with an example that the functor S^G: $TOP^G \to TOP$ does not map reflections of objects of TOP^G in $COMP^G$ onto reflections of objects of TOP in COMP (i.e. S^G does not "preserve reflections").

4.1. Limits, monomorphisms and epimorphisms

4.1.1. In this section we consider mainly subcategories X of TTG which can be described in the following way. Let A and B denote subcategories of TOPGRP and TOP, respectively, and set $X := K^{\leftarrow}[A\times B]$; here K: TTG → TOPGRP×TOP is the functor defined in 3.1.2. Thus, objects in X are all ttgs $\langle G,X,\pi\rangle$ with $(G,X) \in A\times B$; we do *not* require that $\pi: G\times X \to X$ is a morphism in B.

Morphisms in X are all morphisms $\langle\psi,f\rangle$ in TTG with (ψ,f) in $A\times B$. *In this section,* A*,* B *and* X *shall always have the above meaning.*

If A has only one object G and one morphism 1_G, then $K^{\leftarrow}[A\times B]$ will be denoted B^G. Obviously, B^G is a subcategory of TOP^G, namely, $B^G = (S^G)^{\leftarrow}[B]$.

We shall be a little bit careless with respect to notation. The inclusion functors $A\to TOPGRP$, $B\to TOP$ and $X\to TTG$ are always omitted. In addition, the restriction and corestriction of the functor K to X and $A\times B$ will be denoted simply $K: X\to A\times B$; similarly, we write $G: X\to A$, $S: X\to B$ and $S^G: B^G\to B$.

4.1.2. At this point, we investigate which conditions have to be imposed upon A and B in order that the methods of §3 can be used in order to solve the following questions:[1]

(i) When can limits and monomorphisms in X be calculated in $A\times B$ (cf. 3.1.12 and 3.2.5)?

(ii) When can epimorphisms in X be calculated in $A\times B$ (cf. 3.4.10 and 3.2.3)?

Ad (i): In order that the monad (H,η,μ) can be defined in $A\times B$ similar to the definition in 3.1.6, it is necessary and sufficient that the following conditions are fulfilled:

(M1) For each object (G,X) in $A\times B$, the topological product $G\times X$ is an object in B.

(M2) For each object (G,X) in $A\times B$, the continuous functions $\eta_X^G: x\mapsto(e,x): X\to G\times X$ and $\mu_X^G: (s,(t,x))\mapsto(st,x): G\times(G\times X)\to G\times X$ are morphisms in B.

If so, then the category of all H-algebras may be identified with the full subcategory of X, defined by all its objects $\langle G,X,\pi\rangle$ for which $\pi: G\times X\to X$ is a morphism in B (cf. 3.1.8); this is all of X if B is a full subcategory of TOP. Resuming: if B is a full subcategory of TOP and if condition (M1) is fulfilled, then limits and monomorphisms in X can be calculated in $A\times B$.

Ad (ii): In order to imitate the proof of 3.4.10, one has first to prove the analogue of 3.4.9, i.e. that the functor $G: X\to A$ has a right adjoint. This can be done if

---

[1] The analoguous question about *isomorphisms* has obviously the answer: always (i.e. no additional conditions!).

(E1) The category B has a final object.

Then the proof of 3.4.10 works in the present context if

(E2) Epimorphisms in A are surjective.

(E3) For each object $<H,Y,\sigma>$ in X, the quotient mapping c_σ: $Y \to Y/C_\sigma$ belongs to B.

(E4) For each object B in B and subset A of B, the quotient mapping q: $B \to B/R(A)$ and the constant mapping f: $B \to B/R(A)$ sending B into q[A] belong to B; here $R(A) := (A\times A) \cup \{(b,b) \mid b\in B\}$.[1]

We might also try to immitate the proofs indicated in 3.4.16 (cf. also 3.4.8). Then we need, among others, again condition (E3). For a discussion of the conditions we refer to the notes in 4.1.11. It appears that (E3) and (E4) are almost never fulfilled. Therefore, we shall now try to develope methods which do not require these conditions.

4.1.3. LEMMA. *Suppose the inclusion functor of* B *into* TOP *preserves limits. Then the functor* K: $X \to A\times B$ *creates limits.*

PROOF. Let D: $J \to X$ be a diagram, and set $D_j =: <G_j,X_j,\pi_j>$ for each object $j \in J$. Suppose the diagram KD: $J \to A\times B$ has a limiting cone (ψ,f): $(G,X) \to KD$ in $A\times B$; set $(\psi_j,f_j) := (\psi,f)_j$ for $j \in J$. Note that f: $X \to SD$ is a limiting cone for the diagram SD: $J \to TOP$ in TOP. Plainly, the morphisms $\pi_j\circ(\psi_j\times f_j)$: $G\times X \to X_j$ in TOP form a cone $G\times X \to SD$ in TOP. Hence there exists a unique morphism π: $G\times X \to X$ in TOP such that $f_j\circ\pi = \pi_j\circ(\psi_j\times f_j)$ for each $j \in J$. It is routine to show that π is an action of G on X, and that $<\psi,f>$: $<G,X,\pi> \to D$ is a limiting cone in X for the diagram D. □

4.1.4. PROPOSITION. *Suppose that* A *and* B *are complete, and that the inclusion functor of* B *into* TOP *preserves limits. Then the functor* K: $X \to A\times B$ *creates and preserves limits, and* X *is complete. In addition,* K: $X \to A\times B$ *preserves and reflects monomorphisms.*

PROOF. Use 4.1.3 and 0.4.4. □

4.1.5. LEMMA. *Let* Y *be a subcategory of* TTG *and let* $<\psi,f>$: $<G,X,\pi> \to <H,Y,\sigma>$ *be a monomorphism in* Y. *If either*

---

[1] The space Z constructed in the proof of 3.2.3 can be obtained by identification of the subset $c_\sigma f[X]$ of Y/C_σ with a point.

(1) $\forall x \in X : \langle 1_G, \pi_x \rangle : \langle G,G,\lambda \rangle \to \langle G,X,\pi \rangle$ *is in* Y

or Y *is a Hausdorff space and*)1

(2) $\forall x \in X : \langle 1_G, \delta_x \rangle : \langle G,E,\pi^* \rangle \to \langle G,X,\pi \rangle$ *is in* Y,

then f *is injective.*

PROOF. Suppose that (2) is valid and that Y is a Hausdorff space (the proof under assumption of (1) is similar and is left to the reader). Let $x,y \in X$ be such that $f(x) = f(y)$. Then for all $t \in G$,

$$f\pi_x(t) = \sigma(\psi t, fx) = \sigma(\psi t, fy) = f\pi_y(t)$$

whence $f\delta_x(\pi^t) = f\delta_y(\pi^t)$ for all $t \in G$. Since $\bar{\pi}[G]$ is dense in E, it follows that $f\delta_x = f\delta_y$. Consequently, the morphisms $\langle 1_G, \delta_x \rangle$ and $\langle 1_G, \delta_y \rangle$ in Y have equal compositions with the monomorphism $\langle \psi, f \rangle$. Hence $\delta_x = \delta_y$, and $x = y$. This shows that f is injective. □

4.1.6. LEMMA. *If* $\langle \psi, f \rangle : \langle G,X,\pi \rangle \to \langle H,Y,\sigma \rangle$ *is a monomorphism in* X *and* f *is injective, then* ψ *is monic in* A.

PROOF. Let $\alpha, \beta : K \to G$ be morphisms in A such that $\psi\alpha = \psi\beta$. Then for all $s \in K$ and $x \in X$

$$f\pi^\alpha(s,x) = \sigma(\psi\alpha s, fx) = \sigma(\psi\beta s, fx) = f\pi^\beta(s,x).$$

Since f is injective, it follows that $\pi^\alpha = \pi^\beta$. Let $\rho := \pi^\alpha = \pi^\beta$. Then $\langle \alpha, 1_X \rangle$ and $\langle \beta, 1_X \rangle$ are morphisms in X from $\langle K,X,\rho \rangle$ to $\langle G,X,\pi \rangle$, and their composites with $\langle \psi, f \rangle$ are equal to each other. Since $\langle \psi, f \rangle$ is monic in X it follows that $\alpha = \beta$. This shows that ψ is monic in A. □

4.1.7. PROPOSITION. *Suppose that* B *is a full subcategory of* TOP, *and that one of the following conditions is fulfilled:*

(i) $A \subseteq B$.

(ii) $B \subseteq$ HAUS *and* B *is closed under the formation of topological products and closed subspaces.*

Then the functor $K : X \to A \times B$ *preserves and reflects monomorphisms.*

PROOF. Reflection is obvious since K is faithful. Preservation is an easy

---

)1 Cf. 1.4.4(vi) for the notation.

consequence of the preceding lemmas. Condition (i) implies that (1) in 4.1.5 is fulfilled, and (ii) implies that (2) in 4.1.5 is valid. Hence, the conditions of 4.1.6 are trivially fulfilled. □

4.1.8. The preceding lemmas and propositions, from 4.1.3 up to 4.1.7 may be seen as an effort to save as much as possible if the general method, indicated in 4.1.2 for the computation of limits and monomorphisms cannot be used. For epimorphisms, the method indicated in 4.1.2 is not general at all (condition (E3) is very heavy; cf. the notes in 4.1.11 below). So our next proposition can be seen as an improvement on the above mentioned method.

4.1.9. LEMMA. *Let* Y *be a subcategory of* TTG *and let* $\langle\psi,f\rangle\colon \langle G,X,\pi\rangle \to \langle H,Y,\sigma\rangle$ *be an epimorphism in* Y. *In addition, let* A *be an* H*-invariant subset of* Y, $A \supseteq f[X]$, *and let there exist an action* ρ *of* H *on* $Y \cup_A Y$[1] *such that the canonical injections* $f_1,f_2\colon Y \to Y \cup_A Y$ *are morphisms of* H*-spaces. If the morphisms* $\langle 1_H,f_i\rangle\colon \langle H,Y,\sigma\rangle \to \langle H,Y\cup_A Y,\rho\rangle$ *for* $i=1,2$ *belong to* Y, *then* $A = Y$.

PROOF. Plainly $f_1 = f_2$, hence $A = Y$. □

4.1.10. PROPOSITION. *Suppose that* A *and* B *satisfy the following conditions:*

(i) *Epimorphisms in* A *have a dense range.*

(ii) B *is a full subcategory of* HAUS *having a terminal object.*

(iii) *For any object* $Y \in \mathsf{B}$ *and closed subset* A *of* Y *the space* $Y\cup_A Y$ *is an object in* B.

Then the functor $K\colon \mathsf{X} \to \mathsf{A}\times\mathsf{B}$ *preserves and reflects epimorphisms.*

PROOF. Reflection: K is faithful.
Preservation: let $\langle\psi,f\rangle\colon \langle G,X,\pi\rangle \to \langle H,Y,\sigma\rangle$ be an epimorphism in X. Since B has a terminal object, we can use the proof of 3.4.9 in order to prove that $G\colon \mathsf{X}\to\mathsf{A}$ has a right adjoint. In particular, it follows that ψ is epic in A (cf. the discussion in 4.1.2(ii)). By (i), $\psi[G]$ is dense in H. Next, set $A := \mathrm{cl}_Y f[X]$. Then A is H-invariant (cf. 1.4.5). By 1.5.10, there exists an action ρ of H on $Y\cup_A Y$ making $\langle 1_H,f_1\rangle$ and $\langle 1_H,f_2\rangle$ morphisms in TTG from $\langle H,Y,\sigma\rangle$ into $\langle H,Y\cup_A Y,\rho\rangle$. Obviously, these morphisms are in X, hence 4.1.9 implies that $A = Y$. So f has a dense range in Y. Since B is a subcategory of HAUS, it follows that f is epic in B. □

---

[1] For the definition of $Y\cup_A Y$ and of $f_1,f_2\colon Y\to Y\cup_A Y$, cf. 0.4.10.

4.1.11. NOTES. If B is a full subcategory of **TOP**, then (M1) implies (M2), and in (E3) and (E4) we need only to require that the quotient spaces under consideration are objects in B (which is a quite heavy requirement!).

Observe that (M1) is fulfilled whenever $A \subseteq B$ and B is closed with respect to the formation of topological products. Although the condition $A \subseteq B$ seems to be quite natural, it is rather inconvenient. For example, in Topological Dynamics one is interested in actions of discrete groups on compact Hausdorff spaces; here this condition would imply that one could consider only actions of finite discrete groups.[1] Fortunately, the condition $A \subseteq B$ does not occur in 4.1.4, nor in 4.1.7(ii).

A problem, related to the condition $A \subseteq B$, is the following one: if A and B are suitable subcategories of **TOPGRP** and **TOP**, respectively, and if $\langle G,X,\pi\rangle$ is a ttg, under which additional conditions on the action π the assumption $X \in B$ implies $G \in A$? Of course, the condition that π is effective seems to be indispensable. As examples of this general problem we mention two particular problems:

(i) When does metrizability of X imply metrizability of G if $\langle G,X,\pi\rangle$ is an effective ttg?

An answer is included in 1.1.23: X separable and G locally compact Hausdorff.

(ii) When does the condition that X is an n-manifold imply that G is a Lie group, if $\langle G,X,\pi\rangle$ is an effective ttg?

The HILBERT-SMITH conjecture states that compactness of G is a sufficient condition. In its generality, the conjecture is still open. For a survey and for more references to pertinent literature, cf. R.F. WILLIAMS [1968]. See the notes in 3.3.16 for a related problem.

We proceed with a brief discussion of the conditions which are sufficient in order that epimorphisms in X can be calculated in $A \times B$. Let us first observe that the condition on B in 4.1.10 are rather weak. Indeed, many useful full subcategories B of **HAUS** contain a one-point space and satisfy 4.1.10(iii); we mention the following ones:

T_2-spaces, T_3-spaces, Tychonov spaces (easy);
T_4-spaces (cf. [Du], Chap. VII, 3.3(1));
paracompact T_2-spaces ([Du], Chap. VIII, 2.6);
locally compact T_2-spaces (easy);

---

[1] To avoid misunderstanding, actions of finite groups on compact spaces form an important field of mathematical research. Cf. also [MZ], p.222, where the connection with actions of general compact groups is indicated.

k-spaces (easy);
compact T_2-spaces (obvious).

Concerning condition 4.1.10(i), observe that each subcategory A of **TOPGRP** is admitted in which epimorphisms are surjections (e.g. all discrete groups). However, the question whether the subcategory **HAUSGRP** of **TOPGRP** satisfies condition 4.1.10(i), seems still to be unsolved (of course, all morphisms in **HAUSGRP** with a dense range are epic in **HAUSGRP**). Although the conditions (E3) and (E4) do not explicitly impose conditions on A, they are quite unattractive. First, (E4) works only for nice subcategories of **TOP** if we consider *closed* subsets, and then 4.1.10 seems to be preferable. Second, in practice condition (E3) can only be verified for nice subcategories of **TOP** if $A \subseteq$ **COMPGRP**. Indeed, the question under which additional conditions on a ttg $\langle H,Y,\sigma\rangle$ (either on H or on the action σ) the orbit space Y/C_σ inherits nice properties from the phase space Y, has drawn considerable attention in the literature. As a general rule one can state that the orbit space has better properties according as the action looks more like the action of a compact group. In fact, orbit spaces form an important tool in the study of ttgs with a compact phase group. We shall mention now some properties which Y/C_σ inherits from Y if the phase group of $\langle H,Y,\sigma\rangle$ is a compact T_2-group. First, notice that in any ttg $\langle H,Y,\sigma\rangle$ with $H \in$ **COMPGRP** and $Y \in$ **HAUS**, the function $c_\sigma\colon Y \to Y/C_\sigma$ is *perfect* (its fibers are the orbits, and orbits are compact because they are continuous images of H; moreover, c_σ is a closed mapping by Theorem 3.1 of [Br], Chap. I, or [GH], 1.18(5)). In that case one can prove that each of the following properties are inherited from Y by Y/C_σ:

T_2, T_3, metrizable, (cf. [Du], Chap. XI, §5);
paracompact Hausdorff (cf. [Du], Chap. VIII, 2.6);
T_4 (cf. [Du], Chap. VII, 3.3(1));
Tychonov (cf. [Du], Chap. XI, Problem 5.12 on p.254).

The above references do not use the fact that Y/C_σ is the orbit space of a ttg (only the fact that c_σ is a perfect mapping is used). Using the peculiar properties of a given ttg $\langle H,Y,\sigma\rangle$ some of the above "inheritance theorems" can be proved easier or in greater generality. For example, using normalized Haar measure on the compact T_2-group H, it is easy to show that a *metrizable* phase space may be assumed to have an *invariant* metric d. Then it is easy to see that

$$\tilde{d}(c_\sigma x, c_\sigma y) := \inf\{d(u,v) : u \in C_\sigma[x] \ \& \ v \in C_\sigma[y]\}$$

defines a metric on Y/C_σ. This proof generalizes to arbitrary locally compact T_2-groups H, provided Y is a locally compact metrizable space, Y/C_σ is given to be paracompact and the action σ of H on Y is *proper*. Cf. [Ks], Chap. I. Here the property "proper" (cf. also [Bo], Chap. III) may be seen as an "approximation" for the action of a compact group. Yet another "approximation" is *uniform equicontinuity*. And indeed, it is easily shown that for any uniformly equicontinuous ttg $\langle H,Y,\sigma\rangle$ with Y metrizable)1, there exists an invariant metric on Y. Cf. [SK], p.186.

Other conditions on the action σ of an arbitrary topological group H on a space Y implying that Y/C_σ inherits nice properties of Y can be found in [Ks], in [Bo], Chap. III, in R.S. PALAIS [1961], and in O. HAJEK [1970;1971].

4.2. Applications

4.2.1. The notation in this subsection will be as in subsection 4.1, and G will always denote a fixed topological group. We shall apply now the results of proposition 4.1.4, 4.1.7 and 4.1.10 to some special categories A and B. *Since in all examples the categories* A *and* B *are complete and* K: X→A×B *creates (hence preserves!) limits, the category* X *is complete.* We shall not repeat this fact in each case separately.

In the case that A is the category consisting of one object G and one morphism 1_G, we shall also consider briefly some coproducts and coequalizers. Cocompleteness for subcategories of TTG will be considered more intensively in subsection 4.3 (cf. in particular 4.3.3).

4.2.2. A = TOPGRP; B = HAUS.

The inclusion functor of HAUS into TOP creates all limits, so by 4.1.4, the functor K: X→TOPGRP×HAUS creates all limits. In addition, it preserves and reflects all monomorphisms (this would also follow from 4.1.7). Finally, 4.1.10 applies in the present situation to the effect that K preserves and reflects epimorphisms.

)1 In topological dynamics such a ttg is often called *stable in the sense of Liapunov.*

4.2.3. A = HAUSGRP; B = HAUS.

Similar to 4.2.2, except the statement on epimorphisms: we can apply 4.1.10 only if the conjecture that all epimorphisms in HAUSGRP have dense ranges is assumed to be true.

4.2.4. The category $HAUS^G$.

The results concerning limits, mono- and epimorphisms are similar to those in 4.2.2 for $K^{\leftarrow}[TOPGRP \times HAUS]$.

Since coproducts in HAUS can be computed in TOP, the proof of 3.4.2 can be given entirely within the present context. Thus, the functor S^G: $HAUS^G \to HAUS$ creates and preserves all coproducts. {Notice that it follows that the inclusion functor $HAUS^G \to TOP^G$ creates and preserves them as well; use 3.4.2 to prove this.}

Finally, the coequalizer g: $Y \to Z$ in HAUS of a pair of morphisms f_1, f_2: $X \to Y$ in HAUS is always a quotient mapping. Consequently, the proof of 3.4.3 shows that S^G: $HAUS^G \to HAUS$ creates all coequalizers whenever G *is a locally compact Hausdorff group. In this case,* $HAUS^G$ *is cocomplete*)1, *and* S^G *creates and preserves all colimits.*

4.2.5. A = TOPGRP; B = COMP.

Similar to 4.2.2.

4.2.6. A = HAUSGRP; B = COMP.

Similar to 4.2.3.

4.2.7. The category $COMP^G$.

The results about limits, monomorphisms and epimorphisms are similar to those in 4.2.4 for $HAUS^G$.

Observe that all finite coproducts in COMP can be computed in TOP. So similar to 4.2.4 it can be shown that the functor S^G: $COMP^G \to COMP$ creates and preserves all finite coproducts. In addition, coequalizers in COMP are always *perfect* continuous surjections, so in view of the first remark in 3.4.4 we can use the proof of 3.4.3 in order to show that S^G creates all coequalizers. Consequently, $COMP^G$ is finitely cocomplete)1, and S^G: $COMP^G \to$ COMP *creates and preserves all colimits of finite diagrams.*

)1 We shall see in subsection 4.3 that this category is cocomplete for every topological group G. However, S^G may not preserve limits of infinite diagrams.

4.2.8. The category COMP^G for *discrete* G.

For limits, monomorphisms and epimorphisms the situation is similar to 4.2.7.

We shall indicate now why the functor S^G: $\mathsf{COMP}^G \to \mathsf{COMP}$ creates colimits for all diagrams in COMP^G)1. In view of 4.2.7 it will be sufficient to prove that S^G creates all (infinite) coproducts in COMP^G. To this end, one has to apply proposition 4.2.9 below to the (created!) coproduct in HAUS^G of a given set of objects in COMP^G (use the fact that coproducts in COMP are obtained as reflections in COMP of the corresponding coproducts in HAUS).

4.2.9. PROPOSITION. *Let* $\langle G,X,\pi\rangle$ *be a ttg with* G *a discrete group and let* β_X: $X \to \beta X$ *denote the reflection of* X *in* COMP. *Then there exists a unique action* σ *of* G *on* βX *making* β_X *a morphism of* G*-spaces from* X *(with action* π*) into* βX *(with action* σ*).*

PROOF. For every $t \in G$, let σ^t: $\beta X \to \beta X$ be the unique continuous function satisfying $\sigma^t\beta_X = \beta_X\pi^t$. Since G is discrete, we obtain a continuous mapping σ: $G\times\beta X \to \beta X$, and σ is easily seen to meet all requirements. □

4.2.10. There remain several other subcategories of TTG to be considered, for example the cases

A = COMPGRP; B = HAUS.

A = COMPGRP; B = COMP.

In these cases, limits, mono- and epimorphisms)2 in X are created and preserved by K: $X \to A\times B$ (cf. 4.2.2).

4.2.11. The results of this subsection are summarized in the scheme on p.128. Anticipating the results in 5.3.4 on the category KR^G for locally compact Hausdorff groups G, we have also inserted some properties of the functor S^G: $\mathsf{KR}^G \to \mathsf{KR}$.

4.2.13. NOTES. In view of proposition 4.2.9 one might ask under what conditions an action π of a group G on, say, a Tychonov space X can be extended to an action of G (not merely of G_d) on the Stone-Čech compactification

---

)1 In particular, COMP^G is cocomplete. However, we shall show in 4.3.3 that discreteness of G can be omitted as far as it concerns cocompleteness.

)2 Epimorphisms in COMPGRP are surjective; see D. POGUNTKE [1970].

βX of X. This, and related questions are dealt with in D.H. CARLSON [1971] for the case G = ℝ. In general, the action of G on X cannot be extended to an action of G on βX (cf. Theorem 4.10 in the above mentioned paper).

We mentioned some cases in which a subcategory B^G of TOP^G is cocomplete (cf. 4.2.4, 4.2.8). However, if X is any full reflective subcategory of the complete and cocomplete category TTG or TOP^G (or of any other complete and cocomplete subcategory of TTG), and if X is closed with respect to isomorphisms, then X itself is complete and cocomplete. Therefore, the results in our next subsection show among others that $COMP^G$ and $HAUS^G$ are cocomplete for *every* topological group G.

PROPERTIES OF THE FUNCTOR K: X → A×B AND
THE FUNCTOR S^G: B^G → B

<table>
<tr><th></th><th>A = TOPGRP
B = HAUS</th><th>$HAUS^G$</th><th>A = TOPGRP
B = COMP</th><th>$COMP^G$</th><th>KR^G
(G loc. comp. T_2)</th></tr>
<tr><td>products</td><td rowspan="2">} c,p</td><td rowspan="2">} c,p</td><td rowspan="2">} c,p</td><td rowspan="2">} c,p</td><td rowspan="2">} c,p</td></tr>
<tr><td>equalizers</td></tr>
<tr><td>monomorphisms</td><td>r,p</td><td>r,p</td><td>r,p</td><td>r,p</td><td>r,p</td></tr>
<tr><td>coproducts</td><td></td><td>c,p</td><td></td><td>c,p)2</td><td rowspan="2">} c,p</td></tr>
<tr><td>coequalizers</td><td></td><td>c,p)1</td><td></td><td>c,p</td></tr>
<tr><td>epimorphisms</td><td>r,p</td><td>r,p</td><td>r,p</td><td>r,p</td><td>r,p</td></tr>
</table>

)1 only for locally compact Hausdorff groups G

)2 only creation and preservation of finite coproducts; if G is discrete, then of all coproducts.

c = creates

p = preserves

r = reflects

4.3. Reflective subcategories of TTG

4.3.1. Notation will be in accordance with the previous subsections. However, we shall consider now subcategories A_0,A of TOPGRP and B_0,B of TOP, subject to the following conditions:

(R1) $A_0 \subseteq A \subseteq$ TOPGRP; $B_0 \subseteq B \subseteq$ TOP.

(R2) A_0 is a full subcategory of A, closed with respect to isomorphisms in A. Similarly, B_0 is a full subcategory of B, closed with respect to isomorphisms in B.

Let now the subcategories X_0 and X of TTG be given by $X_0 := K^{\leftarrow}[A_0 \times B_0]$ and $X := K^{\leftarrow}[A \times B]$. Obviously, X_0 is a full subcategory of X, closed with respect to isomorphisms in X. Next, let E {M} denote a class of epimorphisms {monomorphisms} in X and suppose that X has the following properties:

(R3) X has the E-M-factorization property.

(R4) X is co-E-small.

(R5) X has all products.

In addition, let X_0 satisfy the following conditions:

(R6) X_0 is closed under the formation of products in X.

(R7) X_0 is closed under the formation of M-subobjects in X.

Under these conditions, X_0 *is an E-reflective subcategory of* X (cf. 0.4.3).

We shall consider now classes E and M which are defined in the following way. Let E_a and E_b {M_a and M_b} denote classes of epimorphisms {monomorphisms} in A and B, respectively, and set $E := K^{\leftarrow}[E_a \times E_b]$, $M := K^{\leftarrow}[M_a \times M_b]$. Since K is faithful, it follows that E is a class of epimorphisms in X and that M is a class of monomorphisms in X[1].

Next, suppose that A_0 and A satisfy the conditions (R3) through (R7) above with respect to E_a and M_a. In addition, let B_0 and B have them with respect to E_b and M_b. {Then A_0 is E_a-reflective in A and B_0 is E_b-reflective in B; however, we shall not use this explicitly.}

Then the categories X_0 *and* X *obviously have the properties* (R4) *and* (R7). *Moreover, if* $K\colon X \to A \times B$ *creates all products in* X, *then also conditions* (R5) *and* (R6) *are satisfied.*

However, in this abstract setting it is not possible to show that X has E-M-factorization. The difficulty is the following one. Suppose we are given a morphism $\langle\psi,f\rangle\colon \langle G,X,\pi\rangle \to \langle H,Y,\sigma\rangle$ in X. Let $G \xrightarrow{\psi'} H' \xrightarrow{\iota} H$ {$X \xrightarrow{f'} Y' \xrightarrow{i} Y$} be the E_a-M_a-{E_b-M_b-} factorization of ψ in A {of f in B}. *Then*

---

1 Here we need only that K *reflects* all epimorphisms and all monomorphisms, and our efforts in obtaining results on *preservation* of such morphisms by K seem to be superfluous. Strictly speaking, this is true. However, if $K\colon X \to A \times B$ preserves all monomorphisms and epimorphisms, the above method yields E and M as general as possible.

$\langle\psi,f\rangle = \langle\iota,i\rangle\langle\psi',f'\rangle$ *is an* E-M-*factorization of* $\langle\psi,f\rangle$ *iff* $\langle\iota,i\rangle$ *and* $\langle\psi',f'\rangle$ *really are morphisms in* TTG, i.e. iff there exists an action σ' of H' on Y' which makes the following diagram commutative:

(1)

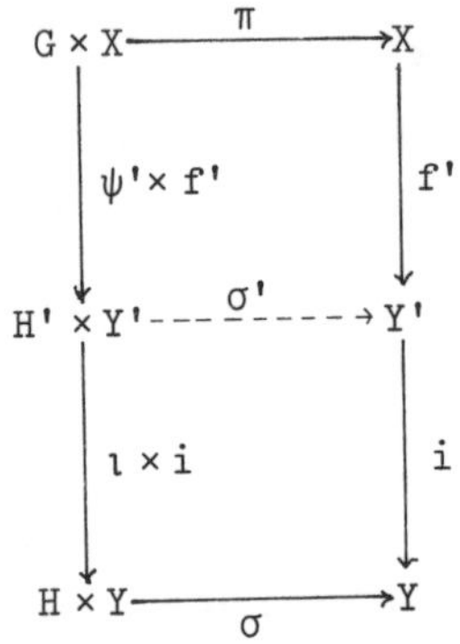

Intuitively, this means that Y' is an H'-invariant subset of Y. We shall present now a few examples where the above described situation is, indeed, as follows: H' is a subgroup of H, Y' is a subspace of Y, and ι and i are embedding mappings. Then such a σ' exists iff Y' is an H'-invariant subspace of Y. In that case, $\sigma' = \sigma|_{H'\times Y'} : H'\times Y' \to Y'$. This condition will be fulfilled in all examples below.

4.3.2. <u>EXAMPLES</u>. The following examples are obtained by specification of A_0, A, B_0, B, etc., taking care that the conditions (R1) through (R7) are satisfied for E_a and M_a with respect to A_0 and A, and for E_b and M_b with respect to B_0 and B.

(i) $K^{\leftarrow}$[TOPGRP×HAUS] *is an* E-*reflective subcategory of* TTG, *where* E *denotes the class of all morphisms in* TTG *whose group and space components both are surjective.*

{To see this, take (in the notation of 4.3.1):

A_0 := A := TOPGRP; B_0 := HAUS; B := TOP;

E_a {E_b}: all surjective morphisms in TOPGRP {TOP};

M_a {M_b}: all topological embeddings in TOPGRP {TOP}.

In diagram (1), we obtain $H' = \psi[G]$, $Y' = f[X]$, and ι and i are embedding mappings. Then by 1.4.5, Y' is an H'-invariant subset of Y, and the arguments in 4.3.1 show that not only conditions (R4) through (R7), are fulfilled, but also (R3). For (R5), notice that the functor K: TTG → TOPGRP×TOP creates products.}

(ii) $K^{\leftarrow}$[HAUSGRP×HAUS] *is an E-reflective subcategory of* TTG, *where E denotes the class of all morphisms* $\langle\psi,f\rangle$ *in* TTG *with surjective* ψ *and* f.
{Similar to (i).}

(iii) $K^{\leftarrow}$[COMPGRP×HAUS] *is E-reflective in the category* $K^{\leftarrow}$[HAUSGRP×HAUS], *where E is the class of all morphisms* $\langle\psi,f\rangle$ *in* $K^{\leftarrow}$[HAUSGRP×HAUS] *such that* ψ *and* f *have dense ranges.*
{In the notation of 4.3.1, take:

A_0 := COMPGRP, A := HAUSGRP; B_0 := B := HAUS;

E_a {E_b}: all morphisms in HAUSGRP {HAUS} with dense ranges;

M_a {M_b}: all closed embeddings in HAUSGRP {HAUS}.

Then the conditions (R4) through (R7) are fulfilled by E,M,X_0 and X (for (R5), observe that K: X→HAUSGRP×HAUS creates all products; cf. 4.2.3). Also condition (R3) is fulfilled. Indeed, in the situation of diagram (1), $H' = cl_H\,\psi[G]$, $Y' = cl_Y\, f[X]$. Hence by one of the remarks in 1.4.5, Y' is an H'-invariant subset of Y. So σ' exists in diagram (1).}

(iv) $K^{\leftarrow}$[HAUSGRP×COMP] *and* $K^{\leftarrow}$[COMPGRP×COMP] *are E-reflective subcategories of the category* $K^{\leftarrow}$[HAUSGRP×HAUS], *where E is as in* (iii).
{Similar to (iii).}

(v) $K^{\leftarrow}$[COMPGRP×COMP] *is E-reflective in* $K^{\leftarrow}$[HAUSGRP×COMP] *and in* $K^{\leftarrow}$[COMPGRP×HAUS], *with E as in* (iii).
{Similar to (iii).}

(vi) *Fix any topological group* G. *Then* $HAUS^G$ *is epi*[)1]*-reflective in* TOP^G *and* $COMP^G$ *is epi*[)2]*-reflective in* $HAUS^G$. *Consequently,* $COMP^G$ *is E-reflective in* TOP^G, *where E denotes the class of all morphisms of G-spaces with dense ranges.*
{Similar to (i) and (iv).}

4.3.3. We can summarize the above examples by saying that the following inclusion functors have left adjoints (hence all their possible composites have):

)1 Recall that epimorphisms in TOP^G are the surjective morphisms of G-spaces.

)2 The epimorphisms in $HAUS^G$ are the morphisms of Hausdorff G-spaces with dense ranges.

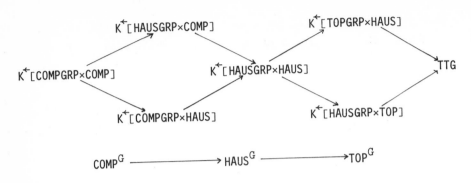

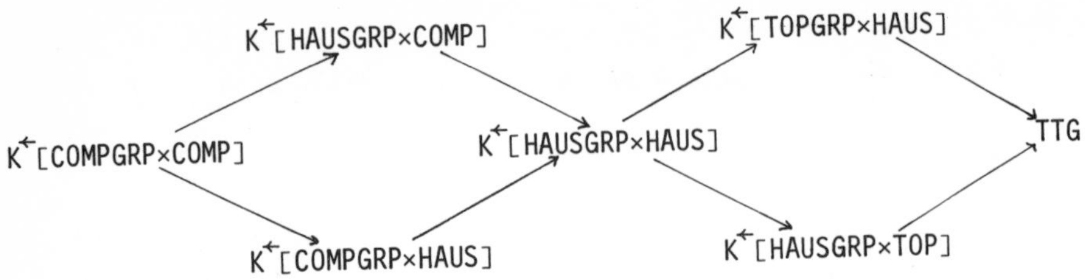

$$\mathsf{COMP}^G \longrightarrow \mathsf{HAUS}^G \longrightarrow \mathsf{TOP}^G$$

In particular, it follows that all subcategories of TTG *mentioned here are complete and cocomplete* (use the last part of 0.4.4 and the fact that TTG and TOP^G are both complete and cocomplete).

4.3.4. It is clear how *colimits* in the above mentioned reflective subcategories of TTG can be computed: for any diagram in the subcategory, first compute the colimit in TTG, and then compute the reflection of the resulting colimiting cone. A similar procedure can be followed for the reflective subcategories of TOP^G. *Limits* can directly be computed in TTG. For the computation of some of the required reflections, cf. 4.3.11 and subsection 4.4.

4.3.5. At this place the reader might expect a theorem like: "*if* A_0 *and* B_0 *are reflective in* A *and* B, *respectively, then* X_0 *is reflective in* X". However, if $\langle G,X,\pi\rangle$ is an object in X and X_0 is reflective in X, as well as A_0 and B_0 are in A and B, then there is in general not a nice connection between the reflection of $\langle G,X,\pi\rangle$ in X_0 and the reflection of X in B_0. See 4.3.13 below. Therefore, it cannot be expected that reflectiveness of A_0 in A and of B_0 in B alone is sufficient for X_0 to be reflective in X. In many cases, however, A_0 and B_0 are known to be reflective in A and B because they satisfy some *stronger* conditions (e.g. the conditions mentioned in 4.3.1, or, according to the FREYD adjoint functor theorem, completeness together with a "solution set condition"). But then these stronger conditions may be used (as was done in 4.3.2) to prove that X_0 is reflective in X. Consequently, it seems to be not worth troubling about conditions under which reflectiveness of A_0 in A and of B_0 in B imply reflectiveness of X_0 in X. Rather, we shall have a brief look in the converse direction. Notation will be as before, but *we shall require only condition* (R1) *for* A_0, A, B_0 *and* B.

4.3.6. PROPOSITION. *Suppose that* X_0 *is a reflective subcategory of* X. *Then:*

(i) *If* B_0 *contains a one-point space, then* A_0 *is a reflective subcategory of* A.

(ii) *If* A_0 *contains a one-point group*[1], *then* B_0 *is a reflective subcategory of* B.

PROOF. We prove only (ii). (The proof of (i) can be given in a similar way.) Let $(*)$ denote a one-point object in A_0, and for any object X in B, let τ_X denote the obvious action of $(*)$ on X. Then the functor

$$\begin{cases} X \mapsto \langle(*),X,\tau_X\rangle & \text{on objects} \\ f \mapsto \langle 1_{(*)},f\rangle & \text{on morphisms} \end{cases}$$

is an embedding of B into X, carrying B_0 into X_0. From this, the result may easily be derived. □

4.3.7. PROPOSITION. *Suppose that* X_0 *is a reflective subcategory of* X *and that* A_0 *is a reflective subcategory of* A. *Then the functor* $G\colon X \to A$ *preserves reflections of objects of* X_0 *into* X. *That is:*

If $\langle G,X,\pi\rangle$ *is an object in* X *and* $\langle\psi,f\rangle\colon \langle G,X,\pi\rangle \to \langle H,Y,\sigma\rangle$ *is its reflection into* X_0, *then* $\psi\colon G \to H$ *is a reflection of* G *into* A_0.

PROOF. Let $\varphi\colon G \to K$ be a reflection of G into A_0. Then $\psi = \bar{\psi}\varphi$ for a unique morphism $\bar{\psi}\colon K \to H$ in A_0. Hence $\langle\psi,f\rangle$ factorizes in X as follows:

$$\langle G,X,\pi\rangle \xrightarrow{\langle\varphi,f\rangle} \langle K,Y,\sigma^{\bar{\psi}}\rangle \xrightarrow{\langle\bar{\psi},1_Y\rangle} \langle H,Y,\sigma\rangle.$$

Obviously, $\langle K,Y,\sigma^{\bar{\psi}}\rangle$ is an object in X_0, so there exists a (unique) morphism $\langle\varphi',f'\rangle\colon \langle H,Y,\sigma\rangle \to \langle K,Y,\sigma^{\bar{\psi}}\rangle$ in X_0 such that $\langle\varphi,f\rangle = \langle\varphi',f'\rangle\langle\psi,f\rangle$. Then we have

$$(\langle\bar{\psi},1_Y\rangle\langle\varphi',f'\rangle)\langle\psi,f\rangle = \langle\bar{\psi},1_Y\rangle\langle\varphi,f\rangle = \langle\psi,f\rangle,$$

whence $\langle\bar{\psi},1_Y\rangle\langle\varphi',f'\rangle = \langle 1_H,1_Y\rangle$ by universality of $\langle\psi,f\rangle$. In particular, $\bar{\psi}\varphi' = 1_H$. On the other hand,

$$(\varphi'\bar{\psi})\varphi = \varphi'\psi = \varphi,$$

[1] See also 4.3.12 below for a particular case where A_0 does *not* contain a one-point group.

whence $\varphi'\bar{\psi} = 1_K$ by universality of φ. It follows that $\bar{\psi}$ is an isomorphism in A_0. In particular, we may conclude that ψ: $G \to H$ is a reflection of G into A_0. □

4.3.8. COROLLARY 1. *If* X_0 *is reflective in* X *and* A_0 *is reflective in* A, *then the reflection in* X_0 *of an object* $\langle G,X,\pi\rangle$ *in* X *having* $G \in A_0$ *may assumed to be of the form* $\langle 1_G,f\rangle$: $\langle G,X,\pi\rangle \to \langle G,Y,\sigma\rangle$.

PROOF. If $G \in A_0$, then 1_G: $G \to G$ is a reflection of G in A_0. □

4.3.9. COROLLARY 2. *The reflection of an object* $\langle G,X,\pi\rangle$ *in* TTG *into* $K^{\leftarrow}$[COMPGRP×COMP] *has the form* $\langle \alpha_G,f\rangle$: $\langle G,X,\pi\rangle \to \langle G^c,Y,\sigma\rangle$, *where* α_G: $G \to G^c$ *is the Bohr-compactification of* G. □

4.3.10. PROPOSITION. *If* $A_0 = A$, *then the following conditions are equivalent:*

(i) X_0 *is a reflective subcategory of* X.

(ii) *For each object* G *of* A, B_0^G *is a reflective subcategory of* B^G.

If these conditions are fulfilled, then for any object $\langle G,X,\pi\rangle$ *of* X *the reflection in* X_0 *coincides with the reflection in* B_0^G.

PROOF. (i) ⇒ (ii): Apply 4.3.8 (plainly, A_0 is reflective in A).
(ii) ⇒ (i): Consider an object $\langle G,X,\pi\rangle \in X$, and let $\langle 1_G,f\rangle$: $\langle G,X,\pi\rangle \to \langle G,Y,\sigma\rangle$ be its reflection into B_0^G. If $\langle\psi,g\rangle$: $\langle G,X,\pi\rangle \to \langle H,Z,\zeta\rangle$ is a morphism in X with $\langle H,Z,\zeta\rangle \in X_0$, then $\langle\psi,g\rangle$ can be factorized as indicated in the following diagram

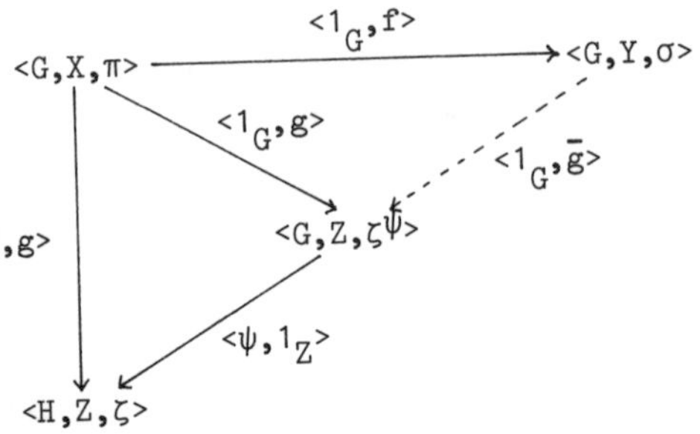

Since $\langle 1_G,f\rangle$ is a universal arrow in B^G from $\langle G,X,\pi\rangle$ into B_0^G, there exists a unique morphism $\langle 1_G,\bar{g}\rangle$: $\langle G,Y,\sigma\rangle \to \langle G,Z,\zeta^{\psi}\rangle$ in B_0^G such that $g = \bar{g}f$. Now it is easily seen that $\langle\psi,\bar{g}\rangle$: $\langle G,Y,\sigma\rangle \to \langle H,Z,\zeta\rangle$ is the *unique* morphism in X_0

such that $\langle\psi,g\rangle = \langle\psi,\bar{g}\rangle\langle 1_G,f\rangle$ (by 3.3.3, any other morphism in X_0 with this property factorizes over $\langle G,Z,\zeta^{\psi}\rangle$ with $\langle\psi,1_Z\rangle$ as a factor). This shows that $\langle 1_G,f\rangle$ is a universal arrow from $\langle G,X,\pi\rangle$ into X_0. In particular, it follows that X_0 is reflective in X. □

4.3.11. Next, we consider the question how to "compute" reflections in general. We shall restrict ourselves to the case that A = TOPGRP and B = TOP, hence X = TTG. In addition, we shall assume that X_0 is a reflective subcategory of TTG, hence also of $K^{\leftarrow}[A_0\times TOP]$, and that $K^{\leftarrow}[A_0\times TOP]$ is a reflective subcategory of TTG. Thus, the following inclusion functors have left adjoints:

$$X_0 = K^{\leftarrow}[A_0\times B_0] \longrightarrow K^{\leftarrow}[A_0\times TOP] \longrightarrow K^{\leftarrow}[TOPGRP\times TOP] = TTG.$$

Moreover, let us assume that A_0 is a reflective subcategory of A (e.g. because B_0 contains a one-point object). Now the reflection of an object $\langle H,Y,\sigma\rangle$ of TTG into X_0 can be obtained in two steps (cf. [ML], p.101).

(i) *The reflection of* $\langle H,Y,\sigma\rangle$ *in* $K^{\leftarrow}[A_0\times TOP]$. Let $\psi: H\to G$ be the reflection of H in A_0. According to 4.3.7, the reflection of $\langle H,Y,\sigma\rangle$ in $K^{\leftarrow}[A_0\times TOP]$ is of the form $\langle\psi,f\rangle: \langle H,Y,\sigma\rangle \to \langle G,X,\pi\rangle$. Then this arrow is at least universal in TTG for all arrows $\langle\psi,g\rangle$ with domain $\langle H,Y,\sigma\rangle$. Hence it coincides (up to isomorphism) with the universal arrow which arises from the unit of adjunction of the functors L_ψ and R_ψ (cf. 3.3.11).)1 Consequently, once the reflection $\psi: H\to G$ of H in A_0 is known, the reflection $\langle\psi,f\rangle: \langle H,Y,\sigma\rangle \to \langle G,X,\pi\rangle$ of $\langle H,Y,\sigma\rangle$ in $K^{\leftarrow}[A_0\times TOP]$ can be computed by means of the methods of subsection 3.3. In particular, $\langle G,X,\pi\rangle = L_\psi\langle H,Y,\sigma\rangle$.

(ii) *The reflection of* $\langle G,X,\pi\rangle$ *in* X_0, *where* $\langle G,X,\pi\rangle$ *is the object of* $K^{\leftarrow}[A_0\times TOP]$ *which was obtained in* (i). According to 4.3.10 this reflection is of the form $\langle 1_G,g\rangle: \langle G,X,\pi\rangle \to \langle G,Z,\zeta\rangle$. Moreover, this morphism is just the reflection of $\langle G,X,\pi\rangle$ in B_0^G.

Thus, we reduced the more general problem to the following one, where G is a fixed topological group:

Given an object $\langle G,X,\pi\rangle$ *in* TOP^G, *determine the universal arrow* $\langle 1_G,k\rangle: \langle G,X,\pi\rangle \to \langle G,Z,\zeta\rangle$ *in* TOP^G *from* $\langle G,X,\pi\rangle$ *to* B_0^G, *whenever* B_0^G *is a reflective*

)1 Because $\psi: H\to G$ is the reflection of H into A_0, the condition mentioned in the footnote to 3.3.11 is fulfilled.

subcategory of $\mathbf{TOP}^G$.

We shall show now that under very weak and quite natural conditions reflectiveness of $\mathbf{B}_0^G$ in $\mathbf{TOP}^G$ implies that $\mathbf{B}_0$ is reflective in $\mathbf{TOP}$. However, even in that case, reflections are in general not preserved by the functor S^G: $\mathbf{TOP}^G \to \mathbf{TOP}$. Examples will be indicated in 4.3.13 below.

4.3.12. If $\mathbf{B}_0^G$ is a reflective subcategory of $\mathbf{B}^G$, then the proof of 4.3.6 cannot be used to show that $\mathbf{B}_0$ is a reflective subcategory of $\mathbf{B}$. However, if for any object X in $\mathbf{B}$, τ_X denotes the trivial action of G on X, and if $\langle 1_G, f\rangle$: $\langle G,X,\tau_X\rangle \to \langle G,Y,\sigma\rangle$ is the reflection of $\langle G,X,\tau_X\rangle$ in $\mathbf{B}_0^G$, then it is easy to show that f: $X \to Y$ is a universal arrow from X to $\mathbf{B}_0$, provided f is an epimorphism in $\mathbf{B}$. Thus, we proved:

Let E *be a class of epimorphisms in* $\mathbf{B}$ *and let* E^G *be the class of all (epi!) morphisms in* $\mathbf{B}^G$ *of the form* $\langle 1_G, f\rangle$ *with* $f \in E$. *If* $\mathbf{B}_0^G$ *is* E^G*-reflective in* $\mathbf{B}^G$, *then* $\mathbf{B}_0$ *is* E*-reflective in* $\mathbf{B}$.

4.3.13. NOTES. Although most results in this subsection could not be traced back in the literature (at least in this form), they are not very surprising. The reflection $\langle \alpha_G, f\rangle$: $\langle G,X,\pi\rangle \to \langle G^c,Y,\sigma\rangle$ of a ttg $\langle G,X,\pi\rangle$ in $K^{\leftarrow}[\mathbf{COMPGRP}\times\mathbf{COMP}]$ has been considered earlier by M.B. LANDSTAD [1972]. There it has been shown that f: $X \to Y$ can be obtained as the Hausdorff completion of X with respect to a certain uniformity on X. (This uniformity is quite similar to the one considered by E.M.ALFSEN & P. HOLM [1962] for topological groups, leading to a construction of the Bohr compactification.) Similar to 2.2.9, there turns out to be a nice relationship between $\langle \alpha_G, f\rangle$ and a certain subalgebra of $C_u(X)$.

In contradistinction to the functor G: $\mathbf{X} \to \mathbf{A}$, the functors S: $\mathbf{X} \to \mathbf{B}$ and S^G: $\mathbf{B}^G \to \mathbf{B}$ behave badly with respect to reflections. For example, $\mathbf{COMP}^G$ is reflective in $\mathbf{TOP}^G$, but the functor S^G does not preserve reflections of objects of $\mathbf{TOP}^G$ in $\mathbf{COMP}^G$. This means, of course, that the space component of the reflection $\langle 1_G, k\rangle$: $\langle G,X,\pi\rangle \to \langle G,Z,\zeta\rangle$ of $\langle G,X,\pi\rangle$ in $\mathbf{COMP}^G$ is in general not the reflection of X in $\mathbf{COMP}$. If it were, then the action of G on Z could be "extended" to an action of G on the reflection βZ of Z in $\mathbf{COMP}$. It has already been indicated in 4.2.13 that this cannot always be done if G is not discrete. Other examples will be given in the next subsection.

Another question is, whether the reflection $\langle 1_G, k\rangle$: $\langle G,X,\pi\rangle \to \langle G,Z,\zeta\rangle$ of an object $\langle G,X,\pi\rangle \in \mathbf{HAUS}^G$ in $\mathbf{COMP}^G$ is such that k is a topological embedding. A necessary condition for this to be so is that X is a Tychonov space, but it is an open problem whether this condition is sufficient. However, if X can equivariantly be embedded in *some* compact Hausdorff G-space Y, say by $\langle 1_G, g\rangle: \langle G,X,\pi\rangle \to \langle G,Y,\sigma\rangle$, then $g = \bar{g}k$ for some equivariant mapping $\bar{g}: Z \to Y$, and it can easily be seen that k has now to be a topological embedding because g is.

This is why we are interested in equivariant embeddings of Tychonov G-spaces in compact G-spaces. This problem will be considered in subsection 7.3. (To be sure, the compactifications considered there are in general not the reflections into COMP^G).

4.4. Some particular reflections

4.4.1. We shall consider in this subsection reflections of a ttg $\langle G,X,\pi\rangle$ in COMP^G and in $K^{\leftarrow}[\mathsf{COMPGRP}\times\mathsf{COMP}]$. As has been pointed out in 4.3.11, the latter reflections can be reduced to the former ones (even to reflections in COMP^H of ttgs of the type $\langle H,Y,\sigma\rangle$ with $H = G^c$, an object in $\mathsf{COMPGRP}$). First, we have to consider reflections of objects of TOP^G into HAUS^G. Essential in the following proposition is that the reflection of any topological space into HAUS is a quotient mapping.

4.4.2. PROPOSITION. *Let* $\langle G,X,\pi\rangle$ *be an object in* TOP^G *and let* $f: X \to Y$ *be the reflection of* X *in* HAUS. *If one of the following conditions is fulfilled, then there exists a unique action* σ *of* G *on* Y *making* f *equivariant. In that case,* $\langle 1_G, f\rangle: \langle G,X,\pi\rangle \to \langle G,Y,\sigma\rangle$ *is the reflection of* $\langle G,X,\pi\rangle$ *into* HAUS^G. *The conditions are:*

(i) f *is an open mapping.*

(ii) f *is a perfect mapping.*

(iii) G *is a locally compact Hausdorff group.*

(iv) $G\times Y$ *is a k-space.*

PROOF. Since $f: X\to Y$ is the reflection of X into HAUS, there exists for each $t \in G$ a unique continuous mapping $\sigma^t: Y \to Y$ such that $\sigma^t f = f\pi^t$. It is easily seen that we obtain in this way an action of G_d on Y such that f is equivariant with respect to the actions π and σ of G_d on X and Y, respectively. Now f is known to be a quotient mapping. It follows immediately from 1.5.7 that $\sigma: G\times Y \to Y$ is continuous whenever one of the conditions (i) through (iv) is fulfilled. Therefore, $\langle G,Y,\sigma\rangle$ is a ttg, and σ is the unique action of G on Y making $\langle 1_G, f\rangle$ a morphism in TOP^G. We claim that $\langle 1_G, f\rangle: \langle G,X,\pi\rangle \to \langle G,Y,\sigma\rangle$

is the reflection of $\langle G,X,\pi\rangle$ in HAUS^G. For if $\langle 1_G,g\rangle\colon \langle G,X,\pi\rangle \to \langle G,Z,\zeta\rangle$ is any morphism in TOP^G with $Z \in \mathsf{HAUS}$, then $g = \bar{g}f$ for some (unique) continuous function $\bar{g}\colon Y \to Z$. Now the equations

$$(\bar{g}\sigma^t)f = \bar{g}f\pi^t = g\pi^t = \zeta^t g = (\zeta^t\bar{g})f$$

($t \in G$) and the fact that f is a surjection imply that $\bar{g}$ is equivariant. So $\langle 1_G,\bar{g}\rangle$ is the unique morphism in HAUS^G such that $\langle 1_G,g\rangle = \langle 1_G,\bar{g}\rangle\langle 1_G,f\rangle$. This proves our claim. □

4.4.3. <u>COROLLARY</u>. *If* G *is a locally compact Hausdorff group then the functor* $S^G\colon \mathsf{TOP}^G \to \mathsf{TOP}$ *preserves all reflections of objects of* TOP^G *into* HAUS^G. *If* G *is any topological group, then the functor* S^G *preserves all reflections into* HAUS^G *of objects* $\langle G,X,\pi\rangle$ *of* TOP^G *with* X *compact.*

<u>PROOF</u>. In both situations, S^G "creates" the reflections)1 into HAUS^G of the objects under consideration (notice that a continous mapping of a compact space onto a T_2-space is perfect). Now the corollary follows from the fact that reflections are unique (up to isomorphism). □

4.4.4. We are now in a position that we can "describe" the reflection of an arbitrary object $\langle G,X,\pi\rangle$ of TOP^G in COMP^G.

First, there is the action π' of G_d on βX making $\beta_X\colon X \to \beta X$ equivariant with respect to the actions π and π' of G_d on X and βX, respectively (cf. proposition 4.2.9).

Next, let $\iota\colon G_d \to G$ be the identity, and consider the arrow $\langle\iota,g\rangle\colon \langle G_d,\beta X,\pi'\rangle \to \langle G,Z,\zeta\rangle$ which is universal for the class of all morphisms $\langle\iota,g'\rangle$ in TTG with domain $\langle G_d,\beta X,\pi'\rangle$ (cf. 3.3.11). By 3.3.13(ii), $g\colon \beta X \to Z$ is a bijection, so that Z is certainly compact (but presumably not Hausdorff). Notice that $\langle 1_G, g\beta_X\rangle\colon \langle G,X,\pi\rangle \to \langle G,Z,\zeta\rangle$ is a morphism in TOP^G.

Finally, let $\langle 1_G,f\rangle\colon \langle G,Z,\zeta\rangle \to \langle G,Y,\sigma\rangle$ be the reflection of $\langle G,Z,\zeta\rangle$ in HAUS. Since Z is compact, it follows from 4.4.3 that $f\colon Z \to Y$ is the reflection of Z in HAUS and that σ is uniquely determined by the condition that f be equivariant. So $\langle G,Y,\sigma\rangle$ may be assumed to be known (cf. also the explanation of our policy in 3.1.1). Since f is surjective and Z is

---

)1 "Creation of reflections" has not been defined, neither in [ML], nor by us. What we mean by it is just what has been described in the preceding proposition.

compact, Y is an object in COMP. Now a straightforward argument shows, that *the arrow*

$$<1_G, fg\beta_X>: <G,X,\pi> \to <G,Y,\sigma>$$

in TOP^G *is universal from* $<G,X,\pi>$ *to* COMP^G, *i.e. it is the reflection of* $<G,X,\pi>$ *in* COMP^G (use the several universality properties of β_X, $<\iota,g>$ and $<1_G,f>$, and the fact that $fg\beta_X$ has a dense range).

If the space X above is *compact* (but not Hausdorff), then the preceding construction may be reduced to its last step. So let $f: X \to Y$ be the reflection of X in HAUS and let σ be the unique action of G on Y making f equivariant. Then $Y \in$ COMP, and it is easy to see that $<1_G,f>: <G,X,\pi> \to <G,Y,\sigma>$ is not only the reflection of $<G,X,\pi>$ into HAUS^G, but that it is also its reflection into COMP^G.

If the group G is compact Hausdorff, then it can be shown that the orbit space Y/C_σ of the reflection of $<G,X,\pi>$ in COMP^G is just the reflection of X/C_π in COMP. See 4.4.13(v) below. {This case is of particular interest because the computation of the reflection of an arbitrary ttg $<H,Z,\zeta>$ in $K^{\leftarrow}$[COMPGRP×COMP] requires computation of the reflection of a G-space $<G,X,\pi>$ in COMP^G with G a compact Hausdorff group, viz. $G = H^c$; cf. 4.3.11.}

4.4.5. Using 4.3.11, 4.3.9 and 4.4.4, we can give the following description of the reflection of a ttg $<G,X,\pi>$ with $X \in$ COMP into $K^{\leftarrow}$[COMPGRP×COMP]. It is the morphism

$$<\alpha, gf>: <G,X,\pi> \to <G^c,Y,\sigma>$$

where α, g, f, Y and σ are obtained as follows:

$\alpha: G \to G^c$ is the Bohr-compactification of G.

$<\alpha,f>: <G,X,\pi> \to L_\alpha<G,X,\pi>$ is the universal arrow according to 3.3.11; notice that the phase space X' of $L_\alpha<G,X,\pi> =: <G^c,X',\pi'>$ is a quotient of $G^c \times X$. In particular, it follows that X' is compact.

$g: X' \to Y$ is the reflection of X' in HAUS (so $Y \in$ COMP).

σ is the unique action of G^c on Y making g equivariant.

The reflection of a ttg $<G,X,\pi>$ with $X \in$ COMP into $K^{\leftarrow}$[COMPGRP×COMP] has obtained considerable attention in the literature. However, there a quite different terminology is used, so that we have to reformulate the matter.

To do so, we introduce a new category, viz. COMPEQ. It is the full subcategory of $K^{\leftarrow}$[TOPGRP×COMP] determined by all objects with an *equicontinuous* action. Thus, a ttg $\langle G,X,\pi\rangle$ is in COMPEQ iff $X \in$ COMP and $\bar{\pi}[G]$ is equicontinuous on X (with respect to the unique uniformity of X).

4.4.6. Obviously, $K^{\leftarrow}$[COMPGRP×COMP] $\subseteq$ COMPEQ. Indeed, an action of a compact group on any uniform space is equicontinuous by a straightforward compactness argument (namely, 0.2.2(ii)).

Moreover, it is not difficult to see that COMPEQ is closed with respect to the formation of products in TTG and with respect to the passage to closed invariant subspaces. Therefore, it can be shown by means of methods similar to the proof of theorem 0.4.3 *that* COMPEQ *is a reflective subcategory of* TTG. However, we shall present a proof which relates the reflection of an object of TTG in COMPEQ with its reflection in $K^{\leftarrow}$[COMPGRP× COMP].

4.4.7. PROPOSITION. *The subcategory* COMPEQ *is reflective in* TTG. *For each object* $\langle G,X,\pi\rangle$ *in* TTG *the reflections in* COMPEQ *and in* $K^{\leftarrow}$[COMPGRP×COMP] *are related as follows: if* $\langle\alpha,k\rangle\colon \langle G,X,\pi\rangle \to \langle G^c,Y,\sigma\rangle$ *is the reflection in* $K^{\leftarrow}$[COMPGRP×COMP], *then the reflection in* COMPEQ *is* $\langle 1_G,k\rangle\colon \langle G,X,\pi\rangle \to \langle G,Y,\sigma^{\alpha}\rangle$.

PROOF. The transition group of $\langle G,Y,\sigma^{\alpha}\rangle$ is a subgroup of the transition group of $\langle G^c,Y,\sigma\rangle$. As $\langle G^c,Y,\sigma\rangle$ is an equicontinuous ttg it follows that $\langle G,Y,\sigma^{\alpha}\rangle$ is equicontinuous. Next, we show that $\langle 1_G,k\rangle\colon \langle G,X,\pi\rangle \to \langle G,Y,\sigma^{\alpha}\rangle$ is the reflection of $\langle G,X,\pi\rangle$ in COMPEQ.

To this end, consider a morphism $\langle\psi,g\rangle\colon \langle G,X,\pi\rangle \to \langle H,Z,\zeta\rangle$ in TTG, where $\langle H,Z,\zeta\rangle$ is an object in COMPEQ. By 1.3.18, the enveloping semigroup E_Z of $\langle H,Z,\zeta\rangle$ is a compact Hausdorff topological homeomorphism group on Z. Thus, we obtain a morphism $\langle\bar{\zeta},1_Z\rangle\colon \langle H,Z,\zeta\rangle \to \langle E_Z,Z,\delta\rangle$ in TTG (cf. 1.4.4(vi)). Now $\langle\bar{\zeta}\psi,g\rangle\colon \langle G,X,\pi\rangle \to \langle E_Z,Z,\delta\rangle$ is a morphism in TTG, where $\langle E_Z,Z,\delta\rangle$ is an object in $K^{\leftarrow}$[COMPGRP×COMP]. Since $\langle\alpha,k\rangle\colon \langle G,X,\pi\rangle \to \langle G^c,Y,\sigma\rangle$ is the reflection of $\langle G,X,\pi\rangle$ in the latter category, it follows that there exists a unique morphism $\langle\varphi,h\rangle\colon \langle G^c,Y,\sigma\rangle \to \langle E_Z,Z,\delta\rangle$ in TTG such that $\langle\bar{\zeta}\psi,g\rangle = \langle\varphi,h\rangle\langle\alpha,k\rangle$.

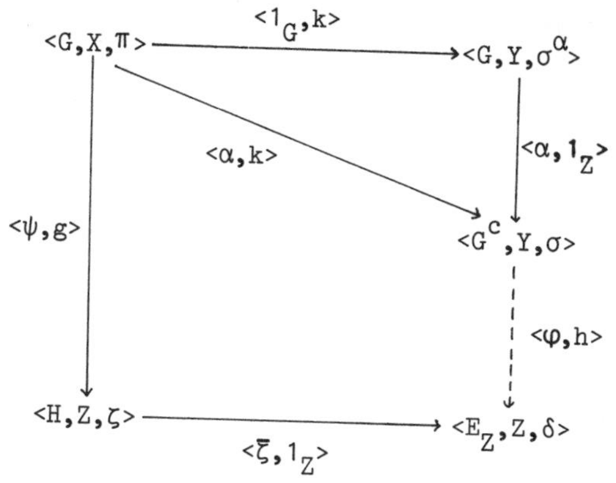

The following calculation shows that $\langle\psi,h\rangle: \langle G,Y,\sigma^{\alpha}\rangle \to \langle H,Z,\zeta\rangle$ is a morphism in **TTG**:

$$h\sigma^{\alpha}(t,y) = h\sigma(\alpha t,y) = \delta(\varphi\alpha t,hy) = \delta(\bar{\zeta}\psi t,hy) = \zeta(\psi t,hy)$$

($t \in G$, $y \in Y$). In addition, $\langle\psi,g\rangle = \langle\psi,h\rangle\langle 1_G,k\rangle$, and $\langle\psi,h\rangle$ is the unique morphism in **TTG** with this property (by 4.3.2 (ii), (iii) and (v), k has a dense range!). This completes the proof. □

4.4.8. As was noticed in the above proof, k has a dense range. Stated otherwise, if E is the class of all morphisms $\langle 1_G,k\rangle$ with $G \in$ **TOPGRP** and with f a continuous mapping with a dense range, then **COMPEQ** is E-reflective in **TTG**.

In the literature the following terminology is often used. If $\langle G,X,\pi\rangle$ is a ttg with $X \in$ **COMP**, then its reflection $\langle 1_G,k\rangle: \langle G,X,\pi\rangle \to \langle G,Y,\sigma^{\alpha}\rangle$ in **COMPEQ** is called the *maximal equicontinuous factor of* $\langle G,X,\pi\rangle$. The enveloping semigroup of $\langle G,Y,\sigma^{\alpha}\rangle$ is an object in **COMPGRP** (cf. 1.3.18). It is called *the structure group of* $\langle G,X,\pi\rangle$.

Notice that in this case $k: X \to Y$ is a *surjection*. It can be described following the lines of 4.4.5 (indeed, k = gf with notation as in 4.4.5).

4.4.9. The reader may have noticed that there is a great similarity between the proofs of 4.4.2 and of 3.4.3. The reader might also have asked himself why the functor S^G: $\mathbf{TOP}^G \to \mathbf{TOP}$ preserves reflections into $\mathbf{HAUS}^G$ if G is locally compact T_2, whereas it does not preserve reflections into $\mathbf{COMP}^G$ (not even if G is compact, as we shall see below). The following lemma will provide a partial answer to these, and similar, questions.

4.4.10. <u>LEMMA</u>. *Let* (P,Q,α,β) *be an adjunction from the category* Y *to the category* C. *Let* Y_0 *be a reflective subcategory of* Y, *say with reflections* $\rho_Y\colon Y \to FY$ $(Y \in Y)$, *and let* C_0 *be a subcategory of* C *such that the following conditions are fulfilled:*

(i) $P[Y_0] \subseteq C_0$ *and for each object* C *in* C_0, *the arrow* $\beta_C\colon PQC \to C$ *is in* C_0.

(ii) $Q[C_0] \subseteq Y_0$ *and for each object* Y *in* Y_0, *the arrow* $\alpha_Y\colon Y \to QPY$ *is in* Y_0.

Then for each object Y *in* Y *the arrow* $P\rho_Y\colon PY \to PFY$ *in* C *is universal for the class of all arrows* $f\colon PY \to C$ *with* $C \in C_0$.

<u>PROOF</u>. First, notice that for any object Y in Y, the object FY is in Y_0, hence PFY is in C_0. Next, consider a morphism $f\colon PY \to C$ in C with $C \in C_0$. Then $Qf \circ \alpha_Y\colon Y \to QC$ is a morphism in Y with $QC \in Y_0$. Hence there exists a morphism $f'\colon FY \to QC$ in Y_0 such that the first one of the following diagrams commutes:

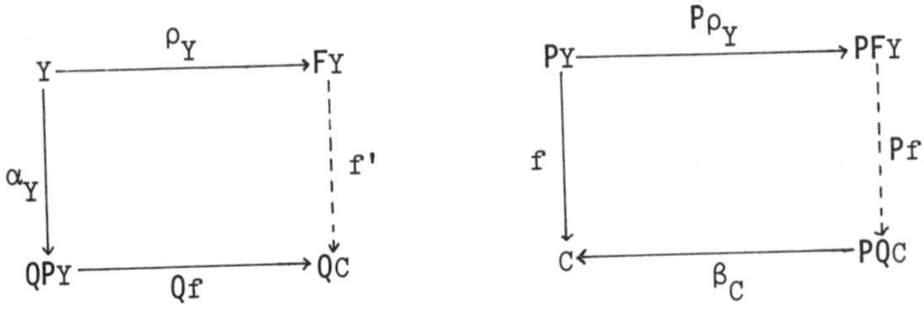

We claim that the second diagram commutes as well. To prove this, observe that

$$\beta_C \circ Pf' \circ P\rho_Y = \beta_C \circ P(f' \circ \rho_Y) = \beta_C \circ P(Qf \circ \alpha_Y).$$

According to 0.4.2 (in particular, diagram (3) and formula (4)), $Qf \circ \alpha_Y$ is the *unique* morphism h in Y such that $\beta_C \circ Ph = f$. So, $f = (\beta_C \circ Pf') \circ P\rho_Y$, as was claimed. Observe that $\beta_C \circ Pf'$ is a morphism in C_0, by condition (i).

Finally, if $g\colon PFY \to C$ is any other morphism in C_0 such that $f = g \circ P\rho_Y$, then $g = \beta_C \circ Pg'$ for some unique morphism $g'\colon FY \to QC$ in Y. Then $f = \beta_C \circ P(g' \circ \rho_Y)$. However, we have seen above, that $Qf \circ \alpha_Y$ is the unique morphism in Y such that $\beta_C \circ P(Qf \circ \alpha_Y) = f$, so $g' \circ \rho_Y = Qf \circ \alpha_Y$. Again according to 0.4.2, $g' = Qg \circ \alpha_{FY}$, so by condition (ii), g' is a morphism in Y_0. Since f' was the *unique* morphism in Y_0 such that $f' \circ \rho_Y = Qf \circ \alpha_Y$, it follows that $f' = g'$. Consequently, $g = \beta_C \circ Pf'$. This shows that $\beta_C \circ Pf'$ is the unique morphism in C_0 whose composite with $P\rho_Y$ is f. □

4.4.11. Notice that the second part of condition (ii) is only used to ensure the uniqueness of the morphism $\beta_C \circ Pf'$ in the above proof. It is clear, that this uniqueness can also be proved if condition (ii) is replaced by the following one

(ii)' For each object C in C_0, $QC \in Y_0$ and, in addition, ρ_Y is an epimorphism in Y for each object $Y \in Y$.

For then the existence of f' in the preceding proof is guaranteed as before, and the uniqueness of $\beta_C \circ Pf'$ follows from the fact that $P\rho_Y$ is epic in C (P preserves epimorphisms because it has a right adjoint).

4.4.12. If in the preceding lemma C_0 is *given* to be a reflective subcategory of C, then obviously $P\rho_Y$ is the reflection of PY into C_0. Thus, the functor P preserves reflections of objects of Y into Y_0.

It is useful to observe that the lemma *implies* that C_0 will be a reflective subcategory of C if, in addition to the conditions (i) and (ii), it is required that P maps the object class of Y_0 onto the object class of C_0.

4.4.13. APPLICATIONS. We shall describe now briefly some applications of the preceding remarks. Most of the details are left to the reader.

(i) Let X, X_0, A, A_0, B, B_0 and $G\colon X \to A$ be as in subsection 4.3. Suppose that B_0 contains a one-point object $(*)$ and that for each object X in B the obvious function $f\colon X \to (*)$ is a morphism in B (so $(*)$ is a final object in B). *Under these conditions, the assumption that* X_0 *is a reflective subcategory of* X *implies that* A_0 *is a reflective subcategory of* A *and, in addition, the functor* $G\colon X \to A$ *preserves the reflections of objects of* X *in* X_0. To prove this, take in 4.4.10, $Y := X$, $Y_0 := X_0$, $C := A$, $C_0 := A_0$, and $P := G$; then the functor $G\colon X \to A$ has a right adjoint Q, namely the functor

$$Q\colon \begin{cases} G \longmapsto \langle G, (*), \tau^G \rangle & \text{on objects} \\ \psi \longmapsto \langle \psi, 1_{(*)} \rangle & \text{on morphisms} \end{cases}$$

(cf. 4.1.2(ii), or the proof of 3.4.9). Then 4.4.10 and 4.4.12 yield the desired results. {Notice that these results can also be proved by using 4.3.6(i) and 4.3.7.}

(ii) Let G be a locally compact Hausdorff group. It will be shown in §6 that the functor S^G: $\mathsf{TOP}^G \to \mathsf{TOP}$ has a right adjoint M^G: $\mathsf{TOP} \to \mathsf{TOP}^G$. The functor M^G is defined by

$$M^G: \begin{cases} X \longmapsto \langle G, C_c(G,X), \tilde{\rho} \rangle & \text{on objects} \\ f \longmapsto \langle 1_G, f \circ - \rangle & \text{on morphisms} \end{cases}$$

(cf. 6.3.6(iii)). In particular, it maps HAUS into HAUS^G, so all requirements of lemma 4.4.10 are satisfied if we take $Y := \mathsf{TOP}^G$, $Y_0 := \mathsf{HAUS}^G$, $C := \mathsf{TOP}$ and $C_0 := \mathsf{HAUS}$. Consequently, the functor S^G preserves the reflections of objects of TOP^G in HAUS^G (cf. also the first part of 4.4.3). {Notice that this proof fails if we try to replace HAUS by COMP: the functor M^G does not send COMP into COMP^G!}

(iii) The functor F: TOPGRP×TOP → TTG which has been described in 3.1.14 has a right adjoint, namely the functor K: TTG → TOPGRP×TOP. Applying 4.4.10 and 4.4.12 to this situation, we see that the functor F preserves reflections of objects of TOPGRP×TOP in COMPGRP×COMP. Consequently, if $\langle G, G\times X, \mu_X^G \rangle$ is any free ttg, then its reflection in $K^{\leftarrow}$[COMPGRP×COMP] is the arrow

$$\langle \alpha_G, \alpha_G \times \beta_X \rangle : \langle G, G\times X, \mu_X^G \rangle \to \langle G^c, G^c \times \beta X, \mu_{\beta X}^{G^c} \rangle .$$

Here α_G: $G \to G^c$ and β_X: $X \to \beta X$ are the reflections of G in COMPGRP and of X in COMP, respectively.

(iv) Let G be a *compact* Hausdorff group. Then the functor F^G: $\mathsf{TOP} \to \mathsf{TOP}^G$ (cf. 3.2.7) maps COMP into COMP^G. So the functor F^G and its right adjoint S^G fit the situation of 4.4.10, and F^G preserves reflections of spaces in COMP. Consequently, if $\langle G, G\times X, \mu_X^G \rangle$ is any free G-space, then its reflection in COMP^G is the arrow

$$\langle 1_G, 1_G \times \beta_X \rangle : \langle G, G\times X, \mu_X^G \rangle \to \langle G, G\times \beta X, \mu_{\beta X}^G \rangle .$$

{Since now $G^c = G$ and $\alpha_G = 1_G$, this is in accordance with (iii) above; cf. 4.3.10.}

(v) Let G be a *compact* Hausdorff group. Then for any object $\langle G, X, \pi \rangle$ in COMP^G the orbit space X/C_π is in COMP (only the fact that X/C_π is a Hausdorff space needs a proof; this is an easy corollary of

1.3.10(iii)). Hence the functor S_1^G: $\mathbf{TOP}^G \to \mathbf{TOP}$ (cf. 3.3.13(iii)) maps $\mathbf{COMP}^G$ into $\mathbf{COMP}$. According to 3.3.13(iii), the functor S_1^G has a right adjoint. Now 4.4.12 can be used to show that S_1^G preserves reflections of arbitrary G-spaces in $\mathbf{COMP}^G$. Thus, if $\langle 1_G, f\rangle: \langle G,X,\pi\rangle \to \langle G,Y,\sigma\rangle$ is the reflection in $\mathbf{COMP}^G$ of the G-space $\langle G,X,\pi\rangle$, then the induced morphism f': $X/C_\pi \to Y/C_\sigma$ is just the reflection of X/C_π in $\mathbf{COMP}$.

4.4.14. Now we can easily provide an example of a G-space such that the space component of its reflection in $\mathbf{COMP}^G$ is not the reflection of the phase space in $\mathbf{COMP}$. To this end, consider any *compact Hausdorff group* G and any Tychonov space X. Then the space component of the reflection of $\langle G, G\times X, \mu_X^G\rangle$ in $\mathbf{COMP}^G$ is, according to 4.4.13(iv), the morphism $1_G \times \beta_X$: $G\times X \to G\times\beta X$ in $\mathbf{TOP}$. The reflection of G in $\mathbf{COMP}$ is 1_G: $G \to G$, so we can write $\beta_G \times \beta_X$: $G\times X \to \beta G\times\beta X$ for this morphism. By a result of I. GLICKSBERG [1959], this can only be the reflection of $G\times X$ in $\mathbf{COMP}$ if $G\times X$ is *pseudocompact*. So we have our desired counterexample if we take for X a non-pseudocompact space. Another example could be provided by the ttg $\langle G,G,\lambda\rangle$ for any *non-compact, non-discrete locally compact Hausdorff group* G.

To this end, we shall first describe some properties of the reflection of $\langle G,G,\lambda\rangle$ in $\mathbf{COMP}^G$, where G is an arbitrary topological group. Let this reflection be denoted by

$$\langle 1_G, g\rangle: \langle G,G,\lambda\rangle \to \langle G,U,\upsilon\rangle.$$

In addition, set $u := g(e)$. An easy calculation shows that $g = \upsilon_u$; hence $g[G]$ is the orbit of u in U. By 4.3.2(vi), g has a dense range in U, that is, *the orbit of* u *is dense in* U.

4.4.15. PROPOSITION. *Let* $\langle G,X,\pi\rangle$ *be any object in* $\mathbf{COMP}^G$ *and let* $x \in X$. *There exists a unique morphism* $\langle 1_G, f\rangle: \langle G,U,\upsilon\rangle \to \langle G,X,\pi\rangle$ *in* $\mathbf{COMP}^G$ *such that* $x = f(u)$, *i.e.* $\pi_x = f\circ\upsilon_u$.

PROOF. For an equivariant mapping $f: U \to X$ the condition $x = f(u)$ is equivalent to the condition $\pi_x = f\upsilon_u$. Notice that $\langle 1_G, \pi_x\rangle: \langle G,G,\lambda\rangle \to \langle G,X,\pi\rangle$ is a morphism in $\mathbf{TOP}^G$ with codomain in $\mathbf{COMP}^G$. So existence and unicity of $\langle 1_G, f\rangle$ as meant in our proposition follow immediately from the universal property of $\langle 1_G, \upsilon_u\rangle$. □

4.4.16. COROLLARY. *Every compact Hausdorff* G*-space which is the orbit-closure of one of its points is the continuous equivariant image of* U. □

4.4.17. PROPOSITION. *The compactification*[1] υ_u: $G \to U$ *of* G *is the unique compactification of* G *(up to isomorphism*[2]*) with the property that* $C^*(\upsilon_u)$: $h \mapsto h \circ \upsilon_u$ *maps* $C(U)$ *onto* $RUC^*(G)$.

PROOF. First, we show that $C(U)$ is mapped into $RUC^*(G)$. Let $h \in C(U)$. By an elementary compactness argument (namely 0.2.2(i), applied to the continuous function $h \circ \upsilon$), it follows that the mapping $t \mapsto h \circ \upsilon^t$: $G \to C_u(U)$ is continuous. Since $C^*(\upsilon_u)$: $C_u(U) \to C_u(G)$ is continuous, it follows that $t \mapsto h \circ \upsilon^t \circ \upsilon_u$: $G \to C_u(G)$ is continuous as well. However, $\upsilon^t \circ \upsilon_u = \upsilon_u \circ \lambda^t$, so the mapping $t \mapsto (h \circ \upsilon_u) \circ \lambda^t$ is continuous from G into $C_u(G)$. Therefore, by the "right" analog of 2.2.2, $h \circ \upsilon_u \in RUC(G)$. Obviously, $h \circ \upsilon_u$ is bounded, hence $h \circ \upsilon_u \in RUC^*(G)$.

Conversely, suppose we are given any $f \in RUC^*(G)$. By 2.1.9, $\langle G, K_{\tilde\rho}[f], \tilde\rho \rangle$ is an object in $COMP^G$, in which f has a dense orbit[3]. By 4.4.15, there exists a morphism of G-spaces k: $U \to K_{\tilde\rho}[f]$ such that $\tilde\rho_f = k \circ \upsilon_u$. If δ_e: $K_{\tilde\rho}[f] \to \mathbb{F}$ denotes evaluation-at-e, then $\delta_e \circ k \in C(U)$, and $C^*(\upsilon_u)(\delta_e \circ k) = \delta_e \circ k \circ \upsilon_u = \delta_e \circ \tilde\rho_f = f$. This proves that $C^*(\upsilon_u)$ maps $C(U)$ onto $RUC^*(G)$. Finally, unicity follows from [Se], 7.7.1 and 7.7.2. □

4.4.18. COROLLARY. *If* G *is a Hausdorff group, then* υ_u: $G \to U$ *is a topological embedding, and* $\langle G, U, \upsilon \rangle$ *is an effective ttg.*

PROOF. By the lemma in 0.2.7, $RUC^*(G)$ separates points and closed subsets of G. Now the result that υ_u: $G \to U$ is a topological embedding is an easy consequence of the fact that $C^*(\upsilon_u)[C^*(U)] = RUC^*(G)$. Finally, if $\upsilon^t = \upsilon^e$ for some $t \in G$, then $\upsilon_u(t) = \upsilon_u(e)$, hence $t = e$. □

4.4.19. Since β_G: $G \to \beta G$ is the unique compactification (up to isomorphism) of G such that $C^*(\beta_G)$: $h \mapsto h \circ \beta_G$ maps $C(\beta G)$ onto $C^*(G)$[4], it is obvious from 4.4.17 that the following statement is true: *the forgetful functor* S^G: $TOP^G \to TOP$ *maps the reflection of* $\langle G, G, \lambda \rangle$ *in* $COMP^G$ *onto a reflection of* G *in* COMP *iff* $RUC^*(G) = C^*(G)$, that is, iff each bounded continuous function on G is uniformly continuous.

---

[1] A *compactification* of G is just a continuous mapping f: $G \to X$ with $X \in COMP$ and $g[G]$ dense in X.

[2] Two compactifications g_i: $G \to X_i$ ($i=1,2$) are said to be *isomorphic* if $g_2 = fg_1$ for some homeomorphism f: $X_1 \to X_2$.

[3] Recall that $K_{\tilde\rho}[f]$ is the closure of $\{\tilde\rho^t f : t \in G\}$ in $C_c(G)$.

[4] Cf. [GJ], 6.5 or [He], 2.3.2 and 2.3.3.

By the results mentioned in Appendix A, the equality of $\mathrm{RUC}^*(G)$ and $C^*(G)$ implies that G is either pseudocompact or a P-space (i.e. every countable intersection of open sets is open). Now suppose that G is a locally compact Hausdorff group. Then pseudocompactness of G implies its compactness. Moreover, if G is a P-space then it is discrete (by [GJ], Exercise 4K2, compact P-spaces are finite!). Consequently, *if* G *is a non-compact, non-discrete locally compact Hausdorff group, then* $\mathrm{RUC}^*(G) \subset C^*(G)$, *and* S^G *does not preserve the reflection of* $\langle G,G,\lambda\rangle$ *in* $\mathbf{COMP}^G$.

We shall mention now some situations in which $\mathrm{RUC}^*(G) = C^*(G)$. First, this is of course true if G is compact and if G is discrete. However, if G is *pseudocompact*, then $\mathrm{RUC}^*(G) = C^*(G)$ as well (cf. Appendix A). In that case, $\beta_G\colon G \to \beta G$ is isomorphic to $\alpha_G\colon G \to G^c$, hence we may assume that the reflection of $\langle G,G,\lambda\rangle$ in $\mathbf{COMP}^G$ is $\langle 1_G,\alpha_G\rangle\colon \langle G,G,\lambda\rangle \to \langle G,G^c,\hat{\alpha}_G\rangle$ (cf. 1.1.6(v) for notation). {Hence *each* compact G-space which is the orbit closure of one of its points is equicontinuous, being the equivariant continuous image of the equicontinuous ttg $\langle G,G^c,\hat{\alpha}_G\rangle$.}

4.4.20. NOTES. The concepts of the maximal equicontinuous factor and the structure group of a ttg $\langle G,X,\pi\rangle$ with $X \in \mathbf{COMP}$ seem to be introduced in R. ELLIS & W. GOTTSCHALK [1960]. The maximal equicontinuous factor of a ttg can be trivial, i.e. an action of G on a one-point space. A lot of research has been done in order to find sufficient conditions for non-triviality of the maximal equicontinuous factor. According to 4.4.7, the construction which has been described in 4.4.5 can be used to obtain the maximal equicontinuous factor of an object $\langle G,X,\pi\rangle$ in $\mathbf{COMP}^G$. This method seems to be new. However, we have not yet explored this alternative description in order to get results about non-triviality of the maximal equicontinuous factor. In the literature, the study of the maximal equicontinuous factor is often related to full subcategories of $\mathbf{COMP}^G$ which are defined by imposing restrictions on the *action* of G (often G is supposed to be discrete, i.e. in most cases the topology of G plays no role). This falls outside the scope of this treatise, but we cannot resist temptation to mention the following class of compact G-spaces: the class of all *minimal* compact Hausdorff G-spaces (a ttg is said to be *minimal* if it contains no proper closed invariant subspaces; by ZORN's lemma, each non-void compact Hausdorff G-space contains a non-void invariant closed subspace which is minimal under the action of G). The classification of compact minimal G-spaces forms an important and largely unsolved problem of Topological Dynamics. For an excellent introduction, cf. [E1]. It has been shown in R. PELEG [1972] that *a minimal ttg* $\langle G,X,\pi\rangle$ *with* $X \in$ COMP *has a non-trivial maximal equicontinuous factor iff* $\langle G,X,\pi\rangle$ *is weakly mixing* (a ttg $\langle G,X,\pi\rangle$ is said to be *weakly mixing* if the product $\langle G,X\times X,\sigma\rangle$ of it with itself in TOP^G is ergodic; a ttg $\langle G,Y,\sigma\rangle$ is *ergodic* whenever every proper closed invariant subset has non-empty interior). More information about the maximal equicontinuous factor of a minimal compact Hausdorff G-space $\langle G,X,\pi\rangle$ can be found in R. ELLIS & H. KEYNES [1971].

Another class of objects in COMP^G which has attracted much attention is the class of ambits. An *ambit* is an object $\langle G,X,x,\pi\rangle$ such that $\langle G,X,\pi\rangle$ is an object in COMP^G and x is a point in X with a dense orbit (in [E1] the term "point transitive" is used). In the literature there are several constructions for a *universal ambit* (or *maximal* ambit, or *greatest* ambit), i.e. an ambit $\langle G,U,u,\upsilon\rangle$ with the property described in 4.4.15. Our proof of its existence seems to be new. Note that *uniqueness* (up to isomorphism) of this universal ambit is trivial, because of the requirement that its base point (i.e. the point with a dense orbit) can be mapped onto the base point of any ambit. {In [E1], Chap. 7, in particular, on p.63, it is shown that there exists a *universal point transitive ttg*: an object $\langle G,X,\pi\rangle$ in COMP^G such that $K_\pi[x] = X$ for some $x \in X$; in addition, if $\langle G,Y,\sigma\rangle$ is any object in COMP^G such that $K_\sigma[y] = Y$ for some $y \in Y$, then there exists an equivariant mapping of X onto Y. Here no uniqueness is required, nor preservation of base points. Yet such a universal point transitive ttg can be shown to be unique up to isomorphism. Using this uniqueness theorem (which is by no means trivial), it follows from 4.4.16 that our ttg $\langle G,U,\upsilon\rangle$ is (isomorphic to) the universal point transitive ttg of ELLIS.}

The property of the universal ambit which we stated in 4.4.17 was used in J. AUSLANDER & F. HAHN [1967] and in R.B. BROOK [1970] as a starting point for their construction of the greatest ambit. Both papers use essentially the theorem that to every suitable left invariant subalgebra A of $\mathrm{RUC}_u^*(G)$ there corresponds a compactification $f\colon G \to Y$ of G such that on the space Y an action of G can be defined so as to obtain an ambit. The papers differ from each other with respect to the *proof* of this theorem (i.e. the construction of a suitable compactification). The former paper invokes Gelfand theory (the space Y is obtained as the maximal ideal space of the algebra A, whereas $f\colon G \to Y$ assigns to each point t of G the maximal ideal $\{g \in A : g(t) = 0\}$). The proof in R.B. BROOK [1970] uses the following procedure: provide G with the weakest uniformity making each $f \in A$ uniformly continuous, and let f: $G \to Y$ be the completion of the uniform space G obtained in this way)1 (since each $f \in A$ is bounded, G is totally bounded in this uniformity, hence Y is compact: cf. [En], Example 1 on page 335). Still other methods can be used to prove this theorem. For a quite general method, cf. [Se], 14.2.2.

The paper W.H. GOTTSCHALK [1968] only *mentiones* the existence of a greatest ambit. It contains no proof, but the paper strongly suggests that it is constructed completely similar to the proof which we presented of the theorem in 0.4.3 (i.e. form the product of a representative set of ambits and consider the closure of the canonical image of G in it). In the paper of P. FLOR [1967], this method is used to obtain a maximal semigroup compactification of G, say $\varphi: G \to S$, such that $C^*(\varphi)[C(S)] = RUC^*(G)$, and $\langle G,S,\hat{\varphi}\rangle$ is a ttg (cf. 1.1.6(v) for notation). It follows from the results in this subsection that $\langle G,S,\varphi(e),\hat{\varphi}\rangle$ must be isomorphic to the maximal ambit. Notice that this implies that the phase space U of the greatest ambit $\langle G,U,u,\upsilon\rangle$ can be given the structure of a semigroup such that $\upsilon_u: G \to U$ is a morphism of semigroups. {This can also be proved directly: if $\langle G,U,u,\upsilon\rangle$ is a maximal ambit, e.g. constructed according to the lines of this subsection, then the ambit $\langle G,E_U,1_U,\upsilon^*\rangle$ has also the properties of a maximal ambit. Hence $\langle G,U,u,\upsilon\rangle$ and $\langle G,E_U,1_U,\upsilon^*\rangle$ are isomorphic.}

It is tempting to mention more full subcategories of $\mathbf{COMP}^G$, defined by means of restrictions on the actions of G. We shall not do so, and we refer the reader to H. CHU [1962], where several subclasses of the object class of $\mathbf{COMP}^G$ are mentioned admitting universal (or "maximal") objects. Cf. also L. AUSLANDER & F. HAHN [1963].

)1 If A consists of all uniformly continuous functions on G, then f: $G \to Y$ is the Samuel compactification of G.

5 - K-ACTIONS OF K-GROUPS ON K-SPACES

As has been pointed out by N.E. STEENROD [1967], topologists should work mainly with k-spaces. We shall do so in this section, by dealing with k-actions. A k-action of a k-group on a k-space is just an ordinary action in which the requirement of continuity on the usual cartesian product of phase group and phase space has been replaced by the (weaker!) requirement of continuity on their product in the category **KR** of all k-spaces. The resulting categories **k-TTG** and $\mathbf{k\text{-}KR}^G$ (G a k-group) behave completely similar to their counterparts **TTG** and $\mathbf{TOP}^G$ as far as it concerns limits. We cannot say much about colimits in **k-TTG**, because we don't know anything about colimits in the category **KRGRP** of all k-groups. Indeed, it is impossible to express colimits in **k-TTG** in terms of **KRGRP** and **KR** without explicit reference to the existence of colimits in **KRGRP**. On the other hand, $\mathbf{k\text{-}KR}^G$ behaves very nicely with respect to colimits: all its colimits can be computed in **KR**. The proof of this fact will be postponed to §6. In fact, all material in the present section should be considered only as preliminaries to the considerations in §6 (in particular, to subsection 6.2).

5.1. General remarks on k-spaces and k-groups

5.1.1. We shall review here briefly some facts about k-spaces. All results can be found in N.E. STEENROD [1967] or [ML], p.181-184. Observe that often k-spaces are called *compactly generated* spaces. Recall that *a k-space* is a T_2-space in which a subset is closed iff its intersection with each compact subset is closed. They can be characterized as T_2-spaces which are quotients of locally compact T_2-spaces.

5.1.2. The full subcategory of **HAUS** defined by the class of all k-spaces will be denoted **KR**. All statements about limits, colimits, epi- and monomorphisms in KR can be derived from the following two facts:

(i) KR is a coreflective subcategory of HAUS, i.e. the inclusion functor KR → HAUS has a right adjoint. Hence KR is complete.

(ii) The inclusion functor KR → HAUS creates all colimits. Hence KR is cocomplete.

Ad (i): For any object $X \in$ HAUS, the coreflection of X in KR is the mapping $1_X: X_1 \to X$, where X_1 is the set X endowed with the finest topology making all inclusion mappings of compact subsets of X into X_1 continuous)1. Limits of diagrams in KR can be obtained as coreflections in KR of the limits which are computed in HAUS. In particular:

If X,Y are objects in KR, then their *product* $X \otimes Y$ in the category KR consists of the coreflection of the cartesian product space $X \times Y$ into KR, together with the "usual" projections.

If $f,g: X \to Y$ are morphisms in KR, then their *equalizer* in KR is the inclusion mapping $i: Z \to X$, where $Z := \{x \in X \,\vdots\, f(x) = g(x)\}$ with the usual relative topology inherited from X (closed subspaces of k-spaces are again k-spaces!).

Notice that the forgetful functor KR → SET preserves all products and equalizers; so it preserves all limits and all monomorphisms (cf. 0.4.4). It follows that *monomorphisms* in KR are just the injective morphisms.

Ad (ii): All *colimits* and, consequently, all epimorphisms in KR can be computed in HAUS. In particular, *epimorphisms* in KR are the morphisms with dense ranges.

5.1.3. If X and Y are objects in KR, then $C_{kc}(X,Y)$ shall denote the k-refinement of the space $C_c(X,Y)$). For each triple X,Y,Z of objects in KR one has

(1) $$C_{kc}(Z\otimes Y,X) \cong C_{kc}(Z,C_{kc}(Y,X)).$$

To be more precise: the mapping

(2) $$f \longmapsto \bar{f}: C_{kc}(Z\otimes Y,X) \to C_{kc}(Z,C_{kc}(Y,X))$$

is a homeomorphism (in particular, it is a bijection); here $\bar{f}: Z \to C_{kc}(Y,X)$ is defined by

)1 We shall call X_1 *the k-refinement of X*. Obviously, the topology of X_1 is finer than the topology of X.

(3) $\bar{f}(z) := f^z\colon y \mapsto f(z,y)\colon Y \to X$

($f \in C(Z \otimes Y, X)$). A proof of this statement can be given by taking k-refinements in 0.2.7(iii). A detailed proof can be found in N.E. STEENROD [1967]; cf. also [ML], p.183,184.

5.1.4. The precise meaning of 5.1.3 is the following one (cf. [ML], p.183; however, justification of the following statements can be given easily in a straightforward way).

Fix an object Y in KR. Then the functor $L^Y\colon \mathrm{KR} \to \mathrm{KR}$, defined by

$$(4)\qquad L^Y\colon \begin{cases} Z \mapsto Z \otimes Y & \text{on objects} \\ f \mapsto f \otimes 1_Y & \text{on morphisms} \end{cases}$$

has a right adjoint, namely $R^Y\colon \mathrm{KR} \to \mathrm{KR}$, where

$$(5)\qquad R^Y\colon \begin{cases} X \mapsto C_{kc}(Y,X) & \text{on objects} \\ f \mapsto f \circ - & \text{on morphisms.} \end{cases}$$

The following explanation of notation may be useful. First, if $f_i\colon X_i \to Y_i$ ($i=1,2$) are morphisms in KR, then $f_1 \times f_2\colon (x_1,x_2) \mapsto (f_1x_1, f_2x_2)\colon X_1 \times X_2 \to Y_1 \times Y_2$ is continuous. Taking k-refinements, we obtain a continuous mapping $X_1 \otimes X_2 \to Y_1 \otimes Y_2$, which will be denoted $f_1 \otimes f_2$. Second, if $f\colon X \to Z$ is a morphism, then $f \circ -\colon C_{kc}(Y,X) \to C_{kc}(Y,Z)$ is defined as the mapping $g \mapsto f \circ g$.

Unit and counit of the adjunction of L^Y and R^Y are given, respectively, by $\gamma^Y\colon I_{\mathrm{KR}} \to R^Y L^Y$ and $\delta^Y\colon L^Y R^Y \to I_{\mathrm{KR}}$, where for each object Z in KR

$$(6)\qquad \gamma^Y_Z\colon Z \to C_{kc}(Y, Z \otimes Y);\ \gamma^Y_Z(z)(y) := (z,y)$$

and

$$(7)\qquad \delta^Y_Z\colon C_{kc}(Y,Z) \otimes Y \to Z;\ \delta^Y_Z(f,y) := f(y).$$

5.1.5. Well-known examples of k-spaces are locally compact T_2-spaces and first countable T_2-spaces. In addition, all Hausdorff quotients of k-spaces are again k-spaces. If Y is a locally compact T_2-space and X is a k-space, then $X \otimes Y = X \times Y$, i.e. the cartesian product $X \times Y$ is already a k-space.

In general, for k-spaces X and Y, the topology of $X \otimes Y$ is strictly finer than the topology of $X \times Y$, i.e. $X \times Y$ is not a k-space. Examples can be found in [Du], p.249. Another example is given in 1.5.11.

5.1.6. The following extension of 0.2.4 holds in **KR**: *If* $f\colon X_1 \to Y_1$ *and* $g\colon X_2 \to Y_2$ *are morphisms in* **KR**, *and both* f *and* g *are quotient mappings, then also* $f \otimes g\colon X_1 \otimes X_2 \to Y_1 \otimes Y_2$ *is a quotient mapping.*

For a proof, cf. N.E. STEENROD [1967], Theorem 4.4. Alternatively, it is sufficient to prove this when $Y_1 = Y_2 = Y$ and $g = 1_Y$. In that case, observe that quotient mappings in **KR** are just the coequalizers (just like in **HAUS**, cf. 5.1.2(ii)), and that the functor L^Y of 5.1.4 preserves coequalizers.

5.1.7. Let **KRGRP** denote the following category. Its objects, the *k-groups*, are the groups G having a topology such that G is a k-space and such that

$$(8) \qquad \lambda\colon (s,t) \mapsto st\colon G \otimes G \to G;\; s \mapsto s^{-1}\colon G \to G$$

are continuous. Its morphisms are the continuous morphisms of groups.

If G is a topological group and the underlying topological space of G happens to be a k-space, then plainly $\lambda\colon G \otimes G \to G$ is continuous. Hence G is an object in **KRGRP**. Thus, considering all relevant categories as subcategories of **TOP**, we can express this symbolicaly by

$$(9) \qquad \mathbf{TOPGRP} \cap \mathbf{KR} \subset \mathbf{KRGRP}.$$

It can be shown that equality in (9) would imply that the free topological group of a k-space would be a k-space as well. According to a result of B.V.S. THOMAS [1974] this need not be true. Hence the inclusion in (9) is strict. Obviously, the category in the left hand side of (9) equals **HAUSGRP** $\cap$ **KRGRP**. It is the full subcategory of **HAUSGRP** defined by all its objects which are k-spaces; alternatively, it is the full subcategory of **KRGRP** determined by all its objects with *simultaneously* continuous multiplication.

Thus, in general, if G is a k-space and a group such that the mappings in (8) are continuous, then $\lambda\colon G \times G \to G$ need not be continuous. However, *for any object* G *in* **KRGRP** *the mapping* $\lambda\colon G \times G \to G$ *is separately continuous.* Indeed, if $s \in G$, then $t \mapsto (s,t)\colon G \to G \times G$ is continuous; taking k-refinements we see that the mapping $t \mapsto (s,t)\colon G \to G \otimes G$ is continuous. Hence the composite of this mapping with $\lambda\colon G \otimes G \to G$ is continuous, i.e. $t \mapsto st\colon G \to G$ is continuous. Similarly, $t \mapsto ts\colon G \to G$ is continuous.

5.1.8. It is easy to see that *closed* subgroups of objects in KRGRP (with the usual relative topology) are still in KRGRP. In addition, using the fact that the formation of products in KR is associative, it is a straightforward exercise to show that the product in KR of a set of objects in KRGRP, endowed with coordinate-wise multiplication, is an object in KRGRP. These observations show, that *the forgetful functor* KRGRP → KR *creates all limits. In particular,* KRGRP *is complete, and limits and monomorphisms can be calculated in* KR (as topological spaces).

Moreover, the forgetful functor KRGRP → GRP has a left adjoint (assigning to each group the group itself with the discrete topology), hence it preserves all limits, in accordance with what we found above.

5.1.9. The coreflector of HAUS into KR induces a functor M: HAUSGRP → KRGRP. Indeed, if G is an object in HAUSGRP, then the k-refinement G_1 of G equals G as a set, hence it can be given the same group structure as G. Let MG denote the space G_1 with this group structure. Since the mappings $(s,t) \longmapsto st$: $G \times G \to G$ and $t \longmapsto t^{-1}$: $G \to G$ are continuous, it follows that $(s,t) \longmapsto st$: $MG \otimes MG \to MG$ and $t \longmapsto t^{-1}$: $MG \to MG$ are continuous, i.e. MG is an object in KRGRP. Moreover, if ψ: $G \to H$ is a morphism in HAUSGRP, then obviously ψ: $MG \to MH$ is continuous, so ψ can be interpreted as a morphism in KRGRP; in doing so, we shall denote it with $M\psi$. In this way a functor M: HAUSGRP → KRGRP is defined. Clearly, M is a faithful functor.

Since the coreflector of HAUS into KR preserves all limits, it follows easily that M: HAUSGRP → KRGRP preserves all limits (use the descriptions of limits in these categories, given in 0.4.11 and 5.1.8). Now we can apply the FREYD adjoint functor theorem (cf. [ML], p.117) to the effect that M *has a left adjoint* N: KRGRP → HAUSGRP. Without any reference to the FREYD adjoint functor theorem, the left adjoint N of M and the corresponding unit of adjunction υ can be obtained in the following way. If G is an object in KRGRP, let $\{T_i : i \in J\}$ be the set of all topologies on G such that (G, T_i) is a topological group and T_i is weaker than the original topology on G (such topologies do exist; e.g. consider the indiscrete topology on G). Let T be the weakest topology on G which is finer than all topologies T_i. Obviously, (G,T) is a topological group (it is the diagonal in $\mathbb{P}_i(G,T_i)$). Set $N'G :=$ (G,T). Obviously, the underlying groups of G and N'G are identical; only the topologies are different. If ψ: $G \to H$ is a morphism in KRGRP then the weakest topology on G making ψ: $G \to N'H$ continuous makes G a topological group and is weaker than the original topology on G. It follows that ψ:

N'G→N'H is continuous. In this way, we obtain a functor N': KRGRP→TOPGRP. Notice that for each object G in KRGRP, 1_G: G→N'G is continuous. Now let N be the composition of N' with the reflector of TOPGRP to HAUSGRP. Then N is left adjoint to the functor M. The unit υ of the adjunction is given by the morphism υ_G: G→MNG, where considered as a mapping, υ_G coincides with the reflection of N'G into HAUSGRP. The straightforward proof is left to the reader.

5.1.10. Many questions about the category KRGRP are left undiscussed here. For example, using 5.1.8, it can be shown that the forgetful functor KRGRP → KR has a left adjoint (the "free k-group functor"). In addition, it can be shown that *the category* KRGRP *is cocomplete*. The existence of coproducts in KRGRP can be shown similar to the existence of coproducts in TOPGRP (see e.g. Theorem 1 in E.T. ORDMAN [1974]). The coequalizer of ψ_1,ψ_2: G→H in KRGRP can be obtained as follows: let q: H→K_0 be the coequalizer of ψ_1,ψ_2 in GRP, give K_0 the quotient topology, induced by q and, finally, let q_0: K_0 → K be the reflection of K_0 in HAUS. Then K is a k-group, and q_0q: H→K is the desired coequalizer. Details will appear elsewhere.

5.2. The category k-TTG

5.2.1. If (G,X) is an object in KRGRP × KR, then the mappings

(1) $$\eta_X^G\colon X\to G\times X;\ \mu_X^G\colon (G\otimes G)\times X\to G\times X,$$

which are defined according to 1.1.1, are continuous. Taking the coreflections in KR of these mappings, we obtain the following morphisms in KR:

(2) $$\eta_X^G\colon X\to G\otimes X;\ \mu_X^G\colon G\otimes(G\otimes X)\to G\otimes X.$$

{Note that it is permitted to identify G ⊗ (G⊗X) with (G⊗G) ⊗ X.}

5.2.2. Let (G,X) be an object in KRGRP × KR. Then *a k-action of* G *on* X is a morphism π: G⊗X→X in KR such that the following diagrams in KR commute:

$$\begin{array}{ccc} X & \xrightarrow{\eta_X^G} & G\otimes X \\ & {\scriptstyle 1_X}\searrow & \downarrow{\scriptstyle \pi} \\ & & X \end{array} \qquad \begin{array}{ccc} G\otimes(G\otimes X) & \xrightarrow{1_G\otimes\pi} & G\otimes X \\ {\scriptstyle \mu_X^G}\downarrow & & \downarrow{\scriptstyle \pi} \\ G\otimes X & \xrightarrow[\pi]{} & X \end{array}$$

A *k-topological transformation group* (abbreviated: a *k-ttg*) is a triple $[G,X,\pi]$ with (G,X) an object in **KRGRP** $\times$ **KR** and π a k-action of G on X.

All terminology and notation concerning ordinary ttgs will also be used for k-ttgs, as far as it is meaningful. Thus, we may speak about transitions, motions, orbits, etc., of k-ttgs. Formally, the definitions are the same as for ordinary ttgs.

5.2.3. <u>PROPOSITION</u>. *If* $[G,X,\pi]$ *is a k-ttg then* $\pi\colon G\times X\to X$ *is separately continuous. Consequently, the transition mapping* $\bar{\pi}\colon t\mapsto \pi^t$ *defines a morphism of groups from* G *into* $H(X,X)$.

<u>PROOF</u>. For each $(t,x)\in G\times X$, the mappings $y\mapsto (t,y)\colon X\to G\times X$ and $s\mapsto (s,x)\colon G\to G\times X$ are continuous. Taking k-refinements, we obtain the continuous mappings $y\mapsto (t,y)\colon X\to G\otimes X$ and $s\mapsto (s,x)\colon G\to G\otimes X$. The compositions of these mappings with the continuous function $\pi\colon G\otimes X\to X$ just equal $\pi^t\colon X\to X$ and $\pi_x\colon G\to X$, respectively. Consequently, π^t and π_x are continuous. □

5.2.4. For any k-ttg $[G,X,\pi]$, π is an action of G_d on X, so that we can speak about the ttg $\langle G_d,X,\pi\rangle$; this is immediate from 5.2.3.

On the other hand, if $(G,X)\in$ (**HAUSGRP** $\cap$ **KRGRP**) $\times$ **KR** is given, and if $\pi\colon G\times X\to X$ is an action of G on X, then $\pi\colon G\otimes X\to X$ is continuous, hence π is a k-action. *So for any ttg* $\langle G,X,\pi\rangle$ *with* $(G,X)\in$ **KRGRP** $\times$ **KR**, *we can speak about the k-ttg* $[G,X,\pi]$.

5.2.5. We shall present now an example which shows that a k-ttg may not be a ttg, even if the phase group is a topological group. First, however, we make the following useful observation: *if* $[G,X,\pi]$ *is a k-ttg and if* G *is a locally compact* T_2*-space, then* π *is an action of* G *on* X, *and we have also the ttg* $\langle G,X,\pi\rangle$. The proof of this observation is a trivial consequence of the fact that now $G\otimes X = G\times X$ (cf. 5.1.5), whereas G is a topological group.

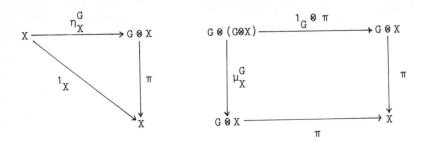

Here follows the example of a k-action of an object in **HAUSGRP** $\cap$ **KR**

on a k-space which is not an action:

For any k-space Z, the mapping $\mu_Z^{\mathbb{Q}}:(s,t,z)\mapsto(s+t,z)\colon \mathbb{Q}\otimes(\mathbb{Q}\otimes Z)\to\mathbb{Q}\otimes Z$ is continuous, i.e. we have the k-ttg $[\mathbb{Q},\mathbb{Q}\otimes Z,\mu_Z^{\mathbb{Q}}]$ (notice that $\mathbb{Q}$ is metrizable, hence a k-space). *Next, take for* Z *the space* $\mathbb{Q}\boxtimes(X/R)$, *considered in* 1.5.11. We have seen in the *Remark* in 1.5.11, that $\mathbb{Q}\times Z$ is not a k-space. Similar to the proof in 1.5.11 one shows that $\mu_Z^{\mathbb{Q}}\colon \mathbb{Q}\times(\mathbb{Q}\otimes Z)\to\mathbb{Q}\otimes Z$ is not continuous (otherwise $(s,0,y)\mapsto(s,y)\colon \mathbb{Q}\times A\to\mathbb{Q}\otimes Z$ would be continuous, where $A := \{(0,y) : y\in Z\}$ may be identified with Z). *So* $\mu_Z^{\mathbb{Q}}$ *is not an action of* $\mathbb{Q}$ *on* $\mathbb{Q}\otimes Z$.

5.2.6. If $[G,X,\pi]$ and $[H,Y,\sigma]$ are k-ttgs, then *a morphism of k-ttgs* $[\psi,f]\colon [G,X,\pi]\to[H,Y,\sigma]$ is a morphism $(\psi,f)\colon (G,X)\to(H,Y)$ in **KRGRP** × **KR** such that the following diagram commutes:

$$\begin{array}{ccc} G\otimes X & \xrightarrow{\ \pi\ } & X \\ \Big\downarrow{\scriptstyle \psi\otimes f} & & \Big\downarrow{\scriptstyle f} \\ H\otimes Y & \xrightarrow[\ \sigma\ ]{} & Y \end{array}$$

So $[\psi,f]\colon [G,X,\pi]\to[H,Y,\sigma]$ is a morphism of k-ttgs iff $\langle\psi,f\rangle\colon \langle G_d,X,\pi\rangle\to\langle H_d,Y,\sigma\rangle$ is a morphism of ttgs and $\psi\colon G\to H$ is continuous. *If we consider only locally compact T_2 phase groups, then the concept of a morphism of k-ttgs is equivalent to that of a morphism of ttgs* (cf. also the remark in 5.2.5).

5.2.7. Let **k-TTG** denote the category whose objects are the k-ttgs of definition 5.2.2, and whose morphisms are the morphisms of k-ttgs, defined in 5.2.6. As composition of morphisms in **k-TTG** we shall use the operation which is defined similar to the composition in **TTG**: if $[\psi,f]\colon [G,X,\pi]\to[H,Y,\sigma]$ and $[\varphi,g]\colon [H,Y,\sigma]\to[K,Z,\zeta]$ are morphisms in **k-TTG**, then

(5) $$[\varphi,g]\circ[\psi,f] := [\varphi\psi,gf] : [G,X,\pi]\to[K,Z,\zeta]$$

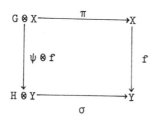

(this is plainly a morphism in k-TTG).

5.2.8. In order to make the notation not too complicated, we shall denote the obvious forgetful functors from k-TTG to KRGRP and KR simply by G and S, respectively (there seems to be no danger of confusion with the notation of 3.1.2). Thus, G and S are defined by

$$(6)\qquad G:\begin{cases}[G,X,\pi]\longmapsto G & \text{on objects;}\\ [\psi,f]\longmapsto \psi & \text{on morphisms;}\end{cases}\qquad S:\begin{cases}[G,X,\pi]\longmapsto X & \text{on objects;}\\ [\psi,f]\longmapsto f & \text{on morphisms.}\end{cases}$$

In addition, let K: k-TTG → KRGRP×KR be defined by

$$(7)\qquad K:\begin{cases}[G,X,\pi]\longmapsto (G,X) & \text{on objects}\\ [\psi,f]\longmapsto (\psi,f) & \text{on morphisms.}\end{cases}$$

5.2.9. In the remainder of this subsection, the category KRGRP × KR will be denoted by C. Let us consider the functor $H\colon C\to C$ which is defined in the following way:

$$(8)\qquad H:\begin{cases}(G,X)\longmapsto (G,G\otimes X) & \text{on objects}\\ (\psi,f)\longmapsto (\psi,\psi\otimes f) & \text{on morphisms.}\end{cases}$$

Then we have natural transformations $\eta\colon I_C\to H$ and $\mu\colon H^2\to H$, where for each object (G,X) in the category C,

$$(9)\qquad \begin{aligned}\eta_{(G,X)} &:= (1_G,\eta_X^G)\colon (G,X)\to(G,G\otimes X)\\ \mu_{(G,X)} &:= (1_G,\mu_X^G)\colon (G,G\otimes(G\otimes X))\to(G,G\otimes X).\end{aligned}$$

Then (H,η,μ) *is a monad.* As in subsection 3.1 it is easy to determine the H-algebras: they correspond uniquely to the k-ttgs [G,X,π]. In fact, *the category of all* H*-algebras is isomorphic to the category* k-TTG. If we identify these categories, the functor K coincides with the standard forgetful functor from the category of all H-algebras to the category C. Consequently, we obtain the following statements as corollaries of the general theory of monads (cf. 0.4.6 and 0.4.7):

First, the functor K has a left adjoint, namely the functor F: C → k-TTG, where

$$F:\begin{cases}(G,X)\longmapsto [G,G\otimes X,\mu_X^G] & \text{on objects}\\ (\psi,f)\longmapsto [\psi,\psi\otimes f] & \text{on morphisms.}\end{cases}$$

Here $[G, G\otimes X, \mu_X^G]$ is called *the free k-ttg on* G *and* X. The unit and counit of the adjunction of F and K are η and ξ, respectively, where η is as above, and ξ is the natural transformation ξ: FK → $I_{k\text{-TTG}}$, defined by

$$\xi_{[G,X,\pi]} := [1_G, \pi]: [G, G\otimes X, \mu_X^G] \to [G,X,\pi]$$

for every object [G,X,π] in k-TTG.

Second, the functor K creates all limits in k-TTG. Since KRGRP and KR are complete, *it follows that* k-TTG *is complete*; in addition, K preserves all limits and K preserves and reflects all monomorphisms. *Shortly, limits and monomorphisms in* k-TTG *can be computed in* C.

5.2.10. It is a rather annoying exercise to determine which properties of the category TTG carry over to the category k-TTG. There seem to arise no difficulties from the fact that in objects of KRGRP multiplication is perhaps not simultaneously continuous. Indeed, in §3 simultane continuity of multiplication in the phase groups of objects in TTG has been used only in subsection 3.1 (continuity of μ_X^G). However, we have seen above that the results of subsection 3.1 do carry over to k-TTG.

In our next subsection, we briefly deal with $k\text{-KR}^G$, the analog of TOP^G. Here the situation turns out to be even better than in TOP^G (cf. subsection 3.2) as far as it concerns colimits. Consequently, we do not need the analog of subsection 3.3 in order to show that $k\text{-KR}^G$ behaves nicely with respect to colimits. Yet we shall see that a version of 3.3.11 is valid (cf. 5.3.8). This will be used, similar to the method in subsection 3.4, that the category k-TTG is cocomplete. First, however, we want to make a few remarks on epimorphisms.

5.2.11. Similar to 3.4.9 one can show that *the functor* G: k-TTG → KRGRP *has a right adjoint; hence* G *preserves all colimits and* G *preserves and reflects all epimorphisms*. Now the proof of 4.1.10 can be adapted to the present case, showing the following statement:

If epimorphisms in KRGRP *have dense ranges*)1 *then the functor* K: k-TTG → C *preserves and reflects epimorphisms*.

)1 Recently it has been announced by W.F. LAMARTIN that this conjecture is false. So it is still an open problem whether K preserves epimorphisms.

In the proof of this statement (which we leave to the reader), one has to use the following version of 1.5.10: *if* $[G,Y,\sigma]$ *is a k-ttg and* A *is a closed invariant subset of* Y, *then there exists a unique k-action* τ *of* G *on* $Y \cup_A Y$ *making the canonical injections* $f_1, f_2: Y \to Y \cup_A Y$ *equivariant.* The difficulty in proving this is of course not that $Y \cup_A Y$ is a k-space (it is a T_2-space and it is the quotient of a k-space, viz. the disjoint union of Y with itself.). The problem is that the unique action τ of G_d on $Y \cup_A Y$ has to be shown to be a k-action of G on $Y \cup_A Y$, i.e. $\tau: G\otimes(Y\cup_A Y) \to Y \cup_A Y$ is continuous. The proof is similar to the one in 1.5.10, except that the reference to 1.5.7(ii) has to be replaced by a reference to the following statement (since we are given only a k-action of G on X, we cannot apply 1.5.7(iv)!):

5.2.12. *Let* $[G,X,\pi]$ *be a k-ttg and let* R *be an invariant equivalence relation in* X *such that* X/R *is a* T_2*-space, i.e. the quotient mapping* $q: X \to X/R$ *is a morphism in* **KR**. *Then there exists a unique k-action* τ *of* G *on* X/R *making* $[1_G, q]$ *a morphism in* **k-TTG**.

The proof is as follows: let τ be the action of G_d on X/R making q equivariant. The only thing that has to be shown is that $\tau: G\otimes(X/R) \to X/R$ is continuous. Obviously, $\tau\circ(1_G\otimes q) = q\circ\pi: G\otimes X \to X$ is continuous. By 5.1.6, $1_G\otimes q: G\otimes X \to G\otimes(X/R)$ is a quotient mapping. Hence $\tau: G\otimes(X/R) \to X/R$ is continuous.

5.2.13. We shall see in 5.3.8 below that the following analog of 3.3.11 holds: *if* $\psi: H \to G$ *is a morphism in* **KRGRP**, *then there exists for each object* $[H,Y,\sigma]$ *in* **k-TTG** *an arrow* $[\psi,f]: [H,Y,\sigma] \to [G,X,\pi]$ *in* **k-TTG** *which is "universal" for all morphisms* $[\psi,g]$ *in* **k-TTG** *with domain* $[H,Y,\sigma]$.[1]

Using this, the proof in 3.4.12 can be modified in such a way that we obtain a proof of the following theorem:

5.2.14. <u>THEOREM</u>. *The category* **k-TTG** *is cocomplete.* □

5.2.15. Although **k-TTG** turns out to be cocomplete, the functor S: **k-TTG** → **KR** does *not* preserve all colimits. This can be shown similar to 3.4.12: the construction of colimits in **k-TTG** is completely similar to the construction of colimits in **TTG**.

---

[1] Here "universal" has the same modified meaning as in 3.3.11 (viz. uniqueness is only with respect to $\mathbf{k\text{-}KR}^H$).

5.3. The category k-KR^G

5.3.1. Fix an object G in KRGRP. Then k-KR^G will denote the subcategory of k-TTG, determined by all objects $[G,X,\pi]$ and all morphisms of the form $[1_G,f]$ [1]. Most facts about the category TOP^G carry over to k-KR^G. In particular, if the functor S^G: k-$KR^G \to KR$ is defined by

$$(1)\qquad S^G: \begin{cases} [G,X,\pi] \mapsto X \text{ on objects} \\ [1_G,f] \mapsto f \text{ on morphisms,} \end{cases}$$

then we obtain the following proposition:

5.3.2. PROPOSITION. *The functor* S^G: k-$KR^G \to KR$ *creates all limits. In particular,* k-KR^G *is a complete category, and* S^G *preserves all limits. In addition,* S^G *preserves and reflects all monomorphisms.*

PROOF. Consider a suitable monad in KR. Cf. 5.2.9. □

5.3.3. PROPOSITION. *The functor* S^G: k-$KR^G \to KR$ *creates all colimits. In particular,* k-KR^G *is a cocomplete category, and* S^G *preserves all colimits. In addition,* S^G *preserves and reflects all epimorphisms.*

PROOF. It is sufficient to show that S^G creates all colimits. This will be done in 6.2.11. We shall show there that k-KR^G may be identified with the category of all coalgebras for a suitable comonad in KR. □

5.3.4. We shall present now two situations in which k-ttgs are just ttgs.

(i) Let G be a *locally compact* T_2 *topological group*. Then for each k-space X, $G \otimes X = G \times X$, hence *the category* k-KR^G *just equals the category* KR^G, *the full subcategory of* TOP^G *determined by all G-spaces with a k-space as a phase space.* So by the previous propositions, *all limits, colimits, monomorphisms and epimorphisms in* KR^G *can be computed in* KR. In particular, since colimits and epimorphisms in KR can be computed in HAUS, all colimits and epimorphisms in KR^G can be computed in HAUS. The reader should compare this result with 3.4.3.

---

[1] Observe that notating KR^G would contradict the terminology of subsection 4.1. Indeed, according to 4.1.1, KR^G would denote a subcategory of TTG (i.e. simultaneously continuous actions!).

(ii) Let G be any object in HAUSGRP ∩ KRGRP. Then for any compact Hausdorff space X, $G \otimes X = G \times X$, hence the full subcategory k-COMP^G of k-KR^G, determined by all k-ttgs with compact Hausdorff phase spaces coincides with the subcategory COMP^G of $\text{KR}^G \subseteq \text{TOP}^G$. {We have seen in 4.2.7, that all limits, monomorphisms, epimorphisms, and all colimits of finite diagrams in COMP^G can be computed in COMP. Hence a similar statement holds for k-COMP^G, thus providing a certain extension of the propositions 5.3.2 and 5.3.3 to a particular subcategory of k-KR^G.}

5.3.5. Let $\psi: H \to G$ be a morphism in KRGRP. For each k-ttg $[G,X,\pi]$, set $\pi^\psi := \pi \circ (\psi \otimes 1_X)$. Then π^ψ is easily seen to be a k-action of H on X. Thus, we can define a functor R_ψ: $\text{k-KR}^G \to \text{k-KR}^H$ by

$$R_\psi: \begin{cases} [G,X,\pi] \longmapsto [H,X,\pi^\psi] & \text{on objects} \\ [1_G,f] \longmapsto [1_H,f] & \text{on morphisms.} \end{cases}$$

(cf. also 3.3.1).

If $[\psi,f]: [H,Y,\sigma] \to [G,X,\pi]$ is any morphism in k-TTG, then $[1_H,f]$: $[H,Y,\sigma] \to [H,X,\pi^\psi]$ and $[\psi,1_X]: [H,X,\pi^\psi] \to [G,X,\pi]$ are morphisms in k-TTG, and $[\psi,f] = [\psi,1_X] \circ [1_H,f]$ (compare this with 3.3.3).

Plainly, R_ψ preserves all limits (apply 5.3.2 to k-KH^G and to k-KH^H). Since KR is a colocally small category (it is a subcategory of HAUS), k-KR^H is colocally small, hence the *solution set condition* in FREYD's adjoint functor theorem is satisfied. Consequently, we obtain the following theorem.

5.3.6. THEOREM. *Let* $\psi: H \to G$ *be a morphism in* KRGRP. *Then the functor* R_ψ: $\text{k-KR}^G \to \text{k-KR}^H$ *has a left adjoint* L_ψ.

PROOF. Cf. the preceding remark. □

5.3.7. We can also repeat the construction of 3.3.5 through 3.3.7, replacing × by ⊗, <...> by [...], etc. We obtain in that way a k-action $\rho: H\otimes(G\otimes Y) \to G\otimes Y$ commuting with the k-action μ_Y^G of G on $G \otimes Y$. So if $(G\otimes Y)/C_\rho$ were a k-space everything could be proved as in 3.3.5 up to 3.3.7 (using 5.2.12 instead of 1.5.8!). But $(G\otimes Y)/C_\rho$ may be not a T_2-space, hence not a k-space. However, it is a quotient space of a k-space. Hence, if g: $(G\otimes Y)/C_\rho \to Z$ is its Hausdorff reflection, then Z is a k-space (g is a quotient mapping). Similar to the proof of 4.4.2 one shows that the equivalence relation on $(G\otimes Y)/C_\rho$ induced by g is invariant under the k-action of G on $(G\otimes Y)/C_\rho$. So 5.2.12 again implies that there is a unique k-action ζ of G on Z making g equivariant. Then $[1_H, gf]: [H,Y,\sigma] \to [G,Z,\zeta^\psi]$ is the desired universal morphism (f as in 3.3.6).

5.3.8. COROLLARY. *Let* $\psi: H \to G$ *be a morphism in* KRGRP *and let* $[H,Y,\sigma]$ *be an object in* k-TTG. *Then there exists an arrow* $[\psi,h]: [H,Y,\sigma] \to [G,Z,\zeta]$ *in* k-TTG *which is "universal"*[1] *for the class of all arrows in* k-TTG *with domain* $[H,Y,\sigma]$ *and with group component* ψ.

PROOF. The arrow $[\psi,h]$ is the composite of $[\psi,1_X]: [H,X,\pi^\psi] \to [G,Z,\zeta] := \mathsf{L}_\psi[H,Y,\sigma]$ and the universal arrow $[1_H,h]: [H,Y,\sigma] \to [H,Z,\zeta^\psi] = \mathsf{R}_\psi\mathsf{L}_\psi[H,Y,\sigma]$, arising from the adjunction of L_ψ and R_ψ. See also the proof of 3.3.11. □

[1] Cf. the footnote to 5.2.13.

6 - THE CATEGORIES TTG_* AND k-TTG_*

In subsection 6.1 we consider the category TTG_*, defined in 1.4.16. Although the obvious forgetful functor K_*: $TTG_* \to TOPGRP^{op} \times TOP$ preserves all colimits, the category TTG_* turns out to be not cocomplete. In addition, it is not complete. Then, in subsection 6.2, we consider the category k-TTG_* of all k-ttgs (i.e. the objects of k-TTG) and all comorphisms between k-ttgs. The category k-TTG_* turns out to be isomorphic to the category of all coalgebras over a suitable comonad. This implies that all colimits can easily be computed. The same methods with similar results can be applied to the categories k-KR^G (with G a k-group) and TOP^G (with G a locally compact Hausdorff group). Incidentally, this provides an explanation for some previously obtained theorems on ttgs with locally compact phase groups (cf. subsection 6.3). Moreover, this forms the basis for some statements about cogenerators (having locally compact phase groups) in TTG_*. This, in turn, will place our considerations in the next section in their proper context. In addition, the result on cogenerators is used in the proof that TTG_* is not complete.

6.1. The category TTG_*

6.1.1. In this section, let A := TOPGRP and B := TOP. Then to the category A we may associate *the opposite category* A^{op}. The objects of A^{op} are the objects of A, the morphisms in A^{op} are arrows ψ^{op}, in a one-one correspondence $\psi \mapsto \psi^{op}$ with the morphisms ψ in A. For each morphism ψ: $G \to H$ in A, the domain and the codomain of the corresponding ψ^{op} are H and G, respectively, so that ψ^{op}: $H \to G$ (the direction is reversed). The composite $\psi^{op}\varphi^{op} := (\varphi\psi)^{op}$ is defined in A^{op} exactly when the composite $\varphi\psi$ is defined in A. Moreover, ψ^{op} is a monomorphism in A^{op} iff ψ is an epimorphism in A, α^{op}: $G \to D^{op}$ is a limiting cone for a diagram D^{op}: $J^{op} \to A^{op}$ iff α: $D \to G$ is a colimiting cone for the diagram D: $J \to A$ (here J^{op} is the opposite category of J, and $D^{op}_j :=$ D_j for every object $j \in J^{op}$, $D^{op}\xi^{op} := (D\xi)^{op}$ for every morphism ξ^{op} in J^{op}), and so on.

6.1.2. If $\langle G,X,\pi\rangle$ and $\langle H,Y,\sigma\rangle$ are ttgs, then a *comorphism* $\langle\psi^{op},f\rangle: \langle G,X,\pi\rangle \to \langle H,Y,\sigma\rangle$ is a morphism $(\psi^{op},f): (G,X) \to (H,Y)$ in $\mathsf{A}\times\mathsf{B}$ for which the following diagram in B commutes for every $t \in H$[)1]:

$$(1)\qquad \begin{array}{ccc} X & \xrightarrow{\;\pi^{\psi(t)}\;} & X \\ \Big\downarrow f & & \Big\downarrow f \\ Y & \xrightarrow{\;\sigma^{t}\;} & Y \end{array} \qquad\qquad \begin{array}{c} G \\ \Big\uparrow \psi \\ H \end{array}$$

The *composite* of two comorphisms $\langle\psi^{op},f\rangle: \langle G,X,\pi\rangle \to \langle H,Y,\sigma\rangle$ and $\langle\eta^{op},g\rangle: \langle H',Y',\sigma'\rangle \to \langle K,Z,\zeta\rangle$ is defined iff $\langle H,Y,\sigma\rangle = \langle H',Y',\sigma'\rangle$; in that case, the composite is the comorphism $\langle\eta^{op},g\rangle \circ \langle\psi^{op},f\rangle := \langle\eta^{op}\psi^{op},gf\rangle: \langle G,X,\pi\rangle \to \langle K,Z,\zeta\rangle$.

6.1.3. Let TTG_* denote the category whose objects are the ordinary ttgs (i.e. the objects of TTG) and whose morphisms are the comorphisms, defined in 6.1.2. In addition, let composition of comorphisms be defined as in 6.1.2.

We have the following "forgetful" functors from TTG_* to $\mathsf{A}^{op}\times\mathsf{B}$, A^{op} and B, respectively:

$$K_*: \mathsf{TTG}_* \to \mathsf{A}^{op}\times\mathsf{B},$$

$$G_*: \mathsf{TTG}_* \to \mathsf{A}^{op}, \quad S_*: \mathsf{TTG}_* \to \mathsf{B},$$

where

$$K_*: \begin{cases} \langle G,X,\pi\rangle \longmapsto (G,X) & \text{on objects} \\ \langle\psi^{op},f\rangle \longmapsto (\psi^{op},f) & \text{on morphisms} \end{cases}$$

$$G_*: \begin{cases} \langle G,X,\pi\rangle \longmapsto G & \text{on objects} \\ \langle\psi^{op},f\rangle \longmapsto \psi^{op} & \text{on morphisms} \end{cases}$$

$$S_*: \begin{cases} \langle G,X,\pi\rangle \longmapsto X & \text{on objects} \\ \langle\psi^{op},f\rangle \longmapsto f & \text{on morphisms.} \end{cases}$$

)1 Obviously, this definition is equivalent with the one, given in 1.4.14.

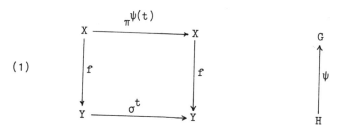

6.1.4. Concerning the preservation and reflection properties of the above defined functors, we have the following trivial observations:

(i) $\langle\psi^{op},f\rangle$ is an isomorphism in $\mathbf{TTG}_*$ iff ψ^{op} is an isomorphism in $\mathbf{A}^{op}$ (i.e. ψ an isomorphism in $\mathbf{A}$) and f is an isomorphism in $\mathbf{B}$ (i.e. f is a homeomorphism).

(ii) K_* is faithful, so K_* reflects monomorphisms and epimorphisms. For example, if $\langle\psi^{op},f\rangle$ is a morphism in $\mathbf{TTG}_*$ and we know that ψ^{op} is monic in $\mathbf{A}^{op}$ (i.e. ψ is epic in $\mathbf{TOPGRP}$) and that f is monic in $\mathbf{B}$, then it follows that $\langle\psi^{op},f\rangle$ is monic in $\mathbf{TTG}_*$.

6.1.5. Obviously, most of the methods in §3 fail if we want to apply them to $\mathbf{TTG}_*$. For instance, there is no natural way to associate to a comorphism $\langle\psi^{op},f\rangle$: $\langle G,X,\pi\rangle \to \langle H,Y,\sigma\rangle$ a morphism $G\times X \to H\times Y$ in $\mathbf{TOP}$ (we only have $\psi\times f$: $H\times X \to G\times Y$, where the phase spaces are multiplied by the wrong groups). There is one proof (viz. the proof of 3.4.9) which can easily be adapted to the present situation:

6.1.6. PROPOSITION. *The covariant functor* G_*: $\mathbf{TTG}_* \to \mathbf{A}^{op}$ *has a right adjoint. Consequently,* G_* *preserves colimits and epimorphisms.*

PROOF. Similar to the proof of 3.4.9. □

6.1.7. PROPOSITION. *The covariant functor* S_*: $\mathbf{TTG}_* \to \mathbf{B}$ *has a right adjoint. Consequently,* S_* *preserves colimits and epimorphisms.*

PROOF. The idea of proof is the same as in 3.4.15. Let the functor R_*: $\mathbf{B} \to \mathbf{TTG}_*$ be defined as follows. Fix a one-point group E. For any object X in $\mathbf{B}$, let τ_X denote the trivial action of E on X, and set $\mathsf{R}_*X := \langle E,X,\tau_X\rangle$. If f: $X \to Y$ is a morphism in $\mathbf{B}$, then $\langle 1_E^{op},f\rangle$: $\langle E,X,\tau_X\rangle \to \langle E,Y,\tau_Y\rangle$ is a comorphism, denoted by R_*f. Then R_* is a covariant functor, and the following diagram shows that R_* is right adjoint to S_*:

(2)

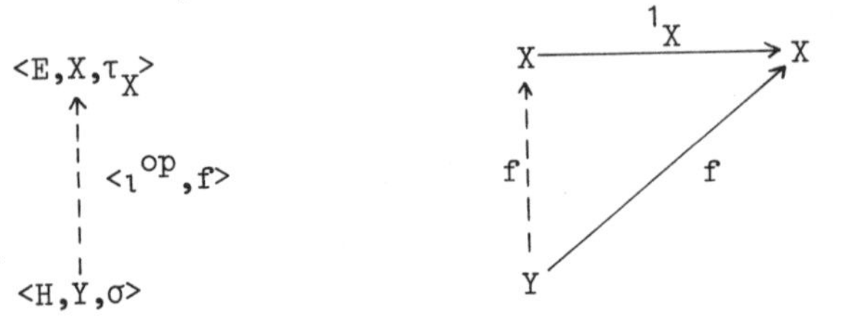

In this diagram, ι^{op}: $H \to E$ is associated to the morphism ι: $E \to H$ in $\mathbf{A}$, where $\iota[E] = \{e\}$. □

6.1.8. <u>COROLLARY</u>. *The functor* K_*: $TTG_* \to A^{op} \times B$ *preserves colimits and epimorphisms.*

<u>PROOF</u>. Use 6.1.6 and 6.1.7 (cf. also 3.1.3). □

6.1.9. We shall show now, that a set of objects in TTG_* always has a *coproduct*. Using 6.1.8, we can easily compute its phase group and its phase space. However, we shall show a little bit more:

6.1.10. <u>PROPOSITION</u>. *The functor* K_*: $TTG_* \to A^{op} \times B$ *creates all coproducts. Consequently,* TTG_* *has all coproducts.*

<u>PROOF</u>. Let $\{\langle G_i, X_i, \pi_i\rangle : i \in J\}$ be a set of objects in TTG_*. The coproduct in $A^{op} \times B$ of the set $\{(G_i, X_i) : i \in J\}$ is formed by the object (G,X) and the coprojections (p_i^{op}, r_i): $(G_i, X_i) \to (G,X)$. Here $G := \mathbb{P}_j G_j$, the product of the groups G_j in A, with projections p_i: $G \to G_i$, and $X := \Sigma_j X_j$, the coproduct of the spaces X_j in B, with coprojections r_i: $X_i \to X$. For each $i \in J$, we can form the object $\langle G, X_i, \pi_i^{p_i}\rangle$ in TOP^G and then we can form the coproduct $\langle G,X,\pi\rangle$ of the set $\{\langle G, X_i, \pi_i^{p_i}\rangle : i \in J\}$ in TOP^G. Now π is easily seen to be the unique action of G on X making each (p_i^{op}, r_i) a comorphism, i.e. a morphism $\langle p_i^{op}, r_i\rangle$: $\langle G_i, X_i, \pi_i\rangle \to \langle G,X,\pi\rangle$ in TTG_*. Finally, a straightforward argument shows that $\langle G,X,\pi\rangle$ is the desired coproduct in TTG_*, with coprojections $\langle p_i^{op}, r_i\rangle$. □

6.1.11. It follows immediately from 6.1.8 that the coequalizer of $\langle \psi_1^{op}, f_1\rangle$, $\langle \psi_2^{op}, f_2\rangle$: $\langle G,X,\pi\rangle \to \langle H,Y,\sigma\rangle$ in TTG_*, *if it exists*, is of the form $\langle \iota^{op}, q\rangle$: $\langle H,Y,\sigma\rangle \to \langle K,Z,\zeta\rangle$ with ι: $K \to H$ the equalizer in A of ψ_1, ψ_2: $H \to G$ and q: $Y \to Z$ the coequalizer in B of f_1, f_2: $X \to Y$.

In particular, if the morphisms $\langle 1_G^{op}, f_1\rangle, \langle 1_G^{op}, f_2\rangle$: $\langle G,X,\pi\rangle \to \langle G,Y,\sigma\rangle$ in TTG_* have a coequalizer, then it is of the form $\langle 1_G^{op}, q\rangle$: $\langle G,Y,\sigma\rangle \to \langle G,Z,\zeta\rangle$, where q: $Y \to Z$ is the coequalizer in B of f_1, f_2: $X \to Y$. Plainly, ζ is the unique (cf. 1.5.5) action of G on Z making the *quotient mapping* q a morphism of G spaces. Consequently, the example in 3.4.4 shows that *not all parallel pairs of morphisms in* TTG_* *have a coequalizer.*

6.1.12. <u>PROPOSITION</u>. *The functor* K_*: $TTG_* \to A^{op} \times B$ *creates all coequalizers of parallel pairs* $\langle \psi_i^{op}, f_i\rangle$: $\langle G,X,\pi\rangle \to \langle H,Y,\sigma\rangle$ $(i=1,2)$ *of morphisms in* TTG_* *for which* G *is a* T_2*-group and* H *is locally compact* T_2.

<u>PROOF</u>. The equalizer of ψ_1, ψ_2: $H \to G$ in A is ι: $K \to H$, where K is the closed (hence locally compact!) subgroup $\{t \in H : \psi_1(t) = \psi_2(t)\}$ of H, and ι is the inclusion mapping. The coequalizer of f_1, f_2: $X \to Y$ in B is a quotient mapping

say $q\colon Y \to Z$.

Consider the ttg $\langle K,Y,\sigma\rangle$ (we use here the convention of 1.3.4). We shall show that there exists an (obviously unique) action ζ of K_d on Z making q an equivariant mapping. To this end, observe that for all $t \in K$,

$$q\sigma^t f_1 = qf_1\pi^{\psi_1(t)} = qf_2\pi^{\psi_2(t)} = q\sigma^t f_2.$$

Since q is the coequalizer of f_1 and f_2, it follows that there exists a unique continuous mapping $\zeta^t\colon Z \to Z$ such that $\zeta^t q = q\sigma^t$. It is easy to see that in this way we obtain the desired action ζ of K_d on Z.

Since K is locally compact, 1.5.7(iv) implies that $\zeta\colon K\times Z \to Z$ is continuous. Hence ζ is the unique action of K on Z for which $\langle \iota^{op},q\rangle\colon \langle H,Y,\sigma\rangle \to \langle K,Z,\zeta\rangle$ is a morphism in $\mathbf{TTG}_*$. Finally, a straightforward argument shows that $\langle \iota^{op},q\rangle$ is the coequalizer of $\langle \psi_1^{op},f_1\rangle,\langle \psi_2^{op},f_2\rangle\colon \langle G,X,\pi\rangle \to \langle H,Y,\sigma\rangle$ in $\mathbf{TTG}_*$. □

6.1.13. We shall pay now some attention to limits in $\mathbf{TTG}_*$. First some remarks on the analogues of subsection 3.3, in particular proposition 3.3.3.

Let $\psi\colon G \to H$ be a morphism in **A**. Then to each object $\langle H,X,\pi\rangle$ in **TTG** there corresponds the object $\langle G,X,\pi^\psi\rangle$ in **TTG** and the morphism $\langle \psi,1_X\rangle\colon \langle G,X,\pi^\psi\rangle \to \langle H,X,\pi\rangle$ in **TTG**. Then we have plainly the morphism

(3) $$\langle \psi^{op},1_X\rangle\colon \langle H,X,\pi\rangle \to \langle G,X,\pi^\psi\rangle$$

in $\mathbf{TTG}_*$. In addition, a straightforward calculation shows that for each morphism $\langle \psi^{op},f\rangle\colon \langle H,X,\pi\rangle \to \langle G,Y,\sigma\rangle$ in $\mathbf{TTG}_*$, there is the morphism $\langle 1_G^{op},f\rangle\colon \langle G,X,\pi^\psi\rangle \to \langle G,Y,\sigma\rangle$, so that $\langle \psi^{op},f\rangle$ can be factorized in $\mathbf{TTG}_*$ in the following way:

(4)

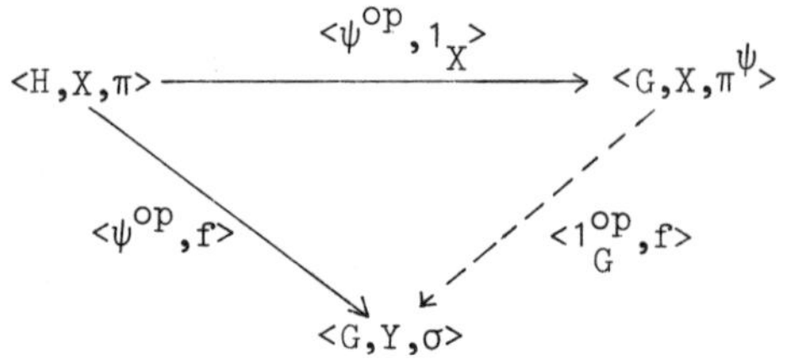

6.1.14. <u>PROPOSITION</u>. *The functor* $\mathbf{G}_*\colon \mathbf{TTG}_* \to \mathbf{A}^{op}$ *preserves all limits. Consequently, it preserves all monomorphisms.*

<u>PROOF</u>. We shall show that G_* preserves all products and all equalizers.

I. Suppose the set $\{\langle G_i, X_i, \pi_i\rangle : i \in J\}$ of objects in $\mathbf{TTG}_*$ has a product with projections $\langle \psi_i^{op}, f_i\rangle : \langle H, X, \pi\rangle \to \langle G_i, X_i, \pi_i\rangle$ $(i \in J)$. Let $\beta_i^{op}: G \to G_i$ be the projections of the product of $\{G_i : i \in J\}$ in $\mathbf{A}^{op}$, i.e. G is the coproduct of the set $\{G_i : i \in J\}$ in $\mathbf{TOPGRP}$, with coprojections $\beta_i : G_i \to G$. The morphisms $\psi_i : G_i \to H$ in $\mathbf{TOPGRP}$ induce a unique morphism $\psi: G \to H$ such that $\psi_i = \psi\beta_i$ for each $i \in J$. So in view of 6.1.13, each morphism $\langle \psi_i^{op}, f_i\rangle$ factorizes over the object $\langle G, X, \pi^{\psi}\rangle$ in $\mathbf{TTG}_*$ in the following way:

(5)

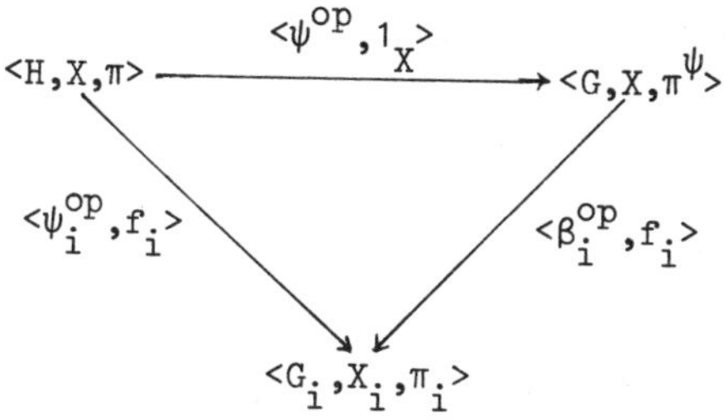

Since $\langle H, X, \pi\rangle$ is the product of the objects $\langle G_i, X_i, \pi_i\rangle$ in $\mathbf{TTG}_*$, the morphisms $\langle \beta_i^{op}, f_i\rangle$ induce a unique morphism $\langle \alpha^{op}, g\rangle : \langle G, X, \pi^{\psi}\rangle \to \langle H, X, \pi\rangle$ such that $\langle \beta_i^{op}, f_i\rangle = \langle \psi_i^{op}, f_i\rangle\langle \alpha^{op}, g\rangle$. Since morphisms to $\langle H, X, \pi\rangle$ are uniquely determined by their composites with all morphisms $\langle \psi_i^{op}, f_i\rangle$ (property of a product in a category), it follows from the equations

$$\langle \psi_i^{op}, f_i\rangle(\langle \alpha^{op}, g\rangle\langle \psi^{op}, 1_X\rangle) = \langle \beta_i^{op}, f_i\rangle\langle \psi^{op}, 1_X\rangle = \langle \psi_i^{op}, f_i\rangle,$$

that $\langle \alpha^{op}, g\rangle\langle \psi^{op}, 1_X\rangle = \langle 1_H^{op}, 1_X\rangle$. In particular, $\psi\alpha = 1_H$. On the other hand, the composites of all morphisms β_i in $\mathbf{TOPGRP}$ with a morphism with domain G completely determine that morphism, because the β_i are the coprojections of the coproduct of the groups G_j in $\mathbf{TOPGRP}$. Hence it follows from

$$(\alpha\psi)\beta_i = \alpha\psi_i = \beta_i$$

that $\alpha\psi = 1_G$ (notice that $\alpha\psi_i = \beta_i$ because $\langle \alpha^{op}, g\rangle$ was such that $\beta_i^{op} = \psi_i^{op}\alpha^{op}$).

It follows that ψ is an isomorphism in $\mathbf{TOPGRP}$, hence $\langle \psi^{op}, 1_X\rangle$ is an isomorphism in $\mathbf{TTG}_*$. Consequently, the morphisms $\langle \beta_i^{op}, f_i\rangle : \langle G, X, \pi^{\psi}\rangle \to \langle G_i, X_i, \pi_i\rangle$ form the projections of the product of the objects $\langle G_i, X_i, \pi_i\rangle$ in $\mathbf{TTG}_*$. Hence G_* preserves products.

II. G_* preserves all equalizers. The proof is similar to the proof of preservation of products, and we leave it to the reader. □

6.1.15. Although the functor G_* preserves all limits, it cannot have a left adjoint, since it does not satisfy the solution set condition in FREYD's adjoint functor theorem. This is due to the fact that any topological group G admits an action on *all* topological spaces (namely, at least the trivial action). Similarly, the functor S_* doesn't satisfy the solution set condition, because any topological space admits an action of all topological groups. In addition, the example in 6.1.17 below shows that *the functor* S_* *does not preserve all limits*. Yet the functor K_* preserves all monomorphisms:

6.1.16. PROPOSITION. *The functor* $K_*: \mathrm{TTG}_* \to A^{op} \times B$ *preserves and reflects all monomorphisms.*

PROOF. Reflection: K_* is faithful.
Preservation: The functor G_* preserves all monomorphisms, by 6.1.14. That $S_*: \mathrm{TTG} \to B$ preserves all monomorphisms can be shown similar to the proof of the first case in 4.1.5. □

6.1.17. EXAMPLE. Let G be a non-trivial group, let E be a one-point group, let τ_G denote the trivial action of E on G, and consider the morphisms

$$\langle G,G,\lambda\rangle \underset{\langle \iota^{op},f_2\rangle}{\overset{\langle \iota^{op},f_1\rangle}{\rightrightarrows}} \langle E,G,\tau_G\rangle \tag{6}$$

in TTG_*, where $\iota: E \to G$ is the obvious injection, $f_1 = 1_G$ and f_2 is the constant mapping with $f_2[G] = \{e\}$. If these morphisms have an equalizer in TTG_*, it has to be of the form

$$\langle G,X,\pi\rangle \xrightarrow{\langle 1_G^{op},g\rangle} \langle G,G,\lambda\rangle,$$

since $1_G^{op}: G \to G$ is the equalizer of $\iota^{op},\iota^{op}: G \to E$ in A^{op}. Hence $g[X]$ is an invariant subset of $\langle G,G,\lambda\rangle$. On the other hand, the condition $f_1 g = f_2 g$ implies that $g[X] \subseteq \{e\}$, hence $g[X]$ cannot be an invariant subset of $\langle G,G,\lambda\rangle$, unless $g[X] = \emptyset$. Since the injection of $\{e\}$ into G is the equalizer of f_1 and f_2 in TOP, it follows that S_* does not preserve equalizers.

6.1.18. REMARK. Since the functor K_* does not preserve all limits, it seems to be difficult to solve the question of whether TTG_* has all limits. It is quite easy to show *that* TTG_* *is not complete*, but for the proof we need a result from subsection 6.4. See 6.4.11 below. We have also seen, that TTG_*

is not cocomplete. But if we restrict ourselves to actions of locally compact T_2-groups, then we obtain a finitely cocomplete subcategory of $\mathbf{TTG}_*$. (see 6.1.12 and 6.1.10, and notice that finite products, hence all finite limits in $\mathbf{A}_0$ can be computed in **TOPGRP**). We shall return to this subcategory of $\mathbf{TTG}_*$ in 6.3.2 below. First, we shall deal with k-ttgs and comorphisms between them, i.e. the category $\mathbf{k\text{-}TTG}_*$.

6.2. The category $\mathbf{k\text{-}TTG}_*$

6.2.1. Let $\mathbf{A} := \mathbf{KRGRP}$, $\mathbf{B} := \mathbf{KR}$, and let $\mathbf{A}^{op}$ denote the opposite category of $\mathbf{A}$. Notation with respect to $\mathbf{A}^{op}$ will be as in 6.1.1. In this section, we consider the category $\mathbf{k\text{-}TTG}_*$, which is related to the category **k-TTG** just in the same way as $\mathbf{TTG}_*$ is related to **TTG**.

The objects of $\mathbf{k\text{-}TTG}_*$ are the k-ttgs $[G,X,\pi]$, where (G,X) is an object in $\mathbf{A}^{op}\times\mathbf{B}$, and π is a k-action of G on X (cf. subsection 5.2). The morphisms in $\mathbf{k\text{-}TTG}_*$ are the comorphisms of k-ttgs. Here a *comorphism of k-ttgs*, $[\psi^{op},f]: [G,X,\pi] \to [H,Y,\sigma]$ is a morphism $(\psi^{op},f): (G,X) \to (H,Y)$ in $\mathbf{A}^{op}\times\mathbf{B}$ such that

$$f\pi(\psi(t),x) = \sigma(t,fx)$$

for all $t\in H$ and $x\in X$ (equivalently: $[1_H,f]: [H,X,\pi^{\psi}] \to [H,Y,\sigma]$ is a morphism of k-ttgs).

Similar to 6.1.3, we define forgetful functors, which will also be denoted by $K_*: \mathbf{k\text{-}TTG}_* \to \mathbf{A}^{op}\times\mathbf{B}$, $G_*: \mathbf{k\text{-}TTG}_* \to \mathbf{A}^{op}$ and $S_*: \mathbf{k\text{-}TTG}_* \to \mathbf{B}$. We shall not write down here the definitions: they may be obtained by replacing in 6.1.3 all brackets $< , >$ by brackets of the form $[,]$.

6.2.2. If (G,X) is an object in $\mathbf{A}^{op}\times\mathbf{B}$, then

$$(1)\qquad H_*(G,X) := (G,C_{kc}(G,X))$$

is also an object in $\mathbf{A}^{op}\times\mathbf{B}$. If $(\psi^{op},f): (G,X)\to(H,Y)$ is a morphism in $\mathbf{A}^{op}\times\mathbf{B}$, then $f\circ\xi\circ\psi \in C_{kc}(H,Y)$ for each $\xi \in C_{kc}(G,X)$. Let $f\circ-\circ\psi$ denote the mapping $\xi \longmapsto f\circ\xi\circ\psi: C_{kc}(G,X) \to C_{kc}(H,Y)$. This is a morphism in $\mathbf{B}$; set

(2) $$H_*(\psi^{op},f) := (\psi^{op}, f\circ - \circ\psi): H_*(G,X) \to H_*(H,Y).$$

Clearly, we have defined a functor $H_*: A^{op}\times B \to A^{op}\times B$. We shall show now that H_* is part of a comonad (H_*,δ,ε).

For this end we have to define natural transformations $\delta: H_* \to I_{A^{op}\times B}$ and $\varepsilon: H_* \to H_*^2$.

6.2.3. LEMMA. *Let* (G,X) *be an object in* $A^{op}\times B$, *and let* e *be the identity of* G. *Then the following statements hold:*

(i) *The mapping* $\delta_X^G: f \mapsto f(e): C_{kc}(G,X) \to X$ *is continuous. Hence it is a morphism in* B.

(ii) *For each* $f \in C_{kc}(G,X)$, *the mapping* $\tilde{\rho}_f: t \mapsto \tilde{\rho}_f t = \tilde{\rho}^t f: G \to C_{kc}(G,X)$ *is continuous*[)1]. *In addition, the mapping* $\varepsilon_X^G: f \mapsto \tilde{\rho}_f: C_{kc}(G,X) \to C_{kc}(G,C_{kc}(G,X))$ *is continuous. Hence it is a morphism in* B.

PROOF.

(i): Obvious.

(ii): If $f \in C_{kc}(G,X)$, then $\tilde{\rho}_f: G \to C_c(G,X)$ is continuous, by 2.1.2. Taking into account that G is its own k-refinement, it follows that $\tilde{\rho}_f: G \to C_{kc}(G,X)$ is continuous. Next, recall that we may identify the space $C_{kc}(G,C_{kc}(G,X))$ with $C_{kc}(G\otimes G,X)$, identifying $\bar{\alpha} \in C_{kc}(G,C_{kc}(G,X))$ with the element $\alpha \in C_{kc}(G\otimes G,X)$, where $\alpha(s,t) = (\bar{\alpha}(s))(t)$ for $s,t \in G$ (cf. 5.1.3). In doing so, it is clear that we obtain $\varepsilon_X^G(f) = \overline{f\circ\rho}$ for each $f \in C_{kc}(G,X)$; here $\rho(s,t) := ts$ for $s,t \in G$. Since the mapping $f \mapsto f\circ\rho: C_c(G,X) \to C_c(G\otimes G,X)$ is continuous (notice, that $\rho: G\otimes G \to G$ is continuous), we see that $f \mapsto f\circ\rho: C_{kc}(G,X) \to C_{kc}(G\otimes G,X)$ is continuous. Consequently, ε_X^G is continuous. □

6.2.4. For each object (G,X) in $A^{op}\times B$, let the morphisms $\delta_{(G,X)}: H_*(G,X) \to (G,X)$ and $\varepsilon_{(G,X)}: H_*(G,X) \to H_*^2(G,X)$ in $A^{op}\times B$ be defined by

(3) $$\delta_{(G,X)} := (1_G^{op},\delta_X^G): (G,C_{kc}(G,X)) \to (G,X)$$

(4) $$\varepsilon_{(G,X)} := (1_G^{op},\varepsilon_X^G): (G,C_{kc}(G,X)) \to (G,C_{kc}(G,C_{kc}(G,X))).$$

)1 As we shall see in 6.2.8 below (in particular, formula (17)), it follows that even $\tilde{\rho}: G\otimes C_{kc}(G,X) \to C_{kc}(G,X)$ is continuous.

Here δ_X^G and ε_X^G are as in the preceding lemma, namely,

(5) $$\delta_X^G(f) := f(e); \quad \varepsilon_X^G(f) := \tilde{\rho}_f\,^{)1}$$

for each $f \in C_{kc}(G,X)$. It follows from the lemma that, indeed, $\delta_{(G,X)}$ and $\varepsilon_{(G,X)}$ are morphisms in $A^{op} \times B$.

6.2.5. PROPOSITION. *With the notation of* 6.2.4, *we have the natural transformations*

(6) $$\delta\colon H_* \to I_{A^{op}\times B}; \quad \varepsilon\colon H_* \to H_*^2,$$

and (H_*,δ,ε) *is a comonad.*

PROOF. First, we have to show that δ and ε are natural transformations, i.e. that for each morphism $(\psi^{op},f)\colon (G,X) \to (H,Y)$ in $A^{op} \times B$ the following diagrams in B commute (plainly, the A^{op}-components of the diagrams which we should consider in $A^{op} \times B$ are commutative; the B-component of $H_*^2(\psi^{op},f)$ is denoted by $H_*^2(\psi^{op},f)_2$):

(7) $$\begin{array}{ccc} C_{kc}(G,X) & \xrightarrow{\delta_X^G} & X \\ \downarrow{\scriptstyle f\circ-\circ\psi} & & \downarrow{\scriptstyle f} \\ C_{kc}(H,Y) & \xrightarrow{\delta_Y^H} & Y \end{array} \qquad \begin{array}{ccc} C_{kc}(G,X) & \xrightarrow{\varepsilon_X^G} & C_{kc}(G,C_{kc}(G,X)) \\ \downarrow{\scriptstyle f\circ-\circ\psi} & & \downarrow{\scriptstyle H_*^2(\psi^{op},f)_2} \\ C_{kc}(H,Y) & \xrightarrow{\varepsilon_Y^H} & C_{kc}(H,C_{kc}(H,Y)) \end{array}$$

For the first diagram to commute it is necessary and sufficient that for each $h \in C_{kc}(G,X)$, $f(h(e_G)) = (f\circ h\circ\psi)(e_H)$. This equality is certainly valid, since $\psi\colon H \to G$ is a morphism of groups, so that $\psi(e_H) = e_G$.

In the second diagram we have first to determine what $H_*^2(\psi,f)$ looks like. To this end we shall use, again, the homeomorphisms $\bar{\alpha} \mapsto \alpha$: $C_{kc}(G,C_{kc}(G,X)) \to C_{kc}(G\otimes G,X)$ and $\bar{\beta} \mapsto \beta$: $C_{kc}(H,C_{kc}(H,Y)) \to C_{kc}(H\otimes H,Y)$. Then it is easily seen that $H_*^2(\psi^{op},f)_2$ corresponds to the continuous mapping $f\circ-\circ(\psi\otimes\psi)\colon C_{kc}(G\otimes G,X) \to C_{kc}(H\otimes H,Y)$. In the proof of 6.2.3 we have seen al-

)1 Recall from §2 that we decided to write always simply $\tilde{\rho}$, where we ought to write $\tilde{\rho}_X^G$. Now the G and X occur in ε_X^G.

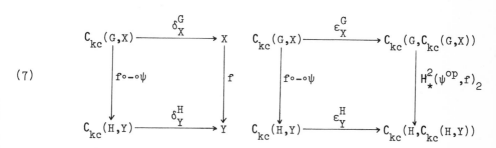

ready that $\varepsilon_X^G h = \overline{h \circ \rho}$ for every $h \in C_{kc}(G,X)$. Since a similar relation holds for each $g \in C_{kc}(H,Y)$, we have to check the commutativity of the following diagram:

$$\begin{array}{ccc} C_{kc}(G,X) & \xrightarrow{\quad -\circ\rho \quad} & C_{kc}(G\otimes G,X) \\ \downarrow{\scriptstyle f\circ-\circ\psi} & & \downarrow{\scriptstyle f\circ-\circ(\psi\otimes\psi)} \\ C_{kc}(H,Y) & \xrightarrow{\quad -\circ\rho \quad} & C_{kc}(H\otimes H,Y) \end{array}$$

Commutativity of this diagram is equivalent to the validity of $f[h(\psi(t)\psi(s))] = (f\circ h\circ\psi)(ts)$ for each $h \in C_{kc}(G,X)$ and $(s,t) \in G\otimes G$. This equality is surely valid, because ψ is a morphism of groups. Consequently, the second diagram in (7) commutes.

Thus, we have shown that δ and ε are natural transformations. In order to prove that (H_*,δ,ε) is a comonad, it is sufficient to check that the following diagrams commute for each object (G,X) in $A^{op}\times B$ (again, we ought to consider diagrams in $A^{op}\times B$, but their A^{op}-components trivially commute):

(8)
$$\begin{array}{ccc} C_{kc}(G,X) & \xrightarrow{\quad \varepsilon_X^G \quad} & C_{kc}(G,C_{kc}(G,X)) \\ \downarrow{\scriptstyle \varepsilon_X^G} & \searrow{\scriptstyle 1_{C_{kc}(G,X)}} & \downarrow{\scriptstyle \delta^G_{C_{kc}(G,X)}} \\ C_{kc}(G,C_{kc}(G,X)) & \xrightarrow{\quad \delta_X^G\circ-\circ 1_G \quad} & C_{kc}(G,X) \end{array}$$

(9)
$$\begin{array}{ccc} C_{kc}(G,X) & \xrightarrow{\quad \varepsilon_X^G \quad} & C_{kc}(G,C_{kc}(G,X)) \\ \downarrow{\scriptstyle \varepsilon_X^G} & & \downarrow{\scriptstyle \varepsilon^G_{C_{kc}(G,X)}} \\ C_{kc}(G,C_{kc}(G,X)) & \xrightarrow{\quad \varepsilon_X^G\circ-\circ 1_G \quad} & C_{kc}(G,C_{kc}(G,C_{kc}(G,X))) \end{array}$$

Commutativity of the first diagram amounts to the equalities

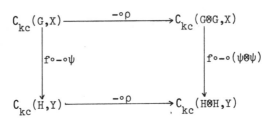

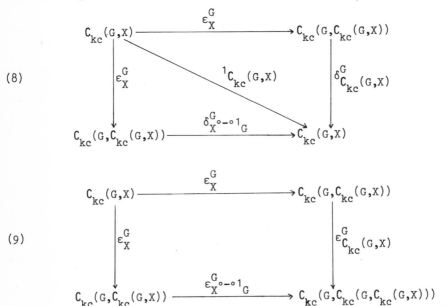

$$\tilde{\rho}_h(e) = h = \delta^G_X \circ \tilde{\rho}_h$$

for all $h \in C_{kc}(G,X)$, i.e. to the equalities $h(te) = h(t) = h(et)$ for all $t \in G$. Therefore, (8) commutes (notice, that the reason is exactly the same as the reason for commutativity of the first diagram in the proof of 3.1.7, namely the identity law in G). As for the diagram (9), here we have to show that

$$(10) \qquad \tilde{\rho}_{\tilde{\rho}_h} = \varepsilon^G_X \circ \tilde{\rho}_h$$

for each $h \in C_{kc}(G,X)$. Since for all $s,t \in G$ and $h \in C_{kc}(G,X)$, $(\tilde{\rho}_{\tilde{\rho}_h}(t))(s) = (\tilde{\rho}^t\tilde{\rho}_h)(s) = \tilde{\rho}_h(st)$, and $[\varepsilon^G_X(\tilde{\rho}_h(t))](s) = \tilde{\rho}^s(\tilde{\rho}_h(t)) = \tilde{\rho}^s\tilde{\rho}^t h$, the equality (10) is equivalent with the equality $\tilde{\rho}^{st}h = \tilde{\rho}^s\tilde{\rho}^t h$ for all $h \in C_{kc}(G,X)$ and $s,t \in G$. This equality is valid by the associative law for the multiplication in G, and it follows that diagram (9) commutes (again, the reason is the same as that of commutativity of the second diagram in the proof of 3.1.7). □

6.2.6. <u>THEOREM</u>. *There exists an isomorphism* J *from the category of all coalgebras for the comonad* (H_*,δ,ε) *onto the category* k-TTG$_*$. *Moreover, if* L *denotes the forgetful functor from the category of all coalgebras for the comonad* (H_*,δ,ε) *to* $A^{op} \times B$, *then* $L = K_* \circ J$.

(11)

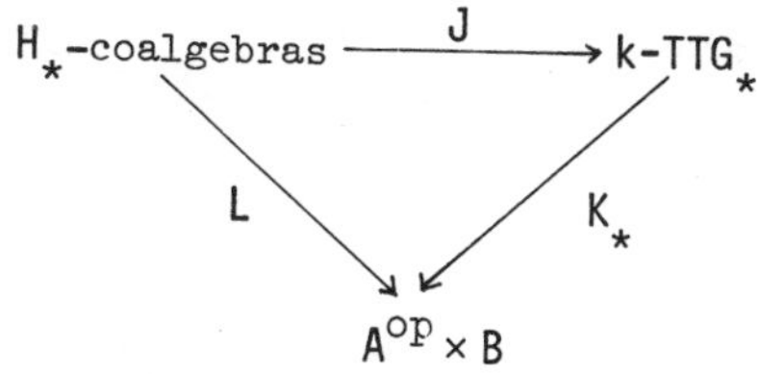

<u>PROOF</u>. By definition, an H_*-coalgebra is a pair $((G,X),(\psi^{op},\alpha))$ with (G,X) an object in $A^{op} \times B$ and $(\psi^{op},\alpha)\colon (G,X) \to (G,C_{kc}(G,X)) = H_*(G,X)$ a morphism in $A^{op} \times B$ such that the following diagrams commute:

(12)

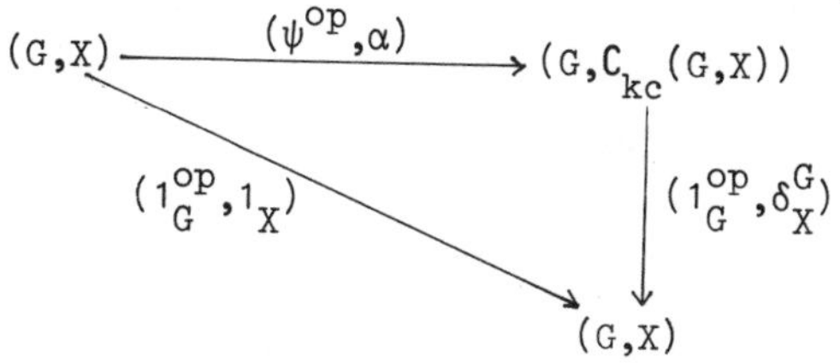

(13)
$$\begin{array}{ccc} (G,X) & \xrightarrow{(\psi^{op},\alpha)} & (G,C_{kc}(G,X)) \\ \downarrow{\scriptstyle(\psi^{op},\alpha)} & & \downarrow{\scriptstyle(\psi^{op},\alpha\circ-\circ\psi)} \\ (G,C_{kc}(G,X)) & \xrightarrow{(1_G^{op},\varepsilon_X^G)} & (G,C_{kc}(G,C_{kc}(G,X))) \end{array}$$

From the first diagram it follows that $\psi = 1_G$, and that

(14) $\qquad \alpha(x)(e) = x$

for all $x \in X$. From the second diagram we obtain now the relation $\tilde{\rho}_{\alpha(x)} = \alpha\circ\alpha(x)$ for all $x \in X$. Hence $\tilde{\rho}^t(\alpha x) = \alpha(\alpha(x)(t))$, that is

(15) $\qquad \alpha(x)(st) = \alpha(\alpha(x)(t))(s)$

Next, we use again the fact that $C(X,C_{kc}(G,X))$ and $C(X\otimes G,X)$ or $C(G\otimes X,X)$ are in a one-one correspondence, as follows: if for any $\xi \in C(X,C_{kc}(G,X))$ we write $\xi'(t,x) := \xi(x)(t)$ $(t\in G, x\in X)$, then $\xi \mapsto \xi'$ is a bijection of $C(X,C_{kc}(G,X)$ onto $C(G\otimes X,X)$. Thus, we may rewrite (14) and (15) as follows:

$$\alpha'(e,x) = x$$
$$\alpha'(st,x) = \alpha'(s,\alpha'(t,x))$$

for all $x \in X$ and $s,t \in G$, or equivalently, α' is a k-action of G on X. We have shown, that $((G,X),(\psi^{op},\alpha))$ is an H_*-coalgebra iff $\psi = 1_G$ and α' is a k-action of G on X. If we write $J((G,X),(1_G^{op},\alpha)) := [G,X,\alpha']$, then J defines a bijection of the class of H_*-coalgebras onto the class of k-ttgs.

We proceed by determining the morphisms of H_*-coalgebras. Suppose $(\psi^{op},f)\colon ((G,X),(1_G^{op},\alpha)) \to ((H,Y),(1_H^{op},\beta))$ is a morphism of H_*-coalgebras. This means that the following diagram commutes:

$$\begin{array}{ccc} (G,X) & \xrightarrow{(1_G^{op},\alpha)} & (G,C_{kc}(G,X)) \\ \downarrow{\scriptstyle(\psi^{op},f)} & & \downarrow{\scriptstyle(\psi^{op},f\circ-\circ\psi)} \\ (H,Y) & \xrightarrow{(1_H^{op},\beta)} & (H,C_{kc}(H,Y)) \end{array}$$

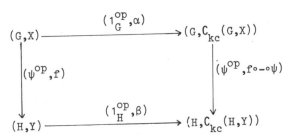

Equivalently, $f\circ\alpha(x)\circ\psi = \beta(fx)$ for all $x\in X$. Using once again the bijections $\xi \mapsto \xi'$: $C(X,C_{kc}(G,X)) \to C(G\otimes X,X)$ and $\eta \mapsto \eta'$: $C(Y,C_{kc}(H,Y)) \to C(H\otimes Y,Y)$, we obtain

$$f(\alpha'(\psi(t),x)) = \beta'(t,f(x))$$

for all $t\in H$ and $x\in X$. Therefore, (ψ^{op},f): $((G,X),(1_G^{op},\alpha)) \to ((H,Y),(1_H^{op},\beta))$ is a morphism of H_*-coalgebras iff (ψ^{op},f) is a comorphism of k-ttgs, $[\psi^{op},f]$: $[G,X,\alpha'] \to [H,Y,\beta']$. If we set $J(\psi^{op},f) := [\psi^{op},f]$ for each morphism (ψ^{op},f) of H_*-coalgebras, then clearly we have obtained a functor J from the category of all H_*-coalgebras to the category $\mathsf{k\text{-}TTG}_*$. In addition, J induces not only a bijection of the object classes, but it also induces bijections of morphism sets. So J is an isomorphism of categories. It is clear from the definitions that we have the relation $L = K_*\circ J$. □

6.2.7. <u>COROLLARY</u>. *The functor* K_*: $\mathsf{k\text{-}TTG}_* \to A^{op}\times B$ *has a right adjoint. Hence* K_* *preserves all colimits and epimorphisms (being faithful,* K_* *also reflects epimorphisms). In addition,* K_* *even creates all colimits, and* $\mathsf{k\text{-}TTG}_*$ *is cocomplete.*

<u>PROOF</u>. Immediate from 6.2.6 and 0.4.9. Hence cocompleteness of $\mathsf{k\text{-}TTG}_*$ follows from cocompleteness of A^{op} and B (cf. 5.1.8 and 5.1.2(ii)). □

6.2.8. Using the general theory of coalgebras, the right adjoint M_* of the functor K_* can be determined as follows. First, the right adjoint R of the functor L is given by

$$R: \begin{cases} (G,X) \longmapsto ((G,C_{kc}(G,X)),(1_G,\varepsilon_X^G)) & \text{on objects} \\ (\psi^{op},f) \longmapsto (\psi^{op},f\circ -\circ\psi) & \text{on morphisms.} \end{cases}$$

In addition, the unit and counit of adjunction of L and R are given, respectively, by the morphisms

$$((G,X),(1_G^{op},\alpha)) \xrightarrow{(1_G^{op},\alpha)} ((G,C_{kc}(G,X)),(1_G^{op},\varepsilon_X^G))$$

for every H_*-coalgebra $((G,X),(1_G^{op},\alpha))$, and

(16) $$(G,C_{kc}(G,X)) \xrightarrow{(1_G^{op},\delta_X^G)} (G,X)$$

for every object (G,X) in $A^{op}\times B$. Cf. 0.4.9 for details.

Since obviously, $M_* := J \circ R$, we obtain from the definition of J (cf. the proof of 6.2.6) that M_* is defined by the assignments

$$(17) \qquad M_*: \begin{cases} (G,X) \longmapsto [G, C_{kc}(G,X), \tilde{\rho}_X^G] & \text{on objects} \\ (\psi^{op}, f) \longmapsto [\psi^{op}, f\circ - \circ\psi] & \text{on morphisms}. \end{cases}$$

Here $\tilde{\rho}_X^G$ stands for $(\varepsilon_X^G)'$, hence for all $t \in G$, $\xi \in C_{kc}(G,X)$:

$$\tilde{\rho}_X^G(t,\xi) := (\varepsilon_X^G \xi)(t) = \tilde{\rho}_\xi(t) = \tilde{\rho}(t,\xi).$$

Thus, $\tilde{\rho}_X^G$ just equals the mapping which was abbreviated to $\tilde{\rho}$ in §2. We shall adopt here the previous usage, and write simply $\tilde{\rho}$ for $\tilde{\rho}_X^G = (\varepsilon_X^G)'$ if there is no risk of ambiguity.

Similar considerations show that the *unit of the adjunction of* K_* *and* M_* is given by the morphisms

$$(18) \qquad [G,X,\pi] \xrightarrow{[1_G^{op}, \underline{\pi}]} [G, C_{kc}(G,X), \tilde{\rho}]$$

for every k-ttg $[G,X,\pi]$. Here $\underline{\pi}: X \to C_{kc}(G,X)$ is defined by $\underline{\pi}(x) := \pi_x$. Recall from 2.1.13 that $\underline{\pi}: X \to C_c(G,X)$ is a topological embedding, *so that* $\underline{\pi}: X \to C_{kc}(G,X)$ *is also a topological embedding*. {We strengthen the topology in the codomain, so $\underline{\pi}$ remains relatively open. Taking k-ations in $\underline{\pi}: X \to C_c(G,X)$, we see that $\underline{\pi}: X \to C_{kc}(G,X)$ is continuous, because X is its own k-ation.}

The *counit of adjunction of* K_* *and* M_* is given by the morphisms of the form (16). If $[H,Y,\sigma]$ is any k-ttg, and $(\psi^{op}, f): (H,Y) \to (G,X)$ is any morphism in $A^{op} \times B$, then there exists a unique morphism in $k\text{-TTG}_*$, namely $M_*(\psi^{op}, f) \circ [1_H^{op}, \underline{\sigma}] = [\psi^{op}, f\circ\underline{\sigma}(-)\circ\psi]: [H,Y,\sigma] \to [G, C_{kc}(G,X), \tilde{\rho}]$, such that the following diagram commutes:

$$(19) \qquad \begin{array}{c} [G, C_{kc}(G,X), \tilde{\rho}] \\ \uparrow {\scriptstyle [\psi^{op}, f\circ\underline{\sigma}(-)\circ\psi]} \\ [H,Y,\sigma] \end{array} \qquad \begin{array}{ccc} (G, C_{kc}(G,X)) & \xrightarrow{(1_G^{op}, \delta_X^G)} & (G,X) \\ & {\scriptstyle (\psi^{op}, f\circ\underline{\sigma}(-)\circ\psi)} \nwarrow \quad \nearrow {\scriptstyle (\psi^{op}, f)} & \\ & (H,Y) & \end{array}$$

6.2.9. The example in 6.1.17 can easily be adapted in order to show that *the functor* $K_*: k\text{-TTG}_* \to A^{op} \times B$ *does not preserve equalizers*. We leave this to the reader. We do not know whether $k\text{-TTG}_*$ is complete (the method of 6.4.11 below does not work in this case).

6.2.10. Fix an object $G \in$ KRGRP, and consider the k-ttgs $[G,X,\pi]$ and $[G,Y,\sigma]$. If $f\colon X \to Y$ is a morphism in KR, then obviously $[1_G^{op},f]\colon [G,X,\pi] \to [G,Y,\sigma]$ is a morphism in k-TTG$_*$ iff $[1_G,f]\colon [G,X,\pi] \to [G,Y,\sigma]$ is a morphism in k-TTG, that is, iff $[1_G,f]$ is a morphism in k-KR^G. *Equivalently,* k-KR^G *could have been defined as the subcategory* $K_*^{\leftarrow}[A_G^{op}\times B]$ *of* k-TTG$_*$, *where* A_G *is the subcategory of* A = KRGRP, *consisting of one object* G *and one morphism* 1_G.

Thus, identifying k-KR^G with $K_*^{\leftarrow}[A_G^{op}\times B]$, we obtain the following results. The proofs are completely similar to 6.2.1 through 6.2.9, replacing A by A_G.

There exists a functor $H_*^G\colon KR \to KR$,

$$(20)\qquad H_*^G\colon \begin{cases} X \longmapsto C_{kc}(G,X) & \text{on objects,} \\ f \longmapsto f\circ - & \text{on morphisms,} \end{cases}$$

and there exist natural transformations $\delta^G\colon H_*^G \to I_{KR}$ and $\varepsilon^G\colon H_*^G \to (H_*^G)^2$,

$$(21)\qquad \delta_X^G\colon f \mapsto f(e)\colon C_{kc}(G,X) \to X,$$

$$(22)\qquad \varepsilon_X^G\colon f \mapsto \tilde{\rho}_f\colon C_{kc}(G,X) \to C_{kc}(G,C_{kc}(G,X)),$$

such that $(H_*^G,\delta^G,\varepsilon^G)$ is a comonad in KR. Moreover, the category of all coalgebras for this comonad is isomorphic to the category k-KR^G.

The functor $S^G\colon$ k-KR$^G \to$ KR has a right adjoint M^G, given by the assignments

$$(23)\qquad M^G\colon \begin{cases} X \longmapsto [G,C_{kc}(G,X),\tilde{\rho}] & \text{on objects} \\ f \longmapsto [1_G,f\circ -] & \text{on morphisms.} \end{cases}$$

The unit of adjunction is given by the morphisms

$$(24)\qquad [G,X,\pi] \xrightarrow{[1_G,\underline{\pi}]} [G,C_{kc}(G,X),\tilde{\rho}]$$

in k-KR^G, for every k-ttg $[G,X,\pi]$. The counit of the adjunction is given by the morphisms

$$(25)\qquad C_{kc}(G,X) \xrightarrow{\delta_X^G} X$$

in KR, for every k-space X. Recall that in (24), $\underline{\pi}\colon X \to C_{kc}(G,X)$ is defined by $\underline{\pi}(x) := \pi_x$ $(x \in X)$, and that $\underline{\pi}$ is a topological embedding of X into $C_{kc}(G,X)$.

6.2.11. If $G \in$ KRGRP is fixed, then by the above remarks the category k-KR^G can be identified with the category of all coalgebras over a suitable comonad in KR, and, consequently, *the functor* S^G: k-KR$^G \to$ KR *not only preserves all colimits, but also creates them. In particular, it follows that* k-KH^G *is cocomplete*. In addition, the functor S^G preserves and reflects all epimorphisms. These results have already been announced in 5.3.3.

Recall from 5.3.2, that the functor S^G: k-KR$^G \to$ KR not only has the *right* adjoint M^G, but that it also has a *left* adjoint F^G, where

$$F^G: \begin{cases} X \longmapsto [G, G\otimes X, \mu_X^G] & \text{on objects} \\ f \longmapsto [1_G, f] & \text{on morphisms} \end{cases}$$

(cf. also 5.2.9 or 3.2.7). In fact, k-KR^G may also be considered as a category of algebras over a suitable monad in KR, viz. (H^G, η^G, μ^G), where

$$H^G: \begin{cases} X \longmapsto G \otimes X & \text{on objects} \\ f \longmapsto 1_G \otimes f & \text{on morphisms.} \end{cases}$$

It follows immediately from 5.1.4 that the functor H^G is left adjoint to the functor H_*^G. It can be shown that the monad (H^G, η^G, μ^G) and the comonad $(H_*^G, \delta^G, \varepsilon^G)$ are adjoint to each other. For a definition of adjointness of monads, cf. for example S. EILENBERG & J.C. MOORE [1965].

6.3. Actions of locally compact Hausdorff groups

6.3.1. In preceding sections it sometimes occurred that a construction could be carried out only if one or more of the phase groups under consideration were locally compact and Hausdorff. Cf. for example 3.4.3, 4.4.3 and 6.1.12. Moreover, as was noticed earlier in 5.3.4, *if* G *is a locally compact* T_2-*group,* then the category k-KR^G equals the category KR^G, which is a subcategory of TOP^G (ordinary actions of G on k-spaces). Then, by 6.2.11, KR^G is both (isomorphic to) a category of algebras over a monad in KR and a category of coalgebras over a comonad in KR. *Consequently,* S^G: KR$^G \to$ KR *has both a left and a right adjoint, and all limits, colimits, monomorphisms and epimorphisms in* KR^G *can be computed in* KR. We shall indicate in 6.3.6, why similar results are valid for all of TOP^G (G locally compact Hausdorff).

6.3.2. In the proofs of 6.2.3, 6.2.5 and 6.2.6, an essential use has been made of the homeomorphisms

(1) $\alpha \mapsto \bar{\alpha}\colon C_{kc}(G\otimes G,X) \to C_{kc}(G,C_{kc}(G,X))$

(2) $\beta \mapsto \underline{\beta}\colon C_{kc}(G\otimes X,X) \to C_{kc}(X,C_{kc}(G,X))$

and their inverses ($G \in$ **KRGRP**, $X \in$ **KR**). So at first sight the previous methods cannot be applied to the category $\mathbf{TTG}_*$. But it follows from 0.2.7(iii) that *for any locally compact T_2-group* G *and any topological space* X *we have the homeomorphisms*

(3) $\alpha \mapsto \bar{\alpha}\colon C_c(G\times G,X) \to C_c(G,C_c(G,X))$

(4) $\beta \mapsto \underline{\beta}\colon C_c(G\times X,X) \to C_c(X,C_c(G,X))$

In addition, in that case $f \mapsto f(e)\colon C_c(G,X) \to X$ and $\tilde{\rho}_f\colon G \to C_c(G,X)$ (with $f \in C_c(G,X)$) are continuous. Therefore, the proofs of 6.2.5 and 6.2.6 can be modified into proofs of the following statements:

Let A_0 be the full subcategory of **TOPGRP**, defined by all locally compact T_2-groups, let $B_0 :=$ **TOP**, and let $X_* := K_*^{\leftarrow}[A_0^{op}\times B_0]$, where $K_*\colon \mathbf{TTG}_* \to \mathbf{TOPGRP}^{op}\times\mathbf{TOP}$ is the usual forgetful functor. Thus, X_* is a full subcategory of $\mathbf{TTG}_*$.

Then we have a comonad (H_*,δ,ε) in $A_0^{op}\times B_0$, where

(5) $$H_*\colon \begin{cases} (G,X) \longmapsto (G,C_c(G,X)) & \text{on objects} \\ (\psi^{op},f) \longmapsto (\psi^{op},f\circ{-}\circ\psi) & \text{on morphisms,} \end{cases}$$

and the natural transformations $\delta\colon H_* \to I_{A_0^{op}\times B_0}$ and $\varepsilon\colon H_* \to H_*^2$ are defined similarly to 6.2.4 with $C_{kc}(G,X)$ replaced by $C_c(G,X)$. *The category of all coalgebras over this comonad* (H_*,δ,ε) *may be identified with the category* X_*, *defined above, in such a way that the standard forgetful functor from the category of coalgebras to* $A_0^{op}\times B_0$ *may be identified with* $K_*\colon X_* \to A_0^{op}\times B_0$.

Consequently, the functor $K_*\colon X_* \to A_0^{op}\times B_0$ has a right adjoint, X_* is finitely cocomplete[1], and all colimits[2] and epimorphisms in X_* can be computed in $A_0^{op}\times B$.

Notice that these results were already obtained in 6.1.10 and 6.1.12. There the restriction to locally compact phase groups might seem somewhat

---

[1] Observe that the category A_0 has at least all finite products, so that A_0^{op} is certainly finitely cocomplete.

[2] If some infinite colimit in X_* exists, it is preserved by K_*, even created by K_*.

unnatural. In the present context it is clear that this restriction arises as a consequence of the passage from $\mathsf{k\text{-}TTG}_*$ to TTG_*.

6.3.3. Let the notation be as in 6.3.2. The counit of the adjunction of K_* and its right adjoint is given by the arrows

(6) $$(1_G^{op},\delta_X^G)\colon (G,\mathsf{C}_c(G,X)) \to (G,X)$$

in $\mathsf{A}_0^{op}\times\mathsf{B}_0$, $(G,X)\in\mathsf{A}_0^{op}\times\mathsf{B}_0$. Cf. also 6.2.8. However, this arrow is universal for a much wider class of arrows than might be expected: the arrows are allowed to have domains outside $\mathsf{A}_0^{op}\times\mathsf{B}_0$. Indeed we have:

6.3.4. *Let* $(G,X)\in\mathsf{A}_0^{op}\times\mathsf{B}_0$. *Then for any object* $\langle H,Y,\sigma\rangle\in\mathsf{TTG}_*$ *and for any morphism* $(\psi^{op},f)\colon (H,Y)\to(G,X)$ *in* $\mathsf{TOPGRP}^{op}\times\mathsf{TOP}$, *there exists a unique morphism* $\langle\psi_1^{op},f_1\rangle\colon \langle H,Y,\sigma\rangle\to\langle G,\mathsf{C}_c(G,X),\tilde\rho\rangle$ *in* TTG_* *such that the following diagram commutes:*

(7) $$\begin{array}{ccccc} \langle G,\mathsf{C}_c(G,X),\tilde\rho\rangle & & (G,\mathsf{C}_c(G,X)) & \xrightarrow{(1_G^{op},\delta_X^G)} & (G,X) \\ \uparrow{\scriptstyle\langle\psi_1^{op},f_1\rangle} & & \uparrow{\scriptstyle(\psi_1^{op},f_1)} & \nearrow{\scriptstyle(\psi^{op},f)} & \\ \langle H,Y,\sigma\rangle & & (H,Y) & & \end{array}$$

The proof is as follows (cf. also (19) in 6.2.8): If such a $\langle\psi_1^{op},f_1\rangle$ exists, then necessarily $\psi_1=\psi$ and (after some straigtforward computations) $f_1 = f\circ\underline{\sigma}(-)\circ\psi\colon y\mapsto f\sigma_y\psi\colon Y\to\mathsf{C}_c(G,X)$. This proves uniqueness. Existence is now easy; indeed, set

(8) $$\langle\psi_1^{op},f_1\rangle := \langle\psi^{op},f\circ\underline{\sigma}(-)\circ\psi\rangle.$$

By 2.1.13, $\underline{\sigma}\colon Y\to\mathsf{C}_c(H,Y)$ is a topological embedding, and since $h\mapsto fh\psi\colon \mathsf{C}_c(H,Y)\to\mathsf{C}_c(G,X)$ is continuous, it follows that the above defined mapping $f_1\colon Y\to\mathsf{C}_c(G,X)$ is continuous. Now it is straightforward to verify that $\langle\psi_1^{op},f_1\rangle$ is a morphism in TTG_* and that it meets all requirements.

Remark. Local compactness of G is used only to ensure that $\tilde\rho\colon G\times\mathsf{C}_c(G,X)\to\mathsf{C}_c(G,X)$ is continuous, i.e. that $\langle G,\mathsf{C}_c(G,X),\tilde\rho\rangle$ is a ttg (cf. 2.1.3). If G is not locally compact, then the above statement remains true if we replace G by G_d at all places where G occurs in its role as phase group.

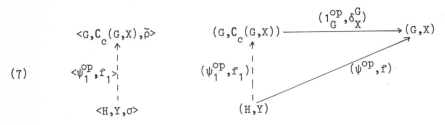

6.3.5. Fix an object $(G,X) \in A_0^{op}\times B_0$, i.e. $(G,X) \in \mathbf{TOPGRP}^{op}\times\mathbf{TOP}$, G locally compact T_2. Then by 6.3.4, *for any object* $<H,Y,\sigma> \in \mathbf{TTG}_*$, *there is a bijection*)1[2]

$$\Psi_{<H,Y,\sigma>}: \mathbf{TOPGRP}^{op}\times\mathbf{TOP}((H,Y),(G,X)) \to \mathbf{TTG}_*(<H,Y,\sigma>,<G,C_c(G,X),\tilde{\rho}>).$$

In fact, it is clear from the proof in 6.3.4, that

$$(9) \qquad \Psi_{<H,Y,\sigma>}(\psi^{op},f) = <\psi^{op},f\circ\underline{\sigma}(-)\circ\psi>$$

for any morphism $(\psi^{op},f)\colon (H,Y)\to(G,X)$ in $\mathbf{TOPGRP}^{op}\times\mathbf{TOP}$, and that

$$(10) \qquad (\Psi_{<H,Y,\sigma>})^{\leftarrow}<\psi_1^{op},f_1> = (\psi_1^{op},\delta_X^G\circ f_1)$$

for any morphism $<\psi_1^{op},f_1>\colon <H,Y,\sigma> \to <G,C_c(G,X),\tilde{\rho}>$ in $\mathbf{TTG}_*$. (Recall, that $\delta_X^G(f) = f(e)$ for $f \in C_c(G,X)$.) In addition, *it is straightforward to show that this bijection* $\Psi_{<H,Y,\sigma>}$ *is natural in* $<H,Y,\sigma>$. {We shall use this in the next subsection in order to prove some facts about *cogenerators* in $\mathbf{TTG}_*$.}

6.3.6. Fix a locally compact T_2-group G. Then $\mathbf{TOP}^G$ is a subcategory of $\mathbf{TTG}$, but it may also be considered as a subcategory of $\mathbf{TTG}_*$; in the latter case, $\mathbf{TOP}^G$ is a subcategory of the category X_*, considered in 6.3.2. Therefore, we do not only have the results and methods of subsection 3.2 for $\mathbf{TOP}^G$, but also the methods of subsection 6.2 (in particular, 6.2.10) can be used, replacing $\otimes$ by $\times$ and C_{kc} by C_c. Collecting all these results together, we have:

(i) $\mathbf{TOP}^G$ is (isomorphic to) the category of all algebras over the monad (H^G,η^G,μ^G) in $\mathbf{TOP}$ in such a way that $S^G\colon \mathbf{TOP}^G\to\mathbf{TOP}$ coincides with the standard forgetful functor which forgets the structure maps of algebras. Consequently, S^G creates and preserves all limits and monomorphisms. In particular, $\mathbf{TOP}^G$ is complete (cf. subsection 3.2).

(ii) $\mathbf{TOP}^G$ is (isomorphic to) the category of all coalgebras over the comonad $(H_*^G,\delta^G,\varepsilon^G)$ in $\mathbf{TOP}$)2. Hence $S^G\colon \mathbf{TOP}^G\to\mathbf{TOP}$ creates and preserves all

)1 The adjointness described in 6.3.2 would give this bijection only for locally compact T_2-groups H; this restriction is shown now to be superfluous.

)2 We shall not write down here the definitions of H_*^G, ε^G and δ^G; the reader may do it himself, using 6.2.10 as a model.

colimits and epimorphisms. In particular, TOP^G is cocomplete (cf. 6.2.10 and 6.2.11; also 3.4.3)

(iii) The functor $S^G: \mathrm{TOP}^G \to \mathrm{TOP}$ has a left adjoint F^G and a right adjoint M^G, defined by

$$F^G: \begin{cases} X \longmapsto \langle G, G\times X, \mu_X^G\rangle & \text{on objects} \\ f \longmapsto \langle 1_G, f\rangle & \text{on morphisms,} \end{cases}$$

and

$$M^G: \begin{cases} X \longmapsto \langle G, C_c(G,X), \tilde{\rho}\rangle & \text{on objects} \\ f \longmapsto \langle 1_G, f\circ -\rangle & \text{on morphisms.} \end{cases}$$

6.3.7. <u>NOTES</u>. With notation as in 6.3.6, it can be shown that the functor $H^G: \mathrm{TOP} \to \mathrm{TOP}$ is left adjoint to the functor $H^G_*: \mathrm{TOP} \to \mathrm{TOP}$ (cf. also 5.1.4 for a similar situation in KR). Moreover, the comonad $(H^G_*, \delta^G, \varepsilon^G)$ turns out to be *adjoint to* the monad (H^G, η^G, μ^G). As was noticed in 6.2.11, a definition of adjointness of monads can be found in S. EILENBERG & J.C. MOORE [1965]. The results in 6.3.6 seem to be known in one form or another, viz. that TOP^G can be seen both as a category of algebras over a monad and as a category of coalgebras over the adjoint comonad. Cf. for instance the first part of C.N. MAXWELL [1966], where this essentially has been shown for locally compact *abelian* T_2-groups (MAXWELL doesn't use the language of monads and comonads, but his results can be interpreted in the above sense; this has been remarked earlier by F.E.J. LINTON in his review of the above mentioned paper; cf. Math. Reviews 1967,#3563). All other results in this subsection, as well as in subsection 6.2 may be seen as extensions or generalizations of this result, viz. that ttgs can be seen as coalgebras if the phase groups are locally compact: we have weakened local compactness of the phase group to the requirement of being a k-group, at the cost of replacing actions by k-actions; moreover, the appropriate morphisms turned out to be the *comor*phisms of k-ttgs.

6.4. <u>Cogenerators in TTG_*</u>

6.4.1. Recall that a *cogenerator* in a category $\mathbf{X}$ is an object $A \in \mathbf{X}$ for which the contravariant functor $\mathbf{X}(-,A): \mathbf{X} \to \mathrm{SET}$ is faithful. This functor is defined by

$$\mathbf{X}(-,A): \begin{cases} X \longmapsto \mathbf{X}(X,A) & \text{on objects} \\ f \longmapsto f^* & \text{on morphisms,} \end{cases}$$

where for every morphism $f: X \to Y$ in $\mathbf{X}$, the function $f^*: \mathbf{X}(Y,A) \to \mathbf{X}(X,A)$ is given by $f^*(g) := g \circ f$ if $g \in \mathbf{X}(Y,A)$ (so $f^* = - \circ f$ in our previous notation).

It is just a reformulation of the above definition to say that an object $A \in \mathbf{X}$ is a cogenerator in $\mathbf{X}$ iff for every parallel pair of morphisms $f_1, f_2: X \to Y$ in $\mathbf{X}$, $f_1 \neq f_2$, there exists a morphism $g: Y \to A$ such that $gf_1 \neq gf_2$.

6.4.2. EXAMPLES. The following examples are standard, and we leave all proofs for the reader. The list is by no means exhaustive: we insert only the examples which we need in the sequel.

(i) The *indiscrete* two-point space E_2 (the only open sets are $\emptyset$ and E_2) is a cogenerator in **TOP**.

(ii) Let F_2 denote the two-point space $\{0,1\}$ with the T_0-topology $\{\emptyset,\{0\},\{0,1\}\}$. Then F_2 is a cogenerator in the full subcategory of **TOP**, determined by the class of all T_0-spaces.

(iii) Let D_2 be the *discrete* two-point space $\{0,1\}$. Then D_2 is a cogenerator in the category of all 0-dimensional Hausdorff spaces.

(iv) The closed unit interval $[0,1]$ is a cogenerator in the category of all Tychonov spaces and also in the category **COMP**.

(v) The category **HAUS** doesn't have a cogenerator. This is due to the fact that for each Hausdorff space Y there exists a Hausdorff space Q containing two points p and q such that each continuous function from X into Q has equal values in p and q. Cf. H. HERRLICH [1965].

(vi) A slight modification of the above mentioned proof in H. HERRLICH [1965] shows that the space Q constructed there may assumed to be a k-space. Consequently, the category **KR** does not have a cogenerator.

(vii) The dual concept of a cogenerator is a *generator*. It is easy to see that the group $\mathbb{Z}$ is a generator in **GRP**. Hence the (discrete!) group $\mathbb{Z}$ is a generator in **TOPGRP** and in any of its subcategories containing $\mathbb{Z}$. In addition, $\mathbb{Z}$ is a generator in **KRGRP**. Consequently, $\mathbb{Z}$ is a cogenerator in $\mathbf{TOPGRP}^{op}$ and in $\mathbf{KRGRP}^{op}$)1.

)1 It is known that the circle group $\mathbb{T}$ is a cogenerator in the category of all locally compact T_2 groups (cf. [HR], 22.17). Hence $\mathbb{T}$ is a generator in the opposite category.

6.4.3. Notice that KR can be seen as a subcategory of the category $\mathsf{k\text{-}TTG}_*$, identifying each k-space Y with the object $[\mathbb{Z}, Y, \tau_Y] \in \mathsf{k\text{-}TTG}_*$, where τ_Y is the trivial action of $\mathbb{Z}$ on Y. It follows easily that A is a cogenerator in KR if $\mathsf{k\text{-}TTG}_*$ has a cogenerator with phase space A. In view of 6.4.2(vi) it follows that $\mathsf{k\text{-}TTG}_*$ cannot have a cogenerator. This is one of the reasons that we turn now our attention to the category TTG_* (another reason is that we are interested in comprehensive objects in TTG_*; see §7). First we prove a general lemma about cogenerators.

6.4.4. LEMMA. *Let* $F\colon \mathsf{X} \to \mathsf{Y}$ *be a faithful functor, let* $X_0 \in \mathsf{X}$, $Y_0 \in \mathsf{Y}$ *and suppose that there exists a natural transformation* $\varphi\colon \mathsf{Y}(F-, Y_0) \to \mathsf{X}(-, X_0)$. *If each* φ_Z *is a bijection of* $\mathsf{Y}(FZ, Y_0)$ *onto* $\mathsf{X}(Z, X_0)$, *then the assumption that* Y_0 *is a cogenerator in* Y *implies that* X_0 *is a cogenerator in* X.

PROOF. Let $f_1, f_2\colon X \to Y$ be morphisms in X such that $f_1 \neq f_2$. For i=1,2, the following diagram commutes:

$$\begin{array}{ccc} \mathsf{X}(X, X_0) & \xleftarrow{\ \varphi_X\ } & \mathsf{Y}(FX, Y_0) \\ \uparrow{\scriptstyle f_i^*} & & \uparrow{\scriptstyle (Ff_i)^*} \\ \mathsf{X}(Y, X_0) & \xleftarrow{\ \varphi_Y\ } & \mathsf{Y}(FY, Y_0) \end{array} \tag{1}$$

If Y_0 is a cogenerator in Y, then $\mathsf{Y}(F-, Y_0)$ is the composition of two faithful functors. Hence $(Ff_1)^* \neq (Ff_2)^*$. Since φ_X and φ_Y are bijections, it follows that $f_1^* \neq f_2^*$. This proves that the functor $\mathsf{X}(-, X_0)$ is faithful. □

6.4.5. If (F, G, φ) is an adjunction from X to Y and F is faithful, then the preceding lemma can be applied with $X_0 := GY_0$. Thus, if Y_0 is a cogenerator in Y, then GY_0 is a cogenerator in X. However, in the situation which we want to consider below, there is no adjointness, so that we have to use the lemma as it is formulated in 6.4.4.

6.4.6. We shall use the following notation in the remainder of this subsection. First, we consider the standard forgetful functor $K_*\colon \mathsf{TTG}_* \to \mathsf{TOPGRP}^{op} \times \mathsf{TOP}$. Further, let A and B denote full subcategories of TOPGRP and TOP, and set $\mathsf{X}_* := K_*^{\leftarrow}[\mathsf{A} \times \mathsf{B}]$. So X_* is a full subcategory of TTG_*. Finally, let the restriction and corestriction of K_* to the domain X_* and the codomain $\mathsf{A}^{op} \times \mathsf{B}$ also be denoted by K_*.

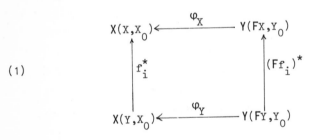

6.4.7. PROPOSITION. *Let the locally compact Hausdorff group* G *be a cogenerator in* $\mathbf{A}^{op}$ *and let* X *be a cogenerator in* $\mathbf{B}$. *If* $C_c(G,X)$ *is an object in* $\mathbf{B}$, *then the ttg* $\langle G, C_c(G,X), \tilde{\rho}\rangle$ *is a cogenerator in* X_*.

PROOF. Observe that (G,X) is a cogenerator in $\mathbf{A}^{op} \times \mathbf{B}$. In view of 6.3.5, we can apply now lemma 6.4.4 with $F := K_*$. □

6.4.8. COROLLARY. *If* G *is a locally compact Hausdorff group and if the category* $\mathbf{B}$ *has a cogenerator* X, *then* $\langle G, C_c(G,X), \tilde{\rho}\rangle$ *is a cogenerator in* $\mathbf{B}^G$, *provided* $C_c(G,X) \in \mathbf{B}$. □

6.4.9. Except **COMPGRP** and its subcategories, each "reasonably nice" subcategory $\mathbf{A}$ of **TOPGRP** contains $\mathbb{Z}$[1]. In such a category $\mathbf{A}$, $\mathbb{Z}$ is a generator, hence $\mathbb{Z}$ is a cogenerator in $\mathbf{A}^{op}$ (cf. also 6.4.2(vii)). In this situation the condition that $C_c(\mathbb{Z},X)$ be in $\mathbf{B}$ for the cogenerator X of $\mathbf{B}$ is rather weak: it means nothing else than that the countable cartesian product of copies of X, viz. the space $X^{\mathbb{Z}}$, is still in $\mathbf{B}$. This condition is fulfilled in all examples mentioned in 6.4.2. In particular, we obtain the following examples of cogenerators in subcategories of $\mathbf{TTG}_*$ (for the notation, cf. 6.4.2):

(i) $\langle \mathbb{Z}, E_2^{\mathbb{Z}}, \tilde{\rho}\rangle$ is a cogenerator in $\mathbf{TTG}_*$. Observe, that here $E_2^{\mathbb{Z}}$ is an indiscrete space.

(ii) $\langle \mathbb{Z}, F_2^{\mathbb{Z}}, \tilde{\rho}\rangle$ is a cogenerator for the full subcategory of $\mathbf{TTG}_*$ determined by the class of all ttgs with a T_0 phase space.

(iii) $\langle \mathbb{Z}, D_2^{\mathbb{Z}}, \tilde{\rho}\rangle$ is a cogenerator for the full subcategory of $\mathbf{TTG}_*$ determined by all ttgs with a 0-dimensional T_2 phase space.

(iv) $\langle \mathbb{Z}, [0,1]^{\mathbb{Z}}, \tilde{\rho}\rangle$ is a cogenerator for the full subcategories of $\mathbf{TTG}_*$, determined by all ttgs with a Tychonov, resp. with a compact T_2, phase space.

6.4.10. Similar applications can be made of the corollary 6.4.8, although here the restriction that $C_c(G,X)$ has to be an object in $\mathbf{B}$ is more serious. However, it is easy to see that $C_c(G,F_2)$ is a T_0-space and $C_c(G,D_2)$ is a 0-dimensional Hausdorff space. In addition, it is clear that $C_c(G,[0,1])$ is a Tychonov space. Thus, 6.4.8 can be used to obtain cogenerators for the categories of all G-spaces with arbitrary, or with T_0, or with 0-dimensional

---

[1] This statement should be considered as the definition of "reasonably nice" subcategories of **TOPGRP**, at least in this context.

T_2, or with Tychonov phase spaces. *But* $C_c(G,[0,1])$ *is compact iff* G *is discrete*, so for non-discrete groups G we cannot apply 6.4.8 to the case B = **COMP**. If $\mathbf{COMP}^G$ has a cogenerator, it seems to be of a quite complicated character. At this moment, it is an open problem whether $\mathbf{COMP}^G$ has a cogenerator or not.

6.4.11. PROPOSITION. *The category* $\mathbf{TTG}_*$ *is not complete.*

PROOF. According to [Pa], p.114, a complete, locally small category with a cogenerator is cocomplete. We have seen above that $\mathbf{TTG}_*$ has a cogenerator. In addition, the category $\mathbf{TOPGRP}^{op}\times\mathbf{TOP}$ is locally small, hence 6.1.16 implies that $\mathbf{TTG}_*$ is such. So if $\mathbf{TTG}_*$ were complete, it would be cocomplete, contradicting the result of 6.1.11. □

6.4.12. NOTES. In the literature the elements of the space $D_2^{\mathbb{Z}}$ are often called *bisequences*. Notice that this space is homeomorphic to the Cantor discontinuum. The action $\tilde{\rho}$ of $\mathbb{Z}$ on $D_2^{\mathbb{Z}}$ is generated by the homeomorphism $\tilde{\rho}^1 : (a_n)_n \mapsto (a_{n+1})_n$; this homeomorphism is often called the *bilateral shift*. The ttg $\langle\mathbb{Z},D_2^{\mathbb{Z}},\tilde{\rho}\rangle$ and, more generally, ttgs of the form $\langle\mathbb{Z},S^{\mathbb{Z}},\tilde{\rho}\rangle$ with S a discrete set, have been investigated intensively in the literature. Cf. [GH], Section 12 and G.A. HEDLUND [1969]. In the present context, such ttgs arise as follows: we shall see in the next section that each ttg $\langle\mathbb{Z},X,\pi\rangle$ with X a compact 0-dimensional topological Hausdorff space can be equivariantly embedded in a product of copies of $\langle\mathbb{Z},D_2^{\mathbb{Z}},\tilde{\rho}\rangle$ in $\mathbf{COMP}^{\mathbb{Z}}$. It is easily seen that a product of κ copies of $\langle\mathbb{Z},D_2^{\mathbb{Z}},\tilde{\rho}\rangle$ in $\mathbf{COMP}^{\mathbb{Z}}$ is just $\langle\mathbb{Z},S^{\mathbb{Z}},\tilde{\rho}\rangle$ with $S := D_2^{\kappa}$.

CHAPTER III
COMPREHENSIVE OBJECTS AND LINEARIZATIONS

7 - COMPREHENSIVE OBJECTS IN TOP^G

An object X_0 in a category $\mathbf{X}$ is said to be *comprehensive* for a class $\mathcal{B}$ of objects in $\mathbf{X}$ whenever each $B \in \mathcal{B}$ admits an "embedding" into X_0. Here an "embedding" is to be understood as an element of a distinguished class of monomorphisms in $\mathbf{X}$. The existence of comprehensive objects for certain classes of objects can be based on the existence of cogenerators. In fact, if in a category $\mathbf{X}$ all powers of the object A exist, then the following statements are easily seen to be equivalent (cf. also [HS], 19.6):

(i) A is a cogenerator in $\mathbf{X}$.

(ii) For each object $X \in \mathbf{X}$ the unique morphism (induced by the product) $X \to A^{\mathbf{X}(X,A)}$ is monic.

(iii) Each object $X \in \mathbf{X}$ is a subobject of some power A^{κ} of A.

However, there is a priori no reason why the monomorphism in (ii) above should belong to our distinguished class of monomorphisms. In the concrete situation which we are interested in, viz. $\mathbf{X}$ is a subcategory of $\mathbf{TOP}^G$ for some given topological group G, the distinguished class of monomorphisms shall be the class of equivariant topological embeddings. Here we feel free to use all known results about $\mathbf{TOP}$ and its subcategories. In particular, we suppose that $\mathbf{B}$ is a full subcategory of $\mathbf{TOP}$ having a cogenerator X such that each object of $\mathbf{B}$ can be *topologically* embedded in some power of X. We shall show that for any locally compact Hausdorff group G each object of $\mathbf{B}^G$ can be equivariantly embedded in some power of $\langle G, C_c(G,X), \tilde{\rho}\rangle$. Notice that if $C_c(G,X)$ is in $\mathbf{B}$, then $\langle G, C_c(G,X), \tilde{\rho}\rangle$ is a cogenerator in $\mathbf{B}^G$ (cf. subsection 6.4), which is completely in accordance with the equivalence of the statements (i), (ii) and (iii) above. We shall not use explicitly this equivalence nor the concept of a cogenerator. The preceding discussion is only included in order to indicate the relationship of subsections 7.1 and 6.4. In subsection 7.2 we present a highly non-categorical modification of the approach of 7.1, which enables us to replace in some cases powers of the space $C_c(G,X)$ by the simpler space $C_c(G\times G,X)$. Finally, in subsection 7.3 we apply the results of 7.1 in order to obtain statements about the existence of compactifications of G-spaces.

7.1. General remarks

7.1.1. An object X in **TOP** will be called *comprehensive for a class* $\mathcal{B}$ *of objects in* **TOP** if for each $Y \in \mathcal{B}$ there exists a topological embedding of Y into X. Observe that we do not require that $X \in \mathcal{B}$.

Similarly, if G is a fixed topological group, then a G-space $\langle G,X,\pi\rangle$ is said to be *comprehensive for a class* $\mathcal{C}$ *of objects in* $\mathbf{TOP}^G$ whenever each $\langle G,Y,\sigma\rangle \in \mathcal{C}$ admits an equivariant topological embedding into $\langle G,X,\pi\rangle$. Again, we do not require that the comprehensive object $\langle G,X,\pi\rangle$ for $\mathcal{C}$ is itself in $\mathcal{C}$.

7.1.2. If $\langle G,X,\pi\rangle$ is comprehensive for a class $\mathcal{C}$ of G-spaces, then obviously X is comprehensive (in **TOP**) for the class $S^G[\mathcal{C}]$. In this section we shall consider comprehensive objects in $\mathbf{TOP}^G$ of the form $\langle G,C_c(G,X),\tilde{\rho}\rangle$. To do so, we have to assume that G is locally compact Hausdorff. In order to avoid trivialities, we shall also assume that G is infinite. *So from now on,* G *is an infinite locally compact Hausdorff group.*

Recall from 6.3.5 that for any G-space $\langle G,Y,\sigma\rangle$ and any topological space X there exists a bijection of $C(Y,X)$ onto $\mathbf{TOP}^G(\langle G,Y,\sigma\rangle,\langle G,C_c(G,X),\tilde{\rho}\rangle)$. For simplicity, we shall denote this bijection here by Ψ_σ. Hence by (9) and (10) in 6.3.5, we have

$$(1) \qquad (\Psi_\sigma f)(y) = \langle 1_G, f\circ\sigma_y\rangle \ ; \ (\overleftarrow{\Psi_\sigma}\langle 1_G,g\rangle)(y) = g(y)(e)$$

for $f \in C(Y,X)$, $y \in Y$ and $\langle 1_G,g\rangle\colon \langle G,Y,\sigma\rangle \to \langle G,C_c(G,X),\tilde{\rho}\rangle$. In particular, if $\langle 1_G,g\rangle$ defines a topological embedding of Y into $C_c(G,X)$, then $f := \overleftarrow{\Psi_\sigma}\langle 1_G,g\rangle\colon Y\to X$ is a continuous function such that

$$(2) \qquad \{f\circ\sigma^t : t\in G\} \text{ separates the points of } Y.$$

Conversely, if $f\colon Y\to X$ is any continuous function satisfying (2), then $\Psi_\sigma f$ induces an equivariant continuous *injection* of Y into $C_c(G,X)$.

Therefore, there are two possibilities to solve the question for what classes the ttg $<G,C_c(G,X),\tilde{\rho}>$ with given X is comprehensive: a direct approach, which provides the equivariant embedding $<1_G,g>$, and an indirect one, where one looks for continuous functions f satisfying (2), such that $\Psi_\sigma f$ is, in addition, relatively open.

We shall choose the first possibility. In addition, we adopt the same point of view as in the preceding chapter, viz. that everything about $\mathbf{TOP}^G$ should be reduced to facts about **TOP**. To be concrete, we shall consider a class $\mathcal{B}$ of topological spaces, and a topological space X_0 such that X_0^I is comprehensive for $\mathcal{B}$ (with I a given index set). Using this as a starting point, we shall search for a comprehensive object in $\mathbf{TOP}^G$ for $(S^G)^{\leftarrow}[\mathcal{B}]$.

7.1.3. EXAMPLES.)1 If κ is a cardinal number, then X_0^κ denotes a product of κ copies of X_o. With this notation, we have for any cardinal κ (finite or transfinite):

(i) $[0,1]^\kappa$ is comprehensive for the class of all Tychonov spaces of weight $\leq \kappa$. Cf. [En], Chap.2, §3, Theorem 8. Obviously, $\mathbb{R}^\kappa$ is also comprehensive for this class. In particular, if $\kappa = \aleph_0$, we infer that $[0,1]^{\aleph_0}$ (and similarly, $\mathbb{R}^{\aleph_0}$) is comprehensive for the class of all separable metrizable spaces.

(ii) Let $D_2 := \{0,1\}$ be the *discrete* space consisting of two points. Then D_2^κ is comprehensive for the class of all 0-dimensional Hausdorff spaces of weight $\leq \kappa$. Cf. [En], Chap.6, §2, Theorem 11. In particular, $D_2^{\aleph_0}$ is comprehensive for the class of all separable metrizable 0-dimensional spaces.

(iii) Let F_2 be the space {0,1} with the T_0-topology $\{\emptyset,\{0\},\{0,1\}\}$. Then for each cardinal number κ, F_2^κ is comprehensive for the class of all T_0-spaces of weight $\leq \kappa$. Cf. [En], Chap.2, §3, Theorem 9.

(iv) If κ is a cardinal number (finite or transfinite), then the space S(κ) will be defined as follows: let I be a set of cardinality κ, and define an equivalence relation in the set I×[0,1] such that the equivalence classes are just all singletons $\{(i,x)\}$ with $i \in I$ and $0 < x \leq 1$ together with the set $\{(i,0) : i\in I\}$. The resulting quotient set may be vizualized as a "star", i.e. a union of κ intervals [0,1] which have their left end points 0 in common; the intervals which constitute

---

)1 As indicated in the introduction, there is a close connection between these examples and those in 6.4.2.

this star shall be called "rays". Now $S(\kappa)$ will denote this star with the topology which is generated by the following metric d:

$$d(x,y) := \begin{cases} |x-y| & \text{if x and y are in the same ray;} \\ |x| + |y| & \text{if x and y are in different rays;} \end{cases}$$

for $x,y \in S(\kappa)$. Note that this topology is *not* the quotient topology inherited from $I\times[0,1]$, unless κ is finite.
A collection $\mathcal{B}$ of subsets of a topological space X is said to be α-*discrete* ($\alpha \geq \aleph_0$) provided $\mathcal{B} = \cup\{\mathcal{B}_j : j\in J\}$ with $|J| \leq \alpha$ and each $\mathcal{B}_j$ a discrete family of subsets of X (i.e. each point in X has a neighbourhood which meets at most one member of $\mathcal{B}_j$). For example, for any cardinal κ, the space $S(\kappa)$ defined above has an $\aleph_0$-discrete base, because [0,1] has a countable base (cf. [Kw], 28.6).
A close examination of the proof of [Kw], 28.7 shows that for any two infinite cardinal numbers α and κ with $\alpha \leq \kappa$ the space $[S(\kappa)]^{\alpha}$ is comprehensive for the class of all T_4-spaces which have an α-discrete base of cardinality $\leq \kappa$ (these spaces have therefore weight $\leq \kappa$). In particular, $[S(\kappa)]^{\kappa}$ is comprehensive for the class of all T_4-spaces of weight $\leq \kappa$.
In addition, $[S(\kappa)]^{\aleph_0}$ is comprehensive for the class of all T_3-spaces having an $\aleph_0$-discrete base of cardinality κ (cf. [Kw], 28.8). Hence by BING's metrization theorem, it is comprehensive for the class of all metrizable spaces of weight $\leq \kappa$ (this can also be found in [En], Chap.4, §4, Theorem 7).

7.1.4. Let $\mathcal{B}$ denote a class of topological spaces. Suppose that the space X_0^I is comprehensive for $\mathcal{B}$ in **TOP**. We shall construct a comprehensive object in $\mathbf{TOP}^G$ with respect to the class $(S^G)^{\leftarrow}[\mathcal{B}]$, provided G and X_0 fulfill some additional conditions.

The first step is the observation that *for any G-space* $\langle G,Y,\sigma\rangle$ *with* $Y \in \mathcal{B}$ *we have the equivariant embedding*

(3) $\underline{\sigma}: Y \to C_c(G,Y)$

of the G-space Y with action σ into the G-space $C_c(G,Y)$ with action $\tilde{\rho}$ (cf. 2.1.3).

Let Y admit the embedding $f: Y \to X_0^I$. Equivalently, there exists a set $\{f_i : i\in I\}$ of continuous mappings of Y into X_0 which separates points and closed sets; then $f: y \mapsto (f_i(y))_i$ is a topological embedding of Y into X_0^I. It is trivial, that the mapping

(4) $$F: g \mapsto f \circ g: C_c(G,Y) \to C_c(G,X_0^I)$$

is a topological embedding. In fact, F *is an equivariant embedding of the* G*-space* $C_c(G,Y)$ *with action* $\tilde{\rho}$ *into the* G*-space* $C_c(G,X_0^I)$ *with action* $\tilde{\rho}$. Observe, that we may define F alternatively by

(5) $$F(g)(s) := (f_i(g(s)))_i$$

for $g \in C_c(G,Y)$ and $s \in G$, where $\{f_i : i \in I\}$ is an (arbitrary, but fixed) collection of continuous mappings of Y into X_0 which separates points and closed sets.

The next step is the observation that the G-space $C_c(G,X_0^I)$ is isomorphic with the product of $|I|$ copies of $\langle G, C_c(G,X_0), \tilde{\rho}\rangle$ in $\mathbf{TOP}^G$. Formally, let $\langle G, C_c(G,X_0)^I, \tilde{\rho}^I\rangle$ denote this product (cf. 3.2.6 for the precise description). If $\eta \in C_c(G,X_0^I)$, then for every $t \in G$, $\eta(t) = (\eta(t,i))_i$ with $\eta(t,i) \in X_0$ for every $i \in I$. Then each $\eta_i: t \mapsto \eta(t,i): G \to X_0$ is continuous, and in this way we obviously obtain a bijection

(6) $$\Phi: \eta \mapsto (\eta_i)_i : C_c(G,X_0^I) \to C_c(G,X_0)^I.$$

It is easy to see that Φ is equivariant with respect to the action $\tilde{\rho}$ of G on $C_c(G,X_0^I)$ and the action $\tilde{\rho}^I$ of G on $C_c(G,X_0)^I$. We show now that Φ is a homeomorphism, *so that* Φ *is an isomorphism of* G*-spaces of* $C_c(G,X_0^I)$ *with action* $\tilde{\rho}$ *and* $C_c(G,X_0)^I$ *with action* $\tilde{\rho}^I$.

That Φ is a homeomorphism can be seen as follows. For any space Z, we may write $Z^I = C_c(I,Z)$, if we give I the discrete topology. Since both G and I are locally compact Hausdorff spaces, we have the homeomorphisms

$$\varphi_1: \alpha \mapsto \bar{\alpha} : C_c(G \times I, X_0) \to C_c(G, C_c(I,X_0)),$$

$$\varphi_2: \beta \mapsto \underline{\beta} : C_c(G \times I, X_0) \to C_c(I, C_c(G,X_0))$$

(cf. 0.2.7(iii)). Plainly $\Phi = \varphi_2\varphi_1^{\leftarrow}$, so Φ is a homeomorphism.

7.1.5. *Resuming, if* <G,Y,σ> *is a ttg with* Y ∈ $\mathcal{B}$, *then we have an equivariant embedding*

$$(7) \qquad \Phi \circ F \circ \underline{\sigma}\colon Y \to C_c(G,X_0)^I$$

of the G-space Y *into the G-space* $C_c(G,X_0)^I$. Note, that if F is given by (5), then

$$(8) \qquad (\Phi \circ F \circ \underline{\sigma})(y) = (f_i \circ \sigma_y)_i$$

for all y ∈ Y. Untill here our construction is "canonical" in the sense that we used only mappings which have some meaning in the categorical context of the preceding sections.

7.1.6. We leave the applications of 7.1.5 to the various classes $\mathcal{B}$, mentioned in 7.1.3, to the reader. If $X_0 = \mathbb{R}$, then we have to do with the G-space $C_c(G)^I$, which is comprehensive for the class of all G-spaces Y such that Y is a Tychonov space of weight $w(Y) \leq |I|$. In the next subsection we shall show that under rather weak restrictions, we can obtain a comprehensive object with phase space $C_c(G\times G)$. Although this space is in a sense simpler than $C_c(G)^I$, the methods in subsection 7.2 will be non-categorical.

7.1.7. NOTES. In 7.1.2 we mentioned an alternative attack of the problem of comprehensive objects, exploring condition (2). This has been done in S. KAKUTANI [1968] in proving that $\langle \mathbb{R}, C_c(\mathbb{R}), \tilde{\rho}\rangle$ is comprehensive for the class of all compact metrizable $\mathbb{R}$-spaces having a fixed point set which is homeomorphic to a subset of $\mathbb{R}$.

7.2. The comprehensive object $\langle G, C_c(G\times G,X_0), \tilde{r}\rangle$

7.2.1. As before, let G denote a locally compact Hausdorff topological group; to avoid trivialities, we assume that G is infinite. In addition, we shall consider an object X_0 ∈ TOP such that X_0^I is comprehensive for a class $\mathcal{B}$ of topological spaces (where the index set I and the class $\mathcal{B}$ are, of course, somehow related to each other; cf. 7.1.3.

We shall show in this subsection that, under certain additional conditions on G, $\mathcal{B}$, X_0 and I, the class $(S^G)^{\leftarrow}[\mathcal{B}]$ admits a comprehensive object with phase space $C_c(G\times G,X_0)$. See 7.2.9 and 7.2.10 below. The action of G on $C_c(G\times G,X_0)$ can be described as follows:

In the usual way, $C_c(G\times G,X_0)$ can be identified with $C_c(G,C_c(G,X_0))$. In doing so, the action $\tilde{\rho}$ of G on $C_c(G,C_c(G,X_0))$ corresponds to an action $\tilde{r}$ of G on $C_c(G\times G,X_0)$, defined by

$$(1) \qquad \tilde{r}^u f(s,t) := f(su,t)$$

for $f \in C_c(G\times G,X_0)$, $u \in G$ and $(s,t) \in G\times G$. It follows from the above correspondence between $\tilde{\rho}$ and $\tilde{r}$, that $\tilde{r}: G\times C_c(G\times G,X_0) \to C_c(G\times G,X_0)$ is continuous, because $\tilde{\rho}$ is continuous by 2.1.3 (of course, continuity of $\tilde{r}$ can also be proved directly). In this way we obtain a ttg $\langle G,C_c(G\times G,X_0),\tilde{r}\rangle$, which is isomorphic to $\langle G,C_c(G,C_c(G,X_0)),\tilde{\rho}\rangle$.

7.2.2. LEMMA. *Suppose* G *is non-compact, and let* I *be a set of cardinality* $|I| = L(G)$, *the Lindelöf degree of* G. *Then there exists a locally finite, disjoint*[1] *family* $\{C_i : i\in I\}$ *of non-empty open subsets of* G. *If* $L(G) > \aleph_0$ *(i.e.* G *not sigma-compact) or if* G *is* 0*-dimensional, then every* C_i *may assumed to be open and closed. In all cases, the family* $\{cl_G C_i : i\in I\}$ *may supposed to be disjoint.*

PROOF. First we consider the case that G is not sigma-compact, i.e. $L(G) > \aleph_0$. Let $U \in \mathcal{V}_e$ be compact and symmetric, and set $H := \cup\{U^n : i\in\mathbb{N}\}$. Then it is well-known (and easy to prove) that H is a subgroup of G, that H is open and closed in G (see [HR], 5.7), and that H is sigma-compact (each U^n is compact). Since the family of all different right cosets of H in G forms an open covering which has no proper subcovering, it is clear that $L(G) \geq |G/H|$. On the other hand, $|G/H| > \aleph_0$, otherwise G would be sigma-compact. Moreover, each of the right cosets of H is open in G and its Lindelöf degree equals $L(H)$ which is $\leq \aleph_0$. Now it is not difficult to see that every open covering of G has a refinement of cardinality $\aleph_0\cdot|G/H| = |G/H|$ (take intersections with cosets). Hence it has a subcovering of cardinality $|G/H|$ and, consequently, $L(G) = |G/H|$. Hence for the family $\{C_i : i\in I\}$ we can take the right cosets of H in G: this collection satisfies all requirements.

If G is sigma-compact then the preceding method fails because it may occur that $H = G$ (e.g. if G is connected). Now we proceed in the following

---

[1] *Disjoint* means: $i \neq j \Rightarrow C_i \cap C_j = \emptyset$. Since each $C_i \neq \emptyset$, this implies plainly that $C_i \neq C_j$ for $i \neq j$.

way. First, note that $L(G) = \aleph_0$, so we may take $I = \mathbb{N}$)1. Again, let U denote a compact neighbourhood of e in G. Since G is not compact, there is a sequence $\{t_i : i \in \mathbb{N}\}$ in G such that $t_{n+1} \notin \bigcup\{t_i U : 1 \le i \le n\}$ for every $n \in \mathbb{N}$. Let V be an open neighbourhood of e such that $V = V^{-1}$ and $V^4 \subseteq U$. Then the family $\{t_i V^2 : i \in \mathbb{N}\}$ is disjoint, hence $\{t_i V : i \in \mathbb{N}\}$ is disjoint and locally finite (if $s \in G$, then sV meets at most one of the sets $t_i V$). Hence we can take $C_i := t_i V$ for $i \in \mathbb{N}$. Observe that $cl_G C_i \subseteq t_i V^2$, so that the sets $cl_G C_i$ are mutually disjoint. If G is 0-dimensional, then V could have been taken open and closed, so that each $C_i = t_i V$ would be open and closed. □

7.2.3. *Suppose that* G *is non-compact* (for compact groups, cf. 7.2.13 below). Fix a locally finite family $\{C_i : i \in I\}$ of non-empty open subsets of G, where I is a set of cardinality $L(G)$, and $cl_G C_i \cap cl_G C_j = \emptyset$ for $i,j \in I$, $i \neq j$. Next, fix a family of continuous functions $\psi_i : G \to [0,1]$ $(i \in I)$ as follows:

If each C_i is open and closed, let ψ_i be the characteristic function of C_i, that is, $\psi_i(t) = 0$ or 1, according to $t \notin C_i$ or $t \in C_i$, respectively. In the other case, fix $t_i \in C_i$ for every $i \in I$. Using complete regularity of G, it follows that there exist continuous functions $\psi_i : G \to [0,1]$ such that $\psi_i(t_i) = 1$ and $\psi_i(t) = 0$ for $t \in G \sim C_i$.

Notice that in both cases we have $\psi_i(t) = 0$ *for* $t \notin C_i$; *in addition, for each* $i \in I$ *there exists* $t_i \in C_i$ *such that* $\psi_i(t_i) = 1$.

7.2.4. With I as in 7.2.3, assume that the space X_0^I is comprehensive in **TOP** with respect to a class $\mathcal{B}$ of topological spaces. Assume that there exists a mapping $m: [0,1] \times X_0 \to X_0$ with the following properties:

(U1) $\exists x_0 \in X_0 : m(0,x) = x_0$ for all $x \in X_0$.

(U2) $m(1,x) = x$ for all $x \in X_0$.

(U3) For every $i \in I$, the mapping $(s,x) \mapsto m(\psi_i(s),x): G \times X_0 \to X_0$ is continuous.

7.2.5. <u>EXAMPLES</u>.

(i) If X_0 is a contractible space, then there exists a *continuous* mapping $m: [0,1] \times X_0 \to X_0$ satisfying (U1) and (U2) of 7.2.4. Condition (U3) is then obviously fulfilled. Notice that for each cardinal number κ the space $S(\kappa)$ (cf. 7.1.3) is contractible. Other contractible spaces are

---

)1 Obviously, $L(G) < \aleph_0$ implies that G is compact (in fact, it is not too difficult to show that $L(G) < \aleph_0$ implies that G is finite).

$[0,1]$ and $\mathbb{R}$. If $X_0 = [0,1]$ or $X_0 = \mathbb{R}$, we can take for m the usual multiplication mapping, $m: (x,y) \mapsto xy$.

(ii) If $X_0 = D_2$ = the discrete space $\{0,1\}$, then define $m: [0,1]\times D_2 \to D_2$ by

$$(2) \qquad m(a,0) = 0 \text{ for all } a \in [0,1] \qquad m(a,1) = \begin{cases} 0 & \text{if } a = 0 \\ 1 & \text{if } 0 < a \leq 1. \end{cases}$$

Obviously, m satisfies (U1) with $x_0 = 0$, and (U2). In addition, if all sets C_i in 7.2.3 could be chosen to be open and closed, then (U3) is also satisfied. {Indeed, then the functions ψ_i have only the values 0 and 1, so $m(\psi_i(s),x) = 0$ for all $s \in G \sim C_i$ and $m(\psi_i(s),x) = x$ for all $s \in C_i$ $(x \in D_2)$. Since both C_i and $G \sim C_i$ are open, continuity of $(s,x) \mapsto m(\psi_i(s),x)$ is obvious.} Thus, if G is 0-dimensional or if $L(G) > \aleph_0$ (cf. 7.2.2) then we may assume that the function m, defined by (2), satisfies (U1), (U2) and (U3) for $X_0 = D_2$.

7.2.6. In the remainder of this subsection, we shall write more concisely $m(s,x) =: sx$ for $(s,x) \in G\times X_0$, if m is as in 7.2.4.

With notation as in 7.2.3 and 7.2.4 we can define unambiguously a function $\Gamma: C_c(G,X_0)^I \to X_0^{G\times G}$ by

$$(3) \qquad \Gamma(\eta)(s,t) := \begin{cases} \psi_i(t)\eta_i(s) & \text{if } t \in \mathrm{cl}_G C_i \\ x_0 & \text{if } t \in G \sim \bigcup_j C_j \end{cases}$$

for $\eta=(\eta_i)_i \in C_c(G,X_0)^I$ and $s,t \in G$. That this is possible follows from the fact that the closures of the sets C_i are disjoint. Moreover, for $t \in \mathrm{cl}_G C_i \cap (G \sim \bigcup_j C_j)$ we have $t \notin C_i$, so $\psi_i(t) = 0$, hence $\psi_i(t)\eta_i(s) = x_0$ by (U1). So the definition is unambiguous.

7.2.7. <u>LEMMA</u>. *The mapping* Γ *defines a topological embedding of* $C_c(G,X_0)^I$ *into* $C_c(G\times G,X_0)$[1].

---

[1] Stated otherwise, Γ induces a topological embedding of $C_c(I\times G,X_0)$ into $C_c(G\times G,X_0)$ or, alternatively, of $C_c(I,C_c(G,X_0))$ into $C_c(G,C_c(G,X_0))$.

PROOF. Consider $\eta=(\eta_i) \in C_c(G,X_0)^I$. First, we have to show that $\Gamma(\eta) \in C_c(G\times G,X_0)$. To this end, observe that for every $i \in I$ the function $(s,t) \mapsto \psi_i(t)\eta_i(s)$: $G\times G \to X_0$ is continuous by (U3). Consequently, the restriction of $\Gamma(\eta)$ to each set $G \times \mathrm{cl}_G C_i$ is continuous. Obviously, the restriction of $\Gamma(\eta)$ to the set $G \times (G \sim \bigcup_j C_j)$ is continuous. The family $\{G\times \mathrm{cl}_G C_i : i\in I\} \cup \{G\times(G \sim \bigcup_j C_j)\}$ is a covering of $G \times G$ by closed sets, and this covering is easily seen to be locally finite. Indeed, $\{C_i : i\in I\}$ and hence $\{\mathrm{cl}_G C_i : i\in I\}$ is a locally finite family in G. Now it is an easy exercise to show that continuity of $\Gamma(\eta)$ on each member of this locally finite, closed covering of $G \times G$ implies continuity of $\Gamma(\eta)$ on $G \times G$. (Cf. also [Du], Chap.III, Theorem 9.4.)

Next, we show that Γ: $C_c(G,X_0)^I \to C_c(G\times G,X_0)$ is continuous. It is sufficient to show that for every subbasical open set of the form $N(K_1\times K_2,V)$ with compact K_1,K_2 in G and open V in X_0, the set $\Gamma^{\leftarrow}[N(K_1\times K_2,V)]$ is open in $C_c(G,X_0)^I$. So consider $\eta \in \Gamma^{\leftarrow}[N(K_1\times K_2,V)]$, i.e. $\eta=(\eta_i)_i \in C_c(G,X_0)^I$ with $\Gamma(\eta)[K_1\times K_2] \subseteq V$. Since $\{\mathrm{cl}_G C_i : i\in I\}$ is locally finite and K_2 is compact, there is a *finite* subset I_0 of I such that $A_i := K_2 \cap \mathrm{cl}_G C_i \neq \emptyset$ iff $i \in I_0$.

For every $i \in I_0$, set $U_i := \{y\in X_0 : \psi_i(t)y \in V \text{ for all } t\in A_i\}$. If $y \in U_i$, then some elementary compactness arguments (namely, an application of 0.2.2(i)) show that y is an interior point of U_i. This proves that U_i is an open subset of X_0. Since $\Gamma(\eta)[K_1\times K_2] \subseteq V$, it follows that $\psi_i(t)\eta_i(s) \in V$ for all $s \in K_1$ and $t \in A_i$. Hence $\eta_i(s) \in U_i$ for all $s \in K_1$, that is, $\eta_i \in N(K_1,U_i)$. Thus, $N(K_1,U_i)$ is an open neighbourhood of η_i in $C_c(G,X_0)$.

Now set $V_i := N_i(K_1,U_i)$ if $i \in I_0$ and $V_i := C_c(G,X_0)$ if $i \in I \sim I_0$. Then $\mathbb{P}_i V_i$ is a neighbourhood of η in $C_c(G,X_0)^I$. Moreover, if $\xi \in \mathbb{P}_i V_i$ then we have for all $(s,t) \in K_1\times K_2$:

$$\Gamma(\xi)(s,t) = \begin{cases} \psi_i(t)\xi_i(s) & \text{if } t \in A_i \\ x_0 & \text{if } t \in K_2\sim \bigcup_j C_j \end{cases}$$

In the first case, $i \in I_0$, hence $\xi_i(s) \in U_i$ and $\psi_i(t)\xi_i(s) \in V$. If, in the other case, $s \in K_1$ and $t \in K_2\sim \bigcup_j C_j$ then $\Gamma(\eta)(s,t) = x_0$, and consequently, $\Gamma(\xi)(s,t) = x_0 \in \Gamma(\eta)[K_1\times K_2] \subseteq V$. In all cases, therefore, we have $\Gamma(\xi)(s,t) \in V$ for $(s,t) \in K_1\times K_2$. We have proved now, that $\Gamma[\mathbb{P}_i V_i] \subseteq N(K_1\times K_2,V)$, and the continuity of Γ follows.

That Γ is injective is easy to see: if $\xi,\eta \in C_c(G,X_0)^I$, $\xi \neq \eta$, then for some $i \in I$ and $s \in G$ we have $\xi_i(s) \neq \eta_i(s)$. Take the element t_i in C_i with $\psi_i(t_i) = 1$. Then, by (U2),

$$\Gamma(\xi)(s,t_i) = \psi_i(t_i)\xi_i(s) = \xi_i(s) \neq \eta_i(s) = \psi_i(t_i)\eta_i(s) = \Gamma(\eta)(s,t_i).$$

Consequently, $\Gamma(\xi) \neq \Gamma(\eta)$.

Finally, we show that Γ is relatively open. It is sufficient (and, by injectiveness of Γ, also necessary) to show the following: given any $\eta \in C_c(G,X_0)^I$ and any neighbourhood V of η in $C_c(G,X_0)^I$, there exists a neighbourhood W of $\Gamma(\eta)$ in $C_c(G\times G,X_0)$ such that

(4) $$\{\xi : \xi \in C_c(G,X_0)^I \ \& \ \Gamma(\xi)\in W\} \subseteq V.$$

We may assume that $V = \mathbb{P}_i V_i$, where for some finite subset I_1 of I, some compact set K in G and some open sets U_i in X_0 $(i \in I_1)$,

$$V_i = \begin{cases} C_c(G,X_0) & \text{if } i \in I \sim I_1 \\ N(K,U_i) & \text{if } i \in I_1. \end{cases}$$

Let $K_1 := \{t_i : i\in I_1\}$ (recall that each $t_i \in C_i$ satisfies the condition that $\psi_i(t_i) = 1$). Then K_1 is a finite, hence compact subset of G. Now for every $i \in I_1$ and $s \in K$ we have

(5) $$\Gamma(\eta)(s,t_i) = \psi_i(t_i)\eta_i(s) = \eta_i(s) \in U_i$$

(use (U2) and the fact that $\eta_i \in V_i = N(K,U_i)$). Consequently, $\Gamma(\eta) \in \bigcap\{N(K\times\{t_i\},U_i) : i\in I_1\} =: W$. Obviously, it follows that W is a neighbourhood of $\Gamma(\eta)$ in $C_c(G\times G,X_0)$. This W satisfies condition (4). Indeed, if $\xi \in C_c(G,X_0)^I$ and $\Gamma(\xi) \in W$, then for any $i \in I_1$ and $s \in K$ we have

(6) $$\xi_i(s) = \psi_i(t_i)\xi_i(s) = \Gamma(\xi)(s,t_i) \in U_i.$$

Hence, $\xi_i \in N(K,U_i) = V_i$ for every $i \in I_1$, and, consequently, $\xi \in V$. □

7.2.8. <u>LEMMA</u>. *The mapping* $\Gamma: C_c(G,X_0)^I \to C_c(G\times G,X_0)$ *defines a morphism of G-spaces from* $C_c(G,X_0)^I$ *with action* $\tilde{\rho}^I$ *(cf. 7.1.4) into* $C_c(G\times G,X_0)$ *with action* $\tilde{r}$.

<u>PROOF</u>. A straightforward computation. □

7.2.9. PROPOSITION. *The ttg* $\langle G, C_c(G\times G, X_0), \tilde{r}\rangle$ *is comprehensive in* TOP^G *with respect to the class* $(S^G)^{\leftarrow}[\mathcal{B}]$, *provided* $X_0^{L(G)}$ *is comprehensive in* TOP *with respect to the class* $\mathcal{B}$, G *is non-compact, and* X_0 *satisfies the conditions* (U1), (U2) *and* (U3) *of* 7.2.4.

PROOF. For any G-space $\langle G, Y, \sigma\rangle$ with $Y \in \mathcal{B}$, we have the equivariant embedding $\Gamma\circ\Phi\circ F\circ\underline{\sigma}$ of Y into $C_c(G\times G, X_0)$ (for $\Phi\circ F\circ\underline{\sigma}$, cf. 7.1.5). □

7.2.10. APPLICATIONS. Suppose G is a non-compact locally compact Hausdorff topological group. Then:

(i) $\langle G, C_c(G\times G, [0,1]), \tilde{r}\rangle$ is comprehensive in TOP^G with respect to the class of all ttgs $\langle G, Y, \sigma\rangle$ with Y a Tychonov space of weight $w(Y) \le L(G)$.

(ii) $\langle G, C_c(G\times G, D_2), \tilde{r}\rangle$ is comprehensive in TOP^G with respect to the class of all ttgs $\langle G, Y, \sigma\rangle$ with Y a 0-dimensional Hausdorff space of weight $w(Y) \le L(G)$, provided either $L(G) > \aleph_0$ or G is 0-dimensional)1.

(iii) $\langle G, C_c(G\times G, S(\kappa)), \tilde{r}\rangle$ is comprehensive in TOP^G with respect to the class of all ttgs $\langle G, Y, \sigma\rangle$ with Y a T_4-space which has an $L(G)$-discrete base of cardinality $\le \kappa$.

If G is sigma-compact (i.e. $L(G) = \aleph_0$), then in (i) and (ii) above, all admitted spaces Y are separable metrizable, and in (iii), Y may be any metrizable space of weight $\le \kappa$.

PROOF. Cf. 7.1.3 and 7.2.5. □

7.2.11. In 7.2.10(i), the space $C_c(G\times G, [0,1])$ may clearly be replaced by $C_c(G\times G, \mathbb{R}) = C_c(G\times G)$. The ttg $\langle G, C_c(G\times G), \tilde{r}\rangle$ seems simple enough to deserve the predicate "nice". On the other hand, this ttg comprises all ttgs $\langle G, Y, \sigma\rangle$ with Y a Tychonov space of weight $\le L(G)$. This implies that $\langle G, C_c(G\times G), \tilde{r}\rangle$ has to have a rather complex structure.

7.2.12. According to 7.1.5, in particular formula (8), and the definition of M in 7.2.6, the equivariant embedding of a ttg $\langle G, Y, \sigma\rangle$ with $Y \in \mathcal{B}$ into the ttg $\langle G, C_c(G\times G, X_0), \tilde{r}\rangle$ mentioned in 7.2.9 may be effected in the following way. Let I be a set with $|I| = L(G)$, let $\{\psi_i : i\in I\}$ be a set of functions from G into [0,1] and let $m: [0,1]\times X_0 \to X_0$ be as in 7.2.3 and 7.2.4 (these data can be fixed with G and X_0). If $\{f_i : i\in I\}$ is a set of continuous functions from Y into X_0 which separates points and closed sets in Y, then the equivariant embedding h of Y into $C_c(G\times G)$ is given by

)1 In neither case G can be connected. Notice that the only action of a connected group on a 0-dimensional Hausdorff space is the trivial one. So the above mentioned restrictions on G are rather weak.

$$(7)\qquad h(y)(s,t) = \begin{cases} \psi_i(t)f_i(\sigma(s,y)) & \text{if } t \in cl_G C_i \\ x_0 & \text{if } t \notin \bigcup_j C_j \end{cases}$$

for $y \in Y$ and $(s,t) \in G\times G$.

{If we identify the space $C_c(G\times G,X_0)$ with $C_c(G,C_c(G,X_0))$ in the usual way, then the action $\tilde{r}$ becomes the action $\tilde{\rho}$ of G on $C_c(G,C_c(G,X_0))$; cf. 7.2.1, where $\tilde{r}$ was defined in this way. Then an equivariant embedding $\bar{h}$ of $\langle G,Y,\sigma\rangle$ into $\langle G,C_c(G,C_c(G,X_0)),\tilde{\rho}\rangle$ is obtained. It is given by

$$(\bar{h}(y)(s))(t) = h(y)(s,t)$$

for $y \in Y$ and $s,t \in G$. According to 7.1.2, the mapping $\Psi_\sigma^{\leftarrow}\langle 1_G,\bar{h}\rangle: Y \to C_c(G,X_0)$ is such that $\{\Psi^{\leftarrow}\langle 1_G,\bar{h}\rangle\circ\sigma^s : s\in G\}$ separates the points of Y. Recall, that here

$$(8)\qquad \Psi_\sigma^{\leftarrow}\langle 1_G,\bar{h}\rangle(y) = \bar{h}(y)(e): t \longmapsto \begin{cases} \psi_i(t)f_i(y) & \text{on } cl_G C_i \\ x_0 & \text{on } G\sim\bigcup_j C_j \end{cases}$$

for every $y \in Y$. We might also have started by defining a mapping $Y \to C_c(G,X_0)$ according to this rule, and then defining $\bar{h}$ as the Ψ_σ-value of this mapping. The technical difficulties, however, would have been the same (i.e. the several parts of the proof of lemma 7.2.7).}

7.2.13. If G is a compact T_2 group, then every locally finite family of subsets of G is finite. So the previous method yields only a ttg which is comprehensive for ttgs $\langle G,Y,\sigma\rangle$ with Y a subset of X_0^n, $n \in \mathbb{N}$ such that G admits a locally finite disjoint family consisting of n non-void open subsets. This can be a considerable class of ttgs: each k-dimensional separable metrizable space Y can be embedded in $[0,1]^{2k+1}$)1. *Consequently, if* G *admits for every* $n \in \mathbb{N}$ *a disjoint family of* n *non-void open subsets*)2*, then* $\langle G,C_c(G\times G,[0,1]),\tilde{r}\rangle$ *is comprehensive for the class of all ttgs* $\langle G,Y,\sigma\rangle$ *with* Y *a separable metrizable space of finite dimension.*

We shall remove now finite dimensionality from the conditions, i.e. we shall prove that 7.2.10(i) is also valid if G is compact, but not finite.

)1 Cf. for example [Na], Theorem IV.8.

)2 Since G is a compact Hausdorff space, this is equivalent to saying that G is not finite.

First we have to find a substitute for lemma 7.2.7.

7.2.14. LEMMA. *Let* G *be an infinite compact Hausdorff topological group. Then there exists a sequence* $\{C_n : n\in\mathbb{N}\}$ *of pairwise disjoint, non-empty open subsets of* G.

PROOF. Since G is not finite, G is not discrete. Hence there exists a sequence $\{V_n : n\in\mathbb{N}\}$ of neighbourhoods of e such that $cl_G V_{n+1} \subset V_n$ for every $n \in \mathbb{N}$. Now set $C_n := V_n \sim cl_G V_{n+1}$ $(n \in \mathbb{N})$. □

7.2.15. Let G be compact and infinite, and fix a sequence $\{C_n : n\in\mathbb{N}\}$ of mutually disjoint, non-empty open subsets of G. As in 7.2.3, let $\{\psi_n : n\in\mathbb{N}\}$ be a sequence of continuous functions from G into $[0,1]$ such that $\psi_n(t) = 0$ for $t \in G\sim C_n$ and $\psi_n(t_n) = 1$ for some $t_n \in C_n$ $(n \in \mathbb{N})$. Define a mapping $\Gamma: C_c(G,[0,1])^{\mathbb{N}} \to [0,1]^{G\times G}$ by

$$(9) \qquad \Gamma(\eta)(s,t) := \sum_{n=1}^{\infty} 2^{-n}\, \psi_n(t)\eta_n(s)$$

for $\eta = (\eta_n)_n \in C_c(G,[0,1])^{\mathbb{N}}$ and $s,t \in G$. Here juxtaposition in the right-hand member of (9) denotes ordinary multiplication in $[0,1]$. Since for every $s,t \in G$ the series in (9) is absolutely dominated by the convergent series $\Sigma_n 2^{-n}$ (which has sum 1), it is clear that $\Gamma(\eta)(s,t)$ is well-defined for every $\eta \in C_c(G,[0,1])^{\mathbb{N}}$ and $s,t \in G$, and that $\Gamma(\eta)(s,t) \in [0,1]$.

We can draw even one more conclusion: the convergence of the series in (9) is uniform in $(s,t) \in G\times G$. For fixed $\eta \in C_c(G,[0,1])^{\mathbb{N}}$, the terms in the series are continuous functions of (s,t) on $G \times G$. Consequently, the sum of the series depends continuously on (s,t), i.e. $\Gamma(\eta) \in C(G\times G,[0,1])$.

7.2.16. LEMMA. *The mapping* Γ *defined in* (9) *is a topological embedding of* $C_c(G,[0,1])^{\mathbb{N}}$ *into* $C_c(G\times G,[0,1])$.

PROOF. Since $G \times G$ is compact, basical neighbourhoods of $\Gamma(\eta)$ in $C_c(G\times G,[0,1])$ have the form

$$\{\xi \in C_c(G\times G,[0,1]) : |\Gamma(\eta)(s,t)-\xi(s,t)| < \varepsilon \text{ for all } s,t \in G\},$$

with $\varepsilon > 0$. Using this, continuity and relative openness of Γ may be proved along the lines of the proof of 7.2.7. In the proof of the continuity of Γ, the finite subset I_0 of $\mathbb{N}$ may be obtained by requiring that $\Sigma\{2^{-n} : n \in \mathbb{N}\sim I_0\}$ is sufficiently small (i.e. I_0 a sufficiently large initial segment in $\mathbb{N}$). □

7.2.17. Neither in 7.2.8, nor in 7.2.1, we used the non-compactness of G. Consequently, 7.2.9 remains valid for compact infinite G, provided we substitute [0,1] for X_0. The class $\mathcal{B}$ for which $[0,1]^{\mathbb{N}}$ is comprehensive is just the class of all separable metrizable spaces, i.e. the class of all Tychonov spaces of weight $\leq \aleph_0$.

7.2.18. THEOREM. *Let* G *be any infinite locally compact Hausdorff topological group. Then the ttg* $\langle G, C_c(G\times G,[0,1]), \tilde{r}\rangle$ *is comprehensive in* TOP^G *with respect to the class of all ttgs* $\langle G,Y,\sigma\rangle$ *with* Y *a Tychonov space of weight* $w(Y) \leq L(G)$.

PROOF. Cf. 7.2.10(i) for the case that G is non-compact. If G is compact, we have $L(G) \leq \aleph_0$ (in fact, $L(G) = \aleph_0$, because $L(G) < \aleph_0$ would imply that G were finite). Hence $w(Y) \leq L(G)$ implies that Y is a separable metrizable space, and we can apply the preceding remark. □

7.2.19. In the above theorem, we may of course replace $C_c(G\times G,[0,1])$ by the space $C_c^*(G\times G)$, or by the space $C_c(G\times G)$. However, it is useful to notice that a *uniformly bounded* invariant subspace of $C_c(G\times G)$, namely $C_c(G\times G,[0,1])$, is comprehensive for the class of G-spaces described in the theorem.
We mention some particular properties of the ttg $\langle G,C_c(G\times G),\tilde{r}\rangle$:

(i) This ttg is effective but not strongly effective. Indeed, if $t \neq e$, then there is $f \in C_c(G\times G)$ such that $f(t,e) \neq f(e,e)$, hence $\tilde{r}^t f \neq f$; on the other hand, $\tilde{r}^t g = g$ for any constant function g.

(ii) The set of invariant points in $\langle G,C_c(G\times G),\tilde{r}\rangle$ is homeomorphic with $C_c(G)$. This follows immediately from the fact that $\langle G,C_c(G\times G),\tilde{r}\rangle$ is isomorphic to $\langle G,C_c(G,C_c(G)),\tilde{\rho}\rangle$. {Indeed, for any space Y, the invariant points in $\langle G,C_c(G,Y),\tilde{\rho}\rangle$ are the constant functions, and they form a subset of $C_c(G,Y)$ which is homeomorphic to Y.} Similarly, the set of invariant points in $\langle G,C_c(G\times G,[0,1]),\tilde{r}\rangle$ is homeomorphic with $C_c(G,[0,1])$.

(iii) If G is *compact*, then $C_c(G\times G) = C_u(G\times G)$, and every $\tilde{r}^t$ is an isometrical mapping of the metric space $C_u(G\times G)$ onto itself (the metric in $C_u(G\times G)$ is of course, the metric generated by the uniform norm).

7.2.20. EXAMPLES. We shall describe here three examples concerning the case that G = $\mathbb{R}$, $\mathbb{Z}$, or $\mathbb{T}$, respectively.

Suppose $G = \mathbb{R}$. For $i=1,2,\ldots$ we can take $C_i := [i-\frac{1}{4}, i+\frac{1}{4}]$, and $\psi_i : \mathbb{R} \to [0,1]$ as follows

$$(10) \qquad \psi_i(t) := \begin{cases} \cos^2 2\pi(t-i) & \text{if } i-\frac{1}{4} \le t \le i+\frac{1}{4} \\ 0 & \text{otherwise.} \end{cases}$$

If $\langle \mathbb{R}, Y, \sigma \rangle$ is any ttg with Y a separable metrizable space and $\{f_i : i \in \mathbb{N}\}$ is any family of continuous functions from Y into $[0,1]$ separating points and closed subsets of Y, then an equivariant embedding h of Y into $C_c(\mathbb{R}\times\mathbb{R},[0,1])$ is given by

$$(11) \qquad h(y)(s,t) = \begin{cases} \cos^2 2\pi(t-i)\cdot f_i(\sigma(s,y)) & \text{if } i-\frac{1}{4} \le t \le i+\frac{1}{4} \\ 0 & \text{if } t \notin \bigcup_j [j-\frac{1}{4}, j+\frac{1}{4}] \end{cases}$$

for $y \in Y$ and $(s,t) \in \mathbb{R}\times\mathbb{R}$. We may interprete this also as an equivariant embedding of Y (with action σ) into $C_c(\mathbb{R}\times\mathbb{R})$ (with action $\tilde{r}$) or into $C_c(\mathbb{R}, C_c(\mathbb{R}))$ (with action $\tilde{\rho}$).

Suppose $G = \mathbb{Z}$. For $i \in \mathbb{Z}$, set $C_i := \{i\}$, and define $\psi_i : \mathbb{Z} \to [0,1]$ by

$$(12) \qquad \psi_i(t) := \begin{cases} 1 & \text{if } t = i \\ 0 & \text{if } t \in \mathbb{Z}\sim\{i\}. \end{cases}$$

If Y is a separable metrizable space and $\{f_i : i \in \mathbb{Z}\}$ is any family of continuous functions of Y into $[0,1]$ separating points and closed subsets of Y, then for any homeomorphism $\sigma^1 : Y \to Y$ (equivalently, for any action σ of $\mathbb{Z}$ on Y; cf. 1.1.6(viii)) we have the following equivariant embedding h of Y into $C_c(\mathbb{Z}\times\mathbb{Z},[0,1]) = [0,1]^{\mathbb{Z}\times\mathbb{Z}}$:

$$(13) \qquad h(y)(s,t) = f_t(\sigma^s y)$$

for $y \in Y$ and $(s,t) \in \mathbb{Z}\times\mathbb{Z}$. Note that the action $\tilde{r}$ of $\mathbb{Z}$ on $[0,1]^{\mathbb{Z}\times\mathbb{Z}}$ is generated by the autohomeomorphism

$$(14) \qquad \tilde{r}^1 : (\xi(i,j))_{i,j} \mapsto (\xi(i+1,j))_{i,j}$$

(bilateral shift in the first coordinate.)

If Y is a separable metrizable 0-dimensional space and $\{f_i : i \in \mathbb{Z}\}$ is a family of continuous functions of Y into $\{0,1\}$ separating points and closed subsets, then for any homeomorphism $\sigma^1 : Y \to Y$, (13) describes an equivariant embedding of Y into $C_c(\mathbb{Z}\times\mathbb{Z},\{0,1\}) = \{0,1\}^{\mathbb{Z}\times\mathbb{Z}}$. In this space, the action is again described by (14).

Suppose $G = \mathbb{T}$. For i=1,2,..., set $C_k := \{\exp(2\pi i t) : t \in D_k\}$, where D_k is the interval

$$\left[\frac{1}{k} - \frac{1}{2k(k+1)}, \frac{1}{k} + \frac{1}{2k(k+1)}\right] = \left[\frac{2k+1}{2k(k+1)}, \frac{2k+3}{2k(k+1)}\right].$$

Define ψ_k by

$$\psi_k(\exp(2\pi i t)) := \begin{cases} \cos^2 k(k+1)\pi(t-k^{-1}) & \text{if } t \in D_k \\ 0 & \text{if } t \notin D_k. \end{cases}$$

If $\langle\mathbb{T},Y,\sigma\rangle$ is a ttg with Y a separable metrizable space and $\{f_i : i\in\mathbb{N}\}$ is a family of continuous functions of Y into [0,1] separating points and closed subsets of Y, then an equivariant embedding of Y into $C_c(\mathbb{T}\times\mathbb{T},[0,1])$ $= C_u(\mathbb{T}\times\mathbb{T},[0,1])$ is obtained by setting

$$h(y)(u,v) = \begin{cases} \cos^2 k(k+1)\pi(t-k^{-1})\cdot f_k(\sigma(u,y)) & \text{if } v = \exp(2\pi i t) \text{ with } t \in D_k \\ 0 & \text{otherwise} \end{cases}$$

for $y \in Y$ and $(u,v) \in \mathbb{T}\times\mathbb{T}$.

7.2.21. NOTES. Fundamental in this subsection is lemma 7.2.2. However, in this lemma it is not essential that G is a group. In fact, the lemma can be proved for any paracompact locally compact Hausdorff space. Cf. J. DE VRIES [1972b].

7.3. Compactifications of G-spaces

7.3.1. For the motivation, or at least, for the connection of the contents of this subsection with the results of Chapter II, we refer to the final remark in 4.3.13. Although all applications will be for locally compact Hausdorff groups G, we shall not make any particular assumption about G up to 7.3.7 (except that it has to be a topological group).

7.3.2. Let $\langle G,X,\pi\rangle$ be a ttg with X a completely regular space (i.e. the topology of X can be generated by a uniformity). Then $\langle G,X,\pi\rangle$ is said to be *bounded with respect to the uniformity* $\mathcal{U}$ provided

(i) $\mathcal{U}$ generates the topology of X.

(ii) $\forall \alpha \in \mathcal{U}, \exists U \in \mathcal{V}_e : (\pi^t x, x) \in \alpha$ for all $t \in U$, $x \in X$.

The ttg $\langle G,X,\pi\rangle$ is said to be *bounded* if it is bounded with respect to some uniformity $\mathcal{U}$. If X is metrizable and $\langle G,X,\pi\rangle$ is bounded with respect to a metrical uniformity (i.e. a uniformity with a countable base), then $\langle G,X,\pi\rangle$ is called *metrically bounded.*

7.3.3. LEMMA. *Let* $\langle G,X,\pi\rangle$ *be a ttg,* X *a uniform space with uniformity* $\mathcal{U}$. *The following conditions are equivalent:*

(i) $\langle G,X,\pi\rangle$ *is bounded with respect to* $\mathcal{U}$.

(ii) *The family* $\{\pi_x : x \in X\}$ *of functions from* G *into* X *is equicontinuous at* e[1].

(iii) *The family* $\{\pi_x : x \in X\}$ *is equi-uniformly continuous on* G, *if* G *is endowed with its right uniformity.*

PROOF.

(i) $\Leftrightarrow$ (ii) : Obvious from the definitions.

(i) $\Rightarrow$ (iii): Let $\alpha \in \mathcal{U}$. Take $U \in \mathcal{V}_e$ such that $(\pi^t y, y) \in \alpha$ for all $t \in U$ and $y \in X$. In particular, for every $s \in G$ and $x \in X$, setting $y := \pi^s x$, we obtain $(\pi_x(ts), \pi_x(s)) \in \alpha$ for all $x \in X$, $s \in G$ and $t \in V$.

(iii) $\Rightarrow$ (ii) : Obvious. □

7.3.4. In contradistinction to 7.3.14 below, we present now an example of a ttg $\langle G,X,\pi\rangle$ with G a sigma-compact locally compact Hausdorff topological group and X a (non-separable!) metrizable space, such that $\langle G,X,\pi\rangle$ is bounded but not metrically bounded.

7.3.5. EXAMPLE. Let I be an *uncountable* set, and let, for every $i \in I$, $\langle H_i, Y_i, \rho_i\rangle$ be a ttg with the following properties:

(i) Y_i is a compact metric space, say with metric d_i and metrical uniformity $\mathcal{U}_i$.

(ii) $\langle H_i, Y_i, \rho_i\rangle$ is *transitive*, i.e. for every $x,y \in Y_i$ there exists $t \in H_i$ such that $\rho_i^t(x) = y$.

(iii) H_i is a sigma-compact locally compact Hausdorff topological group.

In addition, for a fixed finite, non-void subset I_0 of I we require

---

[1] In [GH], a ttg with this property is called *motion equicontinuous.*

that H_i is compact if $i \in I \sim I_0$ and H_i is non-compact if $i \in I_0$. {Observe that such collections $\{\langle H_i, Y_i, \rho_i\rangle : i \in I\}$ of ttgs exist. For example, let $Y_i = \mathbb{T}$ for every $i \in I$, fix $i_0 \in I$, and set $H_{i_0} = \mathbb{R}$, $\rho^t_{i_0}$ = rotation of $\mathbb{T}$ over $2\pi t$ radians. For $i \in I$, $i \neq i_0$, let $H_i = \mathbb{T}$ (as a topological group) and $\rho_i = \lambda$ (= ordinary multiplication in $\mathbb{T}$).}

Since each Y_i is compact, $\mathcal{U}_i$ is the unique uniformity in Y_i which is compatible with the topology of Y_i. We shall use this fact without further reference. In addition, by 7.3.6 below, each $\langle H_i, Y_i, \rho_i\rangle$ is (metrically!) bounded.[1]

Let $\langle G, X, \pi\rangle$ denote the coproduct of the set $\{\langle H_i, Y_i, \rho_i\rangle : i \in I\}$ in TTG_* (cf. 6.1.10), with coprojections $\langle \psi_i^{op}, f_i\rangle : \langle G, X, \pi\rangle \to \langle H_i, Y_i, \rho_i\rangle$. Then G is the product of the set $\{H_i : i \in I\}$ in TOPGRP, with projections $\psi_i : G \to H_i$. So by condition (iii), G is a sigma-compact, locally compact Hausdorff group, but G is not compact. Moreover, X is the disjoint union of the spaces Y_i. Suppressing the canonical injections $f_i : Y_i \to X$, set for $i \in I$ and $n \in \mathbb{N}$

$$U(i,n) := \{(x,y) \in Y_i \times Y_i : d_i(x,y) < n^{-1}\}$$

and for every finite subset J of I

$$V(J,n) := \bigcup\{U(i,n) : i \in J\} \cup \bigcup\{Y_i \times Y_i : i \in I \sim J\}.$$

Then $\mathcal{B} := \{V(J,n) : n \in \mathbb{N}\ \&\ J \text{ a finite subset of } I\}$ is a base for a uniformity $\mathcal{U}$ in X which is compatible with the topology of X. Since for any $\alpha \in \mathcal{U}$ we can have $\alpha \cap (Y_i \times Y_i) \subset Y_i \times Y_i$ for only finitely many $i \in I$ and since $\langle H_i, Y_i, \rho_i\rangle$ is bounded for those i, it is easy to see that $\{\pi_x : x \in X\}$ is equicontinuous with respect to the uniformity $\mathcal{U}$ in X. So by 7.3.3, $\langle G, X, \pi\rangle$ is bounded.

However, it is not difficult to show that $\mathcal{U}$ cannot have a countable base, because I is uncountable. On the other hand, there exist uniformities for X, generating its topology, which have a countable base, because X is obviously metrizable. Let $\mathcal{V}$ denote any such a uniformity. Then for some $\beta \in \mathcal{V}$ the set

---

[1] If we restrict ourselves to the concrete example with each $Y_i = \mathbb{T}$, etc., then this can be seen directly, without any reference to 7.3.6.

$$J(\beta) := \{i \in I \,:\, \beta \cap (Y_i \times Y_i) \neq Y_i \times Y_i\}$$

is infinite. Otherwise, $\mathcal{V}$ would be equal to the uniformity $\mathcal{U}$ which has not a countable base. Fix such a β. Let $V = \mathbb{P}_i V_i$ be a neighbourhood of e in G, with $V_i \neq H_i$ for only a finite number of indices $i \in I$. Since $J(\beta)$ is infinite, there exists $j \in J(\beta)$ such that $V_j = H_j$. In view of condition (ii) and the choice of β, there exists $t_j \in H_j = V_j$ such that $(\rho_j(t_j,y),y) \notin \beta \cap (Y_j \times Y_j)$ for some $y \in Y_j$. Considering y as an element of X, this means that $(\pi(t,y),y) \notin \beta$ for $t = (t_i)_i \in V$, where t_i is the unit of G_i for $i \neq j$ and $t_j \in V_i$ is as above. We have proved now, that there exists $\beta \in \mathcal{V}$ such that every neighbourhood V of e in G contains an element t such that $(\pi^t y,y) \notin \beta$ for some $y \in X$. Thus, $\langle G,X,\pi\rangle$ is not bounded with respect to $\mathcal{V}$. This shows that $\langle G,X,\pi\rangle$ is not metrically bounded.

7.3.6. <u>PROPOSITION</u>. *If the phase space X of a ttg $\langle G,X,\pi\rangle$ is a compact Hausdorff space, then $\langle G,X,\pi\rangle$ is bounded. If X is compact and metrizable, then $\langle G,X,\pi\rangle$ is metrically bounded.*

<u>PROOF</u>. Suppose X is a compact Hausdorff space. By an elementary compactness argument, namely 0.2.2(ii), $\langle G,X,\pi\rangle$ is bounded with respect to the unique uniformity $\mathcal{U}$ of X. The second statement in the proposition is now trivial. □

7.3.7. From a different point of view, we can formulate the proof of 7.3.6 as follows. If X is compact, then $\underline{\pi}[X]$ is a compact subset of $C_c(G,X)$, by 2.1.13. Moreover, the restriction of the evaluation mapping $(\xi,t) \mapsto \xi(t)$: $C_c(G,X) \times G \to X$ to $\underline{\pi}[X] \times G$ is continuous on $\underline{\pi}[X] \times G$; indeed, $\underline{\pi}: X \to \underline{\pi}[X]$ is a homeomorphism, and $(x,t) \mapsto \pi_x(t): X \times G \to X$ is continuous. So by 0.2.8 (in particular, the converse to (iii)), $\underline{\pi}[X]$ is equicontinuous at every point of G, hence $\langle G,X,\pi\rangle$ is bounded by 7.3.3. This proof suggests that it may be useful to have a look at ttgs of the form $\langle G,C_c(G,Y),\tilde{\rho}\rangle$ with Y a uniform space. Although in general local compactness of G is needed to ensure that this is a ttg (cf. 2.1.3), we can dispense with this condition for G in the following proposition.

7.3.8. <u>PROPOSITION</u>. *Let G be a topological group, let Y be a uniform space, and let X be an invariant subset of the ttg $\langle G_d,C_c(G,Y),\tilde{\rho}\rangle$. Consider the following statements:*

(i) *X is equicontinuous on G.*

(ii) *The mapping $\tilde{\rho}$: $G \times X \to X$ is continuous, and the ttg $\langle G,X,\tilde{\rho}\rangle$ is bounded with respect to the relative uniformity of X in $C_c(G,Y)$.*

(iii) $\langle G,X,\tilde{\rho}\rangle$ *admits an equivariant embedding into a ttg* $\langle G,\tilde{X},\tilde{\pi}\rangle$ *with* $\tilde{X}$ *a compact Hausdorff space.*

(iv) $\langle G,X,\tilde{\rho}\rangle$ *is bounded.*

Then (i) $\Leftrightarrow$ (ii) $\Rightarrow$ (iv) *and* (iii) $\Rightarrow$ (iv). *In addition, if* $X \subseteq C^*(G,Y)$, *then also the implication* (i) $\Rightarrow$ (iii) *is valid.*

PROOF. (i) $\Rightarrow$ (ii): By 2.1.6, $\tilde{\rho}: G\times X \to X$ is continuous, so $\langle G,X,\tilde{\rho}\rangle$ is a ttg. Next, consider a compact subset K of G and an element $\alpha \in \mathcal{U}$. Since X is equi-uniformly continuous on K, there exists $V \in \mathcal{V}_e$ such that $(f(s),f(t)) \in \alpha$ for all $s \in K$ and $t \in G$ such that $t^{-1}s \in V$, and for all $f \in X$. Hence $(f,\tilde{\rho}^u f) \in M(K,\alpha)$ for all $f \in X$ and $u \in V^{-1}$.

(ii) $\Rightarrow$ (i): Let $\mathcal{U}$ denote the uniformity of Y, and take $s \in G$, $\alpha \in \mathcal{U}$. Boundedness of $\langle G,X,\tilde{\rho}\rangle$ implies that there exists $U \in \mathcal{V}_e$ such that $(\tilde{\rho}^t f,f) \in M(\{s\},\alpha)$ for all $f \in X$ and $t \in U$, i.e. $(f(st),f(s)) \in \alpha$ for all $f \in X$, $t \in U$. This proves that X is equicontinuous.

(ii) $\Rightarrow$ (iv) is trivial, and (iii) $\Rightarrow$ (iv) is an obvious consequence of 7.3.6. Moreover, if $X \subseteq C^*_c(G,Y)$, then equicontinuity of X implies that the closure $\tilde{X}$ of X in $C_c(G,Y)$ is compact, by the ASCOLI theorem. Therefore, $\tilde{X}$ is a compact invariant subset of $C_c(G,Y)$. Moreover, $\tilde{X}$ is equicontinuous as well (cf. 0.2.8), so $\tilde{\rho}$ is continuous on $G\times\tilde{X}$, by the implication (i) $\Rightarrow$ (ii) for $\tilde{X}$. Thus, (i) $\Rightarrow$ (iii) with $\tilde{\pi} := \tilde{\rho}|_{G\times X}$. □

7.3.9. *If in* 7.3.8 *the group* G *is locally compact and sigma-compact, and* Y *is metrizable, then in* (iii), $\tilde{X}$ *may required to be metrizable, and in* (iv) *we may demand:* $\langle G,X,\tilde{\rho}\rangle$ *is metrically bounded.*

Indeed, this follows immediately from the above proof and the fact fact that in the given situation $C_c(G,Y)$ is metrizable (cf. Appendix C.4, or alternatively, [Du], Chap. XII, 8.5).

7.3.10. EXAMPLES.

(i) Any ttg $\langle G,X,\pi\rangle$ with X locally compact Hausdorff is bounded. If in addition, X is a separable metrizable space, then $\langle G,X,\pi\rangle$ is metrically bounded. Indeed, X admits an equivariant embedding in the compact Hausdorff G-space $\tilde{X} = X\cup\{\infty\}$, the one-point compactification of X, with action $\tilde{\pi}$ defined by $\tilde{\pi}^t|_X = \pi^t$ and $\pi^t(\infty) = \infty$ $(t \in G)$. (See J. DE VRIES [1975c]). Now apply 7.3.6. Notice that $\tilde{X}$ is metrizable if X is separable and metrizable.

(ii) Any ttg $\langle G,X,\pi\rangle$ with X a Tychonov space and G a discrete group is bounded. In fact, $\langle G,X,\pi\rangle$ is bounded with respect to every uniformity which generates the topology of X. This is a trivial consequence of (ii) $\Rightarrow$ (i) in 7.3.3.

We have not been able to find an example of a ttg $\langle G,X,\pi\rangle$ with X a Tychonov space which is not bounded. Observe that such an example would provide an instance of a Tychonov G-space which cannot be embedded in a compact G-space.

7.3.11. The behaviour of boundedness under the application of (co)morphisms of ttgs is very similar to the behaviour of ttgs with a compact phase space. For example:

(i) If $\langle\psi,f\rangle$: $\langle G,X,\pi\rangle \to \langle H,Y,\sigma\rangle$ is a morphism in **TTG**, where f: $X\to Y$ is a topological embedding of X in the Tychonov space Y, then boundedness of $\langle H,Y,\sigma\rangle$ implies boundedness of $\langle G,X,\pi\rangle$. We leave the straightforward proof to the reader. Notice that we have applied this statement several times in the preceding proofs with Y compact and $\psi = 1_G$.

(ii) If $\langle\psi,f\rangle$: $\langle G,X,\pi\rangle \to \langle H,Y,\sigma\rangle$ is a morphism in **TTG**, X and Y Tychonov spaces, f a surjection and ψ an open mapping, then boundedness of $\langle G,X,\pi\rangle$ with respect to a uniformity $\mathcal{U}$ implies boundedness of $\langle H,Y,\sigma\rangle$ with respect to any uniformity $\mathcal{V}$ for which $(f\times f)^{\leftarrow}[\mathcal{V}] \subseteq \mathcal{U}$ (i.e. f *uniformly continuous*). Straightforward.

(iii) If $\langle\psi^{op},f\rangle$: $\langle G,X,\pi\rangle \to \langle H,Y,\sigma\rangle$ is a morphism in $\mathbf{TTG}_*$, X and Y Tychonov spaces, f a surjection, then boundedness of $\langle G,X,\pi\rangle$ with respect to a uniformity $\mathcal{U}$ implies boundedness of $\langle H,Y,\sigma\rangle$ with respect to any uniformity $\mathcal{V}$ in Y which makes f uniformly continuous (no additional conditions on $\langle\psi^{op},f\rangle$). Straightforward.

(iv) Arbitrary products in **TTG** (cf. 3.1.12 for what they look like) of bounded ttgs are again bounded. Similarly, coproducts in $\mathbf{TTG}_*$ of bounded ttgs are bounded (cf. 7.3.5; there the proof that the coproduct $\langle G,X,\pi\rangle$ of the given set of objects in $\mathbf{TTG}_*$ is bounded makes only use of boundedness of each of those objects). We leave the details to the reader.

The preceding statements show that bounded ttgs behave like ttgs with a compact phase space. A link between the two classes of ttgs is provided by our next proposition. First, recall that a Tychonov space X of weight $w(X)$ admits for every compatible uniformity $\mathcal{U}$ a topological embedding f: $x \mapsto (f_i(x))_i$: $X\to[0,1]^I$ such that $|I| = w(X)$ *with the additional property that each* f_i: $X\to[0,1]$ *is uniformly continuous with respect to the uniformity* $\mathcal{U}$ *in* X. Indeed, the usual proof that X can be embedded in $[0,1]^I$ with $|I| = w(X)$ (e.g. the proof of [En], Theorem 2.3.8) can easily be modified to a proof of the previous statement, using the lemma in 0.2.7. *Then* $f\colon X \to [0,1]^I$ *is uniformly continuous, hence the induced topological embedding* $F\colon \xi \mapsto f\circ\xi\colon C_c(G,X) \to C_c(G,[0,1]^I)$ *sends equicontinuous subsets of* $C_c(G,X)$ *into equicontinuous subsets of* $C_c(G,[0,1]^I)$. This will be used in our next result.

7.3.12. THEOREM. *Let* $\langle G,X,\pi\rangle$ *be a ttg with* G *an arbitrary topological group and* X *a Tychonov space. The following conditions are equivalent:*
(i) $\langle G,X,\pi\rangle$ *is bounded.*
(ii) *There exists an equivariant embedding of* X *into a compact Hausdorff* G*-space* $\tilde{X}$ *with*

$$w(\tilde{X}) \le \max\{w(G),w(X)\}.$$

PROOF.
(ii) ⇒ (i) : Apply 7.3.6 and 7.3.11(i).
(i) ⇒ (ii): Suppose $\langle G,X,\pi\rangle$ is bounded with respect to the uniformity $\mathcal{U}$ in X. If X is finite, take $\tilde{X} = X$ and $\tilde{\pi} = \pi$, and there remains nothing to be proved. So we may assume that $w(X) \ge \aleph_0$. By 7.3.3, $\underline{\pi}[X]$ is an equicontinuous subset of $C(G,X)$ with respect to the uniformity $\mathcal{U}$ in X. By the preceding remark, the topological embedding $F\circ\underline{\pi}$ of X into $C_c(G,[0,1]^I)$ maps X equivariantly onto an equicontinuous, invariant subset of the G-space $C_c(G,[0,1]^I)$ (with action $\tilde{\rho}$); here $|I| = w(X)$. By 7.3.8 there exists a compact Hausdorff G-space $\tilde{X}$ in which X can equivariantly be embedded. Recall, that $\tilde{X}$ is the closure of X in $C_c(G,[0,1]^I)$. Hence the inequality $w(\tilde{X}) \le w(X)\cdot w(G)$ can be proved as follows. First, notice that $w(C_c(G,[0,1])) = w(G)\cdot\aleph_0$ (cf. Appendix C). In addition, it is well-known that for any space Z and any infinite cardinal number κ, $w(Z^\kappa) = \kappa\cdot w(Z)$. Combining these results with the fact that $C_c(G,[0,1]^I)$ is homeomorphic to $C_c(G,[0,1])^I$ (cf. for instance 7.1.4), we see that

$$w(C_c(G,[0,1]^I)) = |I|\cdot w(C_c(G,[0,1])) = w(X)\cdot w(G)$$

(here we use that $w(X)\cdot\aleph_0 = w(X)$ because of the assumption $w(X) \ge \aleph_0$). Now $\tilde{X}$ is a subspace of $C_c(G,[0,1]^I)$, so clearly $w(\tilde{X}) \le w(C_c(G,[0,1]^I)) = w(X)\cdot w(G) = \max\{w(X),w(G)\}$. This completes the proof. □

7.3.13. PROPOSITION. *If in* 7.3.12 G *is locally compact and sigma-compact and* X *is a separable metrizable, space, then* $\tilde{X}$ *may also assumed to be separable and metrizable.*

<u>PROOF</u>. Repeat the proof of 7.3.12 with $|I| = \aleph_0$; so now $C_c(G,[0,1]^I)$ is metrizable (cf. Appendix C). Hence $\tilde{X}$ is metrizable and $w(\tilde{X}) = w(X) = \aleph_0$ (use the final remark in 0.2.10). □

7.3.14. <u>COROLLARY 1</u>. *Let* G *be a sigma-compact locally compact Hausdorff topological group and let* X *be a separable metrizable space. For any action* π *of* G *on* X *the following are equivalent:*

(i) $\langle G,X,\pi\rangle$ *is bounded.*

(ii) $\langle G,X,\pi\rangle$ *is metrically bounded.*

<u>PROOF</u>. (i) ⇒ (ii): Apply 7.3.13.
(ii) ⇒ (i): Obvious. □

7.3.15. <u>COROLLARY 2</u>. *Let* $\langle G,X,\pi\rangle$ *be a ttg with* G *a countable discrete group and* X *a separable metrizable space. Then* X *admits an equivariant dense embedding in a compact metrizable* G*-space* $\tilde{X}$.

<u>PROOF</u>. $\langle G,X,\pi\rangle$ is bounded because G is discrete. In addition, G is sigma-compact. Now apply 7.3.13. □

7.3.16. <u>NOTES</u>. The term *bounded* has been borrowed from D.H. CARLSON [1972]. However, what is called there "bounded" is what we call "metrically bounded". The close connection between boundedness and embeddability in compact G-spaces seems to be not earlier recognized. In particular, theorem 7.3.12 seems to be new.

Essential in 7.3.15 is the metrizability of the compactification $\tilde{X}$. Indeed, if G is discrete, the action π of G on X extends in a natural way to an action $\tilde{\pi}$ of G on βX, the Stone-Čech compactification of X (cf. 4.2.9). Then $\langle G,\beta X,\tilde{\pi}\rangle$ is a ttg in which $\langle G,X,\pi\rangle$ can be embedded, but βX is not metrizable (cf. [GJ], 9.6), unless X itself is already compact and metrizable Originally, corollary 7.3.15 is due to J. DE GROOT & R.H. MC DOWELL [1960]. Another proof has been given in [Ba], 3.4.11. The case $G = \mathbb{Z}$ is also handled in R.D. ANDERSON [1968].

In R.B. BROOK [1970] one may find a general compactification theorem for ttgs. Roughly speaking, it is our theorem 7.3.12, except that the actions are not only required to be motion equicontinuous (= bounded), but in addition, each transition has to be a *unimorphism* of the phase space. By our theorem, this latter condition is superfluous.

8 - LINEARIZATION OF ACTIONS

A linearization of a ttg $\langle G,X,\pi\rangle$ may roughly be described as an embedding of X into the phase space Y of a ttg $\langle H,Y,\sigma\rangle$, where Y is a topological linear space and σ an effective action of H on Y such that each σ^t is a linear operator on Y. In addition, each π^t has to be the *restriction* to X of some σ^s. Therefore, a linearization should be a morphism in TTG_*. See also the motivation for the introduction of comorphisms in 1.4.13. Now such linearizations turn out to exist as soon as X can topologically be embedded in *some* topological vector space, i.e. X is a Tychonov space. Therefore some restrictions on the admitted linearizations are considered. First, the linearization has to be *strict*, i.e. it should be a morphism in TOP^G. Second, in constructing a strict linearization $\langle 1_G,f\rangle$: $\langle G,X,\pi\rangle \to \langle G,Y,\sigma\rangle$, one should try to meet the following conditions:

(i) The topological vector space Y should be "nice".

(ii) A large class of other ttgs $\langle G,X',\pi'\rangle$ can also be strictly linearized in $\langle G,Y,\sigma\rangle$.

Of course, these conditions are more or less contradictory. As to condition (i), we shall interprete it in the following sense: topologically, Y should belong to the same distinguished class of spaces as X does (e.g. if X is metrizable, then so should be Y; moreover, it would be nice that Y were a Fréchet space or even a Hilbert space). Condition (ii) obviously relates the problem of linearization to the existence of comprehensive objects, considered in §7.

In subsection 8.1 we shall make some general remarks about linearizations. Then, in subsection 8.2, we consider strict linearizations of metric G-spaces in Fréchet spaces. Using the main result from subsection 7.2, it follows readily that for every infinite locally compact Hausdorff group G, each action of G on any Tychonov space X with $w(X) \le L(G)$ can be strictly linearized in $\langle G, C_c(G\times G), \tilde{r}\rangle$. If G is sigma-compact, then $C_c(G\times G)$ is a Fréchet space, and each action of G on a separable metric space can be strictly linearized in it. Finally, we shall consider strict linearizations in Hilbert spaces. The main result is, that each action of a sigma-compact locally compact Hausdorff group on a metric space X can be strictly linearized in the linear ttg $\langle G, H(\kappa), \sigma(\kappa)\rangle$ (cf. subsection 2.4 for its definition), with $\kappa = w(X)$. In the notes to this subsection we mention some earlier results, which motivated our investigations.

8.1. General remarks on linearization

8.1.1. The action π in a ttg $\langle G, X, \pi\rangle$ is said to be *linear*, and $\langle G, X, \pi\rangle$ is called *a linear ttg* provided

(i) X is a topological vector space.)1

(ii) $\bar{\pi}[G] \subseteq GL(X)$, the group of invertible continuous linear operators on X.

(iii) $\langle G, X, \pi\rangle$ is effective.

8.1.2. Obviously, linear ttgs are in a one-to-one correspondence with subgroups of general linear groups of topological vector spaces, endowed with a topology such that it is a topological homeomorphism group. Classical examples are matrix groups, acting on finite dimensional spaces. Other examples can be found in §2. Indeed, if G is a topological Hausdorff group and Y is a topological vector space, then $C_c(G,Y)$ and $C_u(G,Y)$ are topological vector spaces (note that a topological vector space Y has a uniformity compatible with its topology, viz. the left (= right) uniformity of the underlying additive group of Y). Moreover, each $\tilde{\rho}^t$ is a linear operator, and $\tilde{\rho}^t \neq \tilde{\rho}^e$ for $t \neq e$)2.

Consequently, $\langle G_d, C_c(G,Y), \tilde{\rho}\rangle$, $\langle G_d, C_u(G,Y), \tilde{\rho}\rangle$ and $\langle G, LUC_u(G,Y), \tilde{\rho}\rangle$ are linear ttgs for any topological vector space Y (cf. 2.1.2, 2.2.1 and 2.2.2). Moreover, if G is locally compact, then $\langle G, C_c(G,Y), \tilde{\rho}\rangle$ is a linear ttg (2.1.3). In that case, we have also the linear ttg $\langle G, L^p(G), \tilde{\rho}\rangle$ for $1 \le p < \infty$ (2.3.3) and if G is, in addition, sigma-compact, the linear ttg $\langle G, L^2(G), \sigma\rangle$ defined in 2.4.9.

)1 All topological vector spaces are assumed to have a Hausdorff topology.

)2 Immediate from the fact that C(G,Y) separates the points of Y (note, that $\mathbb{R}$ is topologically embedded in Y, and G is a Tychonov space).

8.1.3. A *linearization of a ttg* $\langle G,X,\pi\rangle$ is a comorphism of ttgs, i.e. a morphism $\langle\psi^{op},f\rangle$: $\langle G,X,\pi\rangle \to \langle H,Y,\sigma\rangle$ in TTG_* such that

(i) $\langle H,Y,\sigma\rangle$ is a linear ttg;

(ii) ψ: $H \to G$ is a surjection and f: $X \to Y$ is a topological embedding.

In that case we say that $\langle G,X,\pi\rangle$ *is linearized in* $\langle H,Y,\sigma\rangle$, or that $\langle G,X,\pi\rangle$ *has a linearization,* viz. $\langle\psi,f\rangle$. A *strict linearization* of $\langle G,X,\pi\rangle$ is a linearization of the form $\langle 1_G^{op},f\rangle$: $\langle G,X,\pi\rangle \to \langle G,Y,\sigma\rangle$, which we may and shall denote in the sequal by $\langle 1_G,f\rangle$.

8.1.4. PROPOSITION. *Let* $\langle G,X,\pi\rangle$ *be a ttg. The following conditions are equivalent:*

(i) $\langle G,X,\pi\rangle$ *has a linearization.*

(ii) X *is embeddable in a topological vector space.*

(iii) X *is a Tychonov space.*

In that case, $\langle G,X,\pi\rangle$ *has a linearization of the form* $\langle 1_G^{op},f\rangle$: $\langle G,X,\pi\rangle \to \langle G_d,Y,\sigma\rangle$. *Moreover, if* G *is a locally compact Hausdorff group then the equivalent conditions* (i), (ii) *and* (iii) *imply that* $\langle G,X,\pi\rangle$ *has a strict linearization.*

PROOF. (i) ⇒ (ii): Obvious.

(ii) ⇒ (iii): Any topological vector space is a Tychonov space, and subspaces of Tychonov spaces are still Tychonov spaces.

(iii) ⇒ (i): If X is a Tychonov space, it can be topologically embedded in $[0,1]^I$, hence in $\mathbb{R}^I$, where I is some index set (in fact, we may assume that $|I| = w(X)$, but this is irrelevant here). Let $E := \mathbb{R}^I$. Then E is a topological vector space (ordinary product topology and coordinate wise linear operations), and we may assume that $X \subseteq E$. Then $\langle G_d,C_c(G,E),\tilde{\rho}\rangle$ is a linear ttg by 8.1.2, and using 2.1.13 it is easy to see that $\underline{\pi}$: $X \to C_c(G,X) \subseteq C_c(G,E)$ is an equivariant embedding. Thus we obtain the linearization $\langle 1_G^{op},\underline{\pi}\rangle$: $\langle G,X,\pi\rangle \to \langle G_d,C_c(G,E),\tilde{\rho}\rangle$. If G is locally compact, then $\tilde{\rho}$: $G\times C_c(G,E) \to C_c(G,E)$ is continuous, and $\langle 1_G,\underline{\pi}\rangle$: $\langle G,X,\pi\rangle \to \langle G,C_c(G,E),\tilde{\rho}\rangle$ is a strict linearization of $\langle G,X,\pi\rangle$. This proves (i) and the remaining statements in our proposition. □

8.1.5. The topological vector space $C_c(G,E)$ in the preceding proof is independant of the particular choice of the space X, except that the index set I used in its definition is such that X can be embedded in $[0,1]^I$. Thus, the only requirement is that $w(X) \leq |I|$. It follows (cf. also 7.1.4) that we have, in fact, also a result about comprehensive objects. Stated otherwise, the above proposition meets condition (ii) of the introduction to this section. In this context, one might also ask if there is a linear ttg in which all ttgs from a certain class can be linearized, where the ttgs of that class do not have identical phase groups. See 8.2.12 and 8.2.14 below.

8.1.6. The preceding proposition shows that an action can always be linearized as soon as its phase space can be embedded in a topological vector space E. However, the space $C_c(G,E)$ in the above proof is isomorphic to $C_c(G)^I$ (I as above), hence it is not always metrizable if X is.[1] Stated otherwise, the space $C_c(G,E)$ seems to be too complicated. This is why we shall consider other methods in the following subsection. Incidentally, it should be observed that the above proof of (iii) ⇒ (i) is similar to the first part of 7.1.4. In the next subsection, we shall replace this by the results of subsection 7.2. A second motivation for the next subsection is that, by the preceding proposition, linearizations are not very interesting: they do always exist if X is Tychonov. Hence *strict* linearizations shall deserve our attention.

8.2. Strict linearizations in Fréchet spaces and in Hilbert spaces

8.2.1. In this subsection, G shall always be an infinite locally compact Hausdorff topological group. Recall that a Fréchet space is a locally convex topological vector space which is metrizable in such a way that it becomes a complete metric space.

8.2.2. *The space* $C_c(G\times G)$ *is a complete locally convex topological vector space.* Indeed, a local base at 0 in $C_c(G\times G)$ is formed by the collection of all sets $\{f : |f(s,t)| < \varepsilon$ for $(s,t) \in K\}$ with $\varepsilon > 0$ and $K \subseteq G\times G$ compact. These sets are easily seen to be convex. So $C_c(G\times G)$ is locally convex. Completeness follows from [Bo], Chap. X, §1.5, Theorem 1, taking into account that the uniformity of $C_c(G\times G)$ induced by its topological vector space structure coincides with the uniformity of convergence on compact sets (the theorem in [Bo] deals with the latter uniformity).

If G *is sigma-compact, then* $C_c(G\times G)$ *is a Fréchet space.* For G×G is sigma-compact and locally compact, so we can apply results from Appendix C.

---

[1] Unless, of course, $|I| \le \aleph_0$ and G is sigma-compact; see Appendix C.

8.2.3. THEOREM. *Let* G *be an infinite locally compact Hausdorff topological group. Then any ttg* $\langle G,X,\pi\rangle$ *with* X *a Tychonov space of weight* $w(X) \leq L(G)$, *can be strictly linearized in the linear ttg* $\langle G,C_c(G\times G),\tilde{r}\rangle$.

PROOF. Apply 7.2.18 and observe, that $C_c(G\times G,[0,1])$ may be replaced there by $C_c(G\times G)$. Moreover, $\langle G,C_c(G\times G),\tilde{r}\rangle$ is plainly a linear ttg (for effectiveness, cf. 7.2.19(i)). □

8.2.4. COROLLARY. *Any action of an infinite locally compact, sigma-compact Hausdorff group* G *on a separable metric space can be strictly linearized in a Fréchet space, viz. in* $C_c(G\times G)$ *with action* $\tilde{r}$ *of* G.

PROOF. Apply 8.2.2 and 8.2.3. □

8.2.5. In the above corollary we have obtained linearization of an important class of G-spaces in a quite simple Fréchet space. Now we shall consider topological linearization in Hilbert spaces.

Recall from subsection 2.4 that for any sigma-compact locally compact Hausdorff group H and any weight function w_0 on H we have the ttg $\langle H,L^2(H),\sigma\rangle$. Moreover, for any uniformly bounded compact invariant subset A of $C_c(H)$ the mapping $F|_A: f \mapsto w_0 f: A \to L^2(H)$ is an equivariant embedding of the H-space A (with action $\tilde{\rho}$) into the H-space $L^2(H)$ (with action σ).

We shall apply this with $H = G\times G$. However, the action σ of $G\times G$ on $L^2(G\times G)$ will be replaced by the action $\tilde{\sigma} := \sigma^{\psi}$ of G on $L^2(G\times G)$, where $\psi: G \to G\times G$ is the morphism in **TOPGRP** defined by $\psi(s) := (s,e)$. The weight function w_0 on $G\times G$ will be defined by $w_0(s,t) := w(s)\,w(t)$ for $s,t \in G$, where w is a weight function on G (cf. Appendix B.2). Then $\tilde{\sigma}$ is defined by

$$(1) \qquad \tilde{\sigma}^s f(u,v) = \frac{w(u)}{w(us)} f(us,v)$$

for $f \in L^2(G\times G)$, $s \in G$ and $(u,v) \in G\times G$. Moreover, it is not difficult to see that the above mentioned mapping $F|_A$ is also equivariant if we consider the action $\tilde{r}$ of G on $A \subseteq C_c(G\times G)$ and the action $\tilde{\sigma}$ of G on $L^2(G\times G)$. Indeed, $\tilde{r} = \tilde{\rho}^{\psi}$, where $\tilde{\rho}$ is the usual action of $G\times G$ on $C_c(G\times G)$, and ψ is as above.

Using these preparatory remarks, we can prove:

8.2.6. PROPOSITION. *Let* G *be an infinite locally compact sigma-compact Hausdorff topological group. Then every ttg* $\langle G,X,\pi\rangle$ *with* X *a compact metric space can be strictly linearized in the linear ttg* $\langle G,L^2(G\times G),\tilde{\sigma}\rangle$.

<u>PROOF</u>. By 7.2.18, X can be equivariantly embedded in $C_c(G\times G)$ (with action $\tilde{r}$) as a uniformly bounded subset {$C_c(G\times G,[0,1])$ is, indeed, a uniformly bounded subset of $C_c(G\times G)$.} Therefore, we may assume that X is a compact, uniformly bounded, invariant subset of the ttg $\langle G,C_c(G\times G),\tilde{r}\rangle$, and that π is the restriction to X of the action $\tilde{r}$. So we can apply the preceding remark. □

8.2.7. The Hilbert space $L^2(G\times G)$ occurring in 8.2.6 has dimension $w(G\times G) = w(G)$ (cf. 2.3.15). The same is true for $L^2(G)$. Consequently, there exists an isomorphism of Hilbert spaces (i.e. a linear inner product preserving bijection) between $L^2(G\times G)$ and $L^2(G)$. Via this isomorphism the action $\tilde{\sigma}$ defined above induces plainly a linear action τ of G on $L^2(G)$ such that $\langle G,L^2(G),\tau\rangle$ and $\langle G,L^2(G\times G),\tilde{\sigma}\rangle$ are isomorphic as G-spaces.[1] So we proved:

If G *is a locally compact sigma-compact Hausdorff topological group, then there exists a linear action* τ *of* G *on* $L^2(G)$ *such that each ttg* $\langle G,X,\pi\rangle$ *with* X *a compact metric space can be strictly linearized in* $\langle G,L^2(G),\tau\rangle$.

By 7.3.13, compactness of X may be replaced by the conditions that X is an arbitrary separable metric space and that π is a bounded action of G on X. We shall show now that there exists a linear action τ' of G on $L^2(G)$ such that $\langle G,L^2(G),\tau'\rangle$ is comprehensive for the class of *all* ttgs $\langle G,X,\pi\rangle$ with X a metrizable space of weight $w(X) \le w(G)$. (Since $w(G) = w(L^2(G))$, the condition $w(X) \le w(G)$ is obviously necessary for X to be embeddable in $L^2(G)$). Cf. 8.2.13 below.

As a motivation for the proof, recall that the basical step in the proof of 8.2.6 is the application of 7.2.18, and that in the proof of 7.2.18 it is used that a separable metric space can be embedded in $[0,1]^{\aleph_0}$ or $\mathbb{R}^{\aleph_0}$ by means of a suitable sequence of continuous functions. For metric spaces, however, we can take this sequence subject to certain additional conditions, and this enables a more direct approach. In this approach, the mapping F used in 8.2.5 (hence 8.2.6) is used in the construction from the beginning.

8.2.8. <u>LEMMA</u>. *Let* X *be a metrizable space of weight* κ. *Then there exist a set* I *with* $|I| = \kappa$ *and a set* $\{f_i : i\in I\} \subseteq C(X,[0,1])$ *such that for every*

[1] ~~Observe that we~~ only noticed the *existence* of the linear action τ; we cannot describe it more explicitely. For a proof, that two Hilbert spaces of the same dimension are isomorphic, see for instance p.30 in P.R. HALMOS, *Introduction to Hilbert Space*, 2nd ed., Chelsea Publishing Company, New York, 1957.

$x \in X$, $f_i(x) \neq 0$ *for at most countably many* $i \in I$, *and* $\Sigma_i f_i(x)^2 \leq 1$. *Moreover, by*

(2) $$r(x,y) := \Big(\sum_i |f_i(x)-f_i(y)|^2\Big)^{\frac{1}{2}}$$

$(x,y \in X)$ *a metric* r *is defined in* X, *and* r *generates the topology of* X. *In this metric,* X *has a finite diameter (in fact,* $r(x,y) \leq 2$ *for all points* x,y *in* X).

PROOF. It is well-known that X can be topologically embedded in the unit sphere of a Hilbert space H of dimension κ (cf. the proof of the Nagata-Smirnov metrization theorem as given in [Du],p.194). Let $\{\xi_i : i\in I\}$ be an orthonormal base of H. Then we have $|I| = \kappa$. For $i \in I$, set $f_i(x) := (x|\xi_i)$, where $(..|..)$ denotes the inner product in H. So $f_j(s)$ is the j-th Fourier coefficient of x with respect to the base $\{\xi_i : i\in I\}$. Hence by elementary Hilbert space theory, $f_i(x) \neq 0$ for at most countably many $i \in I$, $\Sigma_i f_i(x)^2 = \|x\|^2 \leq 1$, and the metric which X enherits from H is given by $r(x,y)^2 = \|x-y\|^2 = \Sigma_i|(x-y|\xi_i)|^2 = \Sigma_i|(x|\xi_i)-(y|\xi_i)|^2 = \Sigma_i|f_i(x)-f_i(y)|^2$. This proves our lemma. □

8.2.9. Recall from 2.4.14 and 2.4.16 that, given a locally compact sigma-compact Hausdorff topological group G and a weight function w on it, we can construct a ttg $\langle G,H(\kappa),\sigma(\kappa)\rangle$ for every cardinal number κ. This ttg $\langle G,H(\kappa),\sigma(\kappa)\rangle$ is obtained as a Hilbert sum of κ copies of $\langle G,L^2(G),\sigma\rangle$, with σ defined according to 2.4.5. Therefore, it is a linear ttg.

8.2.10. THEOREM. *Let* $\langle G,X,\pi\rangle$ *be a ttg with* G *a sigma-compact, locally compact Hausdorff group, and* X *a metrizable space. Then the action* π *can be strictly linearized in the linear ttg* $\langle G,H(\kappa),\sigma(\kappa)\rangle$ *with* $\kappa = w(X)$.

PROOF. Fix a set $\{f_i : i\in I\}$ of continuous functions of X into [0,1] according to 8.2.8. For each $i \in I$, we have the equivariant, continuous mapping $f_i\circ \underline{\pi}$: $X \to C_c(G,[0,1]) \subseteq C_c^*(G)$ (X with action π and $C_c^*(G)$ with action $\tilde{\rho}$). Recall that the mapping F introduced in 2.4.10 is equivariant with respect to the actions $\tilde{\rho}$ on $C_c^*(G)$ and σ in $L^2(G)$. It follows that $F_i := F\circ f_i\circ\underline{\pi}$: $X \to L^2(G)$ is an equivariant mapping of G-spaces, from X with action π into $L^2(G)$ with action σ. In this way, we obtain the mapping F': $x \mapsto (F_i(x))_i : X \to (L^2(G))^I$.

First, we show that $F'[X] \subseteq H(\kappa)$. To this end, we have to show that

$\Sigma_i \| F_i(x) \|_2^2 < \infty$ for every $x \in X$. Since $F_i(x)(t) = w(t) f_i(\pi(t,x))$, we obtain

$$\sum_i \| F_i(x) \|_2^2 = \sum_i \int_G w(t)^2 \; f_i(\pi(t,x))^2 \; dt$$

$$(2) \qquad = \int_G w(t)^2 \sum_i f_i(\pi(t,x))^2 \; dt$$

$$\leqq \int_G w(t)^2 \; dt < \infty.$$

{Here the exchange of integration and summation can be justified by the Lebesgue theorem. Moreover, we have used the fact that $\Sigma_i f_i(y)^2 \leq 1$ for all $y \in X$.} So we have $F'[X] \subseteq H(\kappa)$.

Next, $F' \colon X \to H(\kappa)$ is continuous. Indeed, similar to the above computation, we have for every $x,y \in X$, using formula (2):

$$\| F'(x) - F'(y) \|^2 = \sum_i \| F_i(x) - F_i(y) \|_2^2$$

$$(3) \qquad = \int_G w(t)^2 \sum_i | f_i(\pi(t,x)) - f_i(\pi(t,y)) |^2 \; dt$$

$$= \int_G w(t)^2 \; r(\pi^t x, \pi^t y)^2 \; dt.$$

Let $\varepsilon > 0$. In view of formula (10) in 2.4.10, there exists a compact subset K of G such that

$$\int_{G \sim K} w(t)^2 \; dt < \varepsilon^2.$$

Fix $x \in X$. Then 0.2.2(i) implies that $r(\pi^t x, \pi^t y) < \varepsilon^2$ for all y in some neighbourhood U of x and for all $t \in K$. Bearing in mind that X has diameter ≤ 2, we see that

$$\| F'(x) - F'(y) \|^2 \leq 4 \int_{G \sim K} w(t)^2 \; dt + \varepsilon^2 \int_K w(t)^2 \; dt$$

$$\leq 4\varepsilon^2 + \varepsilon^2 \int_G w(t)^2 \; dt = (4 + \| w \|_2^2) \varepsilon^2,$$

for all $y \in U$. This proves continuity of F'.

In order to show that F' is relatively open and injective, it is sufficient to show that for any $x \in X$ and $\varepsilon > 0$, there exists $\delta > 0$ such that

$$(4) \qquad \forall y \in X : \|F'(x)-F'(y)\| < \delta \Rightarrow r(x,y) \leq \varepsilon.$$

Suppose the contrary. Then for some $x \in X$ and $\varepsilon > 0$ there exists a sequence $\{y_n : n\in\mathbb{N}\}$ in X such that $\|F'(x)-F'(y_n)\| < 1/n$ and $r(x,y_n) > \varepsilon$ for all n. Then (3) implies for every $n \in \mathbb{N}$

$$\int_G w(t)^2\, r(\pi^t x,\pi^t y_n)^2\, dt = \|F'(x)-F'(y_n)\|^2 \leq n^{-2}.$$

If we set $f(t) := \inf\{r(\pi^t x,\pi^t y_n)^2 : n\in\mathbb{N}\}$, then obviously

$$0 \leq \int_G w(t)^2 f(t)\, dt \leq \inf_{n\in\mathbb{N}} n^{-2} = 0.$$

Hence $f(t) = 0$ for almost all $t \in G$ (recall that $w(t) > 0$ for all $t \in G$). However, $f(t) = 0$ for some $t \in G$ implies that there is a subsequence $\{n_i\}_i$ of $\mathbb{N}$ such that $\lim_{n_i} \pi^t y_{n_i} = \pi^t x$, whence $\lim_{n_i} y_{n_i} = x$. This contradicts the choice of the points y_n subject to the condition $r(x,y_n) > \varepsilon$. Consequently, for any $x \in X$ and $\varepsilon > 0$, there exists $\delta > 0$ such that (4) holds.

Thus, F': $X \to H(\kappa)$ is a topological embedding. Notice that F' is equivariant with respect to the given action π on X and the action $\sigma(\kappa)$ on $H(\kappa)$, because each F_i: $X \to L^2(G)$ is equivariant with respect to π and σ. □

8.2.11. <u>COROLLARY 1</u>. *Let* G *be a sigma-compact locally compact Hausdorff topological group, and let* κ *denote any cardinal number. Then the linear ttg* $\langle G,H(\kappa),\sigma(\kappa)\rangle$ *is comprehensive for the class of all ttgs* $\langle G,X,\pi\rangle$ *with* X *a metrizable space of weight* $\leq \kappa$. □

8.2.12. <u>COROLLARY</u> 2. *Let* G *and* κ *be as above, and let* $\langle G',X,\pi\rangle$ *be any ttg satisfying the conditions*

(i) *there exists a surjective morphism* ψ: $G \to G'$ *in* TOPGRP;

(ii) X *is a metric space of weight* $\leq \kappa$.

Then $\langle G',X,\pi\rangle$ *can be linearized in* $\langle G,H(\kappa),\sigma(\kappa)\rangle$.

PROOF. If $\langle G',X,\pi\rangle$ satisfies the conditions (i) and (ii), then $\langle G,X,\pi^{\psi}\rangle$ can be equivariantly embedded in the ttg $\langle G,H(\kappa),\sigma(\kappa)\rangle$, i.e. there exists an equivariant topological embedding $f\colon X \to H(\kappa)$. It is easy to see that $\langle\psi^{op},f\rangle\colon \langle G',X,\pi\rangle \to \langle G,H(\kappa),\sigma(\kappa)\rangle$ is a morphism in $\mathbf{TTG}_*$. Since ψ is given to be a surjection, $\langle\psi^{op},f\rangle$ is the desired linearization. □

8.2.13. COROLLARY 3. *Let* G *be an infinite sigma-compact locally compact Hausdorff topological group. Then there exists a linear action* σ^* *of* G *on* $L^2(G)$ *such that* $\langle G,L^2(G),\sigma^*\rangle$ *is comprehensive in* $\mathbf{TOP}^G$ *with respect to the class of all ttgs* $\langle G,X,\pi\rangle$ *with* X *a metrizable space of weight* $\leq w(G)$.

PROOF. Since G is infinite, $w(G) \geq \aleph_0$. It follows from 2.3.15 that $L^2(G)$ has Hilbert dimension $w(G)$. Consequently, for any cardinal number κ, $H(\kappa)$ has Hilbert dimension $\kappa\cdot w(G) = \max\{\kappa,w(G)\}$. In particular, if $\kappa = w(G)$, $H(\kappa)$ and $L^2(G)$ have the same Hilbert dimension. In that case, there exists an isomorphism of Hilbert spaces $g\colon H(\kappa)\to L^2(G)$. Let σ^* be the unique action of G on $L^2(G)$ such that g is equivariant with respect to the action $\sigma(\kappa)$ of G on $H(\kappa)$ and σ^* of G on $L^2(G)$. Thus, $\sigma^{*t} = g\circ\sigma(\kappa)^t\circ g^{\leftarrow}$ for all $t \in G$. Then obviously σ^* is a linear action, and $\langle G,L^2(G),\sigma^*\rangle$ is isomorphic to $\langle G,H(\kappa),\sigma(\kappa)\rangle$, where $\kappa = w(G)$. Now apply 8.2.11 with $\kappa = w(G)$. □

8.2.14. COROLLARY 4. *Let* G *be an infinite sigma-compact locally compact Hausdorff topological group, and let* $\langle G,L^2(G),\sigma^*\rangle$ *be as in* 8.2.13. *Then any ttg* $\langle G',X,\pi\rangle$ *satisfying the conditions*

(i) *there exists a surjective morphism* $\psi\colon G\to G'$ *in* **TOPGRP**,

(ii) X *is a metric space of weight* $\leq w(G)$,

can be linearized in $\langle G,L^2(G),\sigma^*\rangle$.

PROOF. Similar to 8.2.12.

8.2.15. If G is *compact*, then we may take as a weight function on G the function $w\colon t\longmapsto 1\colon G\to\mathbb{R}$. In that case, we have $\sigma^t f(s) = f(st)$, for $f \in L^2(G)$ and $s,t \in G$, so that $\sigma = \tilde{\rho}$ on $L^2(G)$. So for any cardinal number κ, the action $\sigma(\kappa)$ of G on $H(\kappa)$ is by means of *unitary operators* (orthogonal operators, if we consider only $\mathbb{R}$-valued functions as elements of $L^2(G)$, in which case $H(\kappa)$ is a real Hilbert space).

A close examination of the proof of 8.2.13 shows that in the case that G is an infinite compact Hausdorff topological group we may assume that the action σ^* of G on $L^2(G)$ with the properties mentioned in 8.2.13 is by means of unitary operators as well.

8.2.16. If G is discrete and sigma-compact, then G is countable. In that case, $L^2(G)$, is isomorphic to the (separable) Hilbert space $l^2(\aleph_0)$ (cf. [Du],p.191 for the notation). In particular, if G = $\mathbb{Z}$, then for any cardinal number κ, $H(\kappa)$ is isomorphic to the Hilbert sum of κ copies of the space $l^2(\aleph_0)$. A weight function on $\mathbb{Z}$ is defined by $w(n) := 2^{-|n|}$ for $n \in \mathbb{Z}$. So the action σ of $\mathbb{Z}$ on $l^2(\aleph_0) = L^2(\mathbb{Z})$ is the action generated by the homeomorphism σ^1, where

$$(5) \qquad (\sigma^1 x)_n = \begin{cases} 2\, x_{n+1} & \text{if } n \geq 0 \\ \frac{1}{2}\, x_{n+1} & \text{if } n \leq -1 \end{cases}$$

for $x = (x_n)_{n\in\mathbb{Z}} \in L^2(\mathbb{Z})$. Now let I be a set with $|I| = \kappa$. Plainly, an element $((x_{ni})_{n\in\mathbb{Z}})_{i\in I}$ in $H(\kappa)$, may be identified with the element $((x_{ni})_{i\in I})_{n\in\mathbb{Z}}$ in the Hilbert sum of $|\mathbb{Z}|$ copies of the Hilbert space $l^2(\kappa)$ of dimension κ. In this way we obtain an isomorphism of the Hilbert space $H(\kappa)$ onto the Hilbert sum K of $|\mathbb{Z}|$ copies of $l^2(\kappa)$. Under this isomorphism, the action $\sigma(\kappa)$ of $\mathbb{Z}$ on $H(\kappa)$ carries over to an action of $\mathbb{Z}$ on K which may also be described by (5), now interpreting the x_n as elements of $l^2(\kappa)$ for $n \in \mathbb{Z}$. {This action was described for the first time in J.H. COPELAND & J. DE GROOT [1961]}.

8.2.17. NOTES. The question whether certain ttgs can be embedded in a ttg whose phase space is a topological vector space and whose action is by means of a linear representation of G is almost as old as the theory of ttgs itself. In connection with the existence of comprehensive objects for certain classes of ttgs, one of the most notable early results is BEBUTOV's theorem (the literature gives conflicting references to the original; see for instance V.V. NEMYCKIĬ [1949]). In our terminology, it reads as follows:

The ttg $\langle\mathbb{R}, C_c(\mathbb{R}), \tilde{\rho}\rangle$ *is comprehensive for the class of all ttgs* $\langle\mathbb{R}, X, \pi\rangle$ *with* X *a compact metric space and with an action* π *such that* X *contains at most one invariant point.*

In S. KAKUTANI [1968] this theorem has been strengthened in the sense that the condition that $\langle\mathbb{R}, X, \pi\rangle$ has at most one critical point may be replaced by the condition that *the set of invariant points in* X *is homeomorphic with a subset of* $\mathbb{R}$. In O. HAJEK [1971] a further modification was presented:

The ttg $\langle\mathbb{R}, C_c(\mathbb{R}, \mathbb{R}^n), \tilde{\rho}\rangle$ *is comprehensive for the class of all ttgs* $\langle\mathbb{R}, X, \pi\rangle$ *with* X *a locally compact separable metric space, such that the set of invariant points in* X *is homeomorphic to a closed subset of* $\mathbb{R}^n$.

It should be noticed that in these theorems certain restrictions are imposed on the *actions* in order to describe the class of ttgs for which the above mentioned objects are comprehensive. However, D.H. CARLSON [1972] described a linear ttg $<\mathbb{R}, C_u(\mathbb{R}^2), \tau>$ which is comprehensive for the class of all ttgs $<\mathbb{R}, X, \pi>$ with X a separable metrizable space. The action τ of $\mathbb{R}$ on $C_u(\mathbb{R}^2)$ in this comprehensive object are "weighted" translations; in fact,

$$\tau^t f(u,v) = e^{(u+v)t+t^2} f(u+t, v+t).$$

In this context, our theorem 7.2.18 (≅ proposition 8.2.6) is on the one hand a generalization of the results of BEBUTOV, KAKUTANI and HAJEK, and on the other hand it is a simplification and generalization of the result of CARLSON.)1

Euclidean spaces and Hilbert spaces appear for instance in work of L. ZIPPIN, D. MONTGOMERY, R.H. BING and others. Most of these results are special cases of results of G.D. MOSTOV [1957]. We quote one of MOSTOV's theorems:

If G *is a compact Lie group and* X *is a separable metrizable* G-*space of finite dimension and with a finite number of orbit types, then any action of* G *on* X *can be strictly linearized in a Euclidean* G-*space where the action is by means of orthogonal linear transformations.*

For a nice proof, cf. R.S. PALAIS [1960]. In R.S. PALAIS [1961], these results are generalized to non-compact Lie groups: if G is a matrix group and X a separable finite dimensional metrizable G-space with a *proper* action, having only finitely many orbit types, then X admits an equivariant embedding in a linear G-space of finite dimension. In the same paper, PALAIS shows that *if* G *is any Lie group and* X *is a separable metrizable* G-*space with a proper action, then* X *admits an equivariant embedding in a real Hilbert* G-*space where the action is by means of orthogonal linear transformations.*)2

)1 To be honest, although the action τ of $\mathbb{R}$ on $C_u(\mathbb{R}^2)$ in the CARLSON system is not as simple as the action $\tilde{r}$, his system is related to the solution space of a first order partial differential equation.

)2 The paper of PALAIS does not contain statements about comprehensive objects, nor seem such statements to be obtainable from it.

Meanwhile, theorems on linearization in Hilbert spaces were also obtained by J.H. COPELAND & J. DE GROOT [1961] for cyclic groups and in J. DE GROOT [1962] for compact groups and discrete countable groups. These results were extended to more general locally compact groups by P.C. BAAYEN. Cf. Chap. 4 in [Ba], and also P.C. BAAYEN & J. DE GROOT [1968]. These "more general locally compact groups" were described as locally compact Hausdorff groups admitting weight functions ("W-groups"). However, they did not incorporate 2.4.2(ii) in the definition of a weight function, and consequently, they obtained only linearizations, no *strict* linearizations. Their main result was that *for any such a W-group* G *and any cardinal number* κ *there exists a Hilbert space* H *such that every ttg* $\langle G,X,\pi\rangle$ *with* X *a metrizable space of weight* $\leq \kappa$ *admits a morphism* $\langle\psi,f\rangle$: $\langle G_d,X,\pi\rangle \to \langle \mathrm{GL}(H)_d,H,\delta\rangle$ *in* TTG *with* ψ *injective and* f *a topological embedding.* Here δ is the obvious action of $\mathrm{GL}(H)_d$ on H. (Our methods for e.g. the proof of 8.2.10 are similar to those of BAAYEN). In a subsequent note (P.C. BAAYEN [1967]) it was shown that in the above mentioned theorem, ψ: $G \to \mathrm{GL}(H)$ is a topological embedding if GL(H) is given its strong operator topology, provided G admits a *continuous* weight function. In that case, however, it was not yet clear that a strict linearization in the sense of 8.1.3 had been obtained. Indeed, it was not yet shown that in this case the subgroup $\psi[G]$ of GL(H) with the strong operator topology is a topological homeomorphism group on H (this is our corollary 2.4.16). The results in the present section became possible by the paper of A.B. PAALMAN - DE MIRANDA [1971], who proved that the locally compact Hausdorff groups admitting weight functions are exactly the sigma-compact ones. Some of our results in this section have been published earlier in J. DE VRIES [1972a; 1975a].

Finally, it should be noticed, that [Ba] contains many results on comprehensive objects in TTG; however, most classes of ttgs considered there have *discrete* phase groups, this in contradistinction with our results in subsection 7.3 and in §8. More information about the history of this subject can be found in the paper P.C. BAAYEN & M.A. MAURICE, Johannes de Groot 1914-1972, *General Topology and Appl.* 3 (1973), 3-32. Cf. also section 6 in "The topological works of J. DE GROOT", a lecture by P.C. BAAYEN, contained in *Topological Structures* (Proceedings of a Symposium, organized by the Wiskundig Genootschap of the Netherlands on November 7, 1973, in honour of J. de Groot (1914-1972)), Mathematical Centre Tracts 52, Mathematisch Centrum, Amsterdam, 1974.

APPENDIX A

Pseudocompactness for topological groups

A.1. In this appendix, G shall always denote a topological Hausdorff group. Recall that G is *totally bounded* whenever for every $U \in \mathcal{V}_e$, G can be covered by finitely many left translates of U. This means that G is precompact in its left uniformity. If G is totally bounded, then the left and right uniformities on G coincide. The following is well-known:

A.2. LEMMA. *The following statements are equivalent:*

(i) $\alpha_G: G \to G^c$ *is a topological embedding.*

(ii) G *is totally bounded.*

(iii) G *is a subgroup of a compact Hausdorff group* H.

In this case, $\alpha_G: G \to G^c$ *may be identified with the inclusion mapping of* G *into* $cl_H G$ *for any compact Hausdorff group* H *in which* G *is topologically embedded as a subgroup. In addition,* $AP(G) = LUC^*(G)$.

PROOF. That (i) ⇒ (ii) is trivial. In order to prove that (ii) ⇒ (iii), consider the completion H of G with respect to its left uniformity, and apply [Bo], Chap. IV, §3.4. Next, assume (iii). Then every continuous morphism of groups from G into a compact Hausdorff group K, being a uniformly continuous function into a complete uniform Hausdorff space, can be extended to $cl_H G$. This extension is obviously a morphism of groups. So $cl_H G$ may be identified with the reflection of G in COMPGRP, i.e. the Bohr compactification of G. Similarly, each $f \in LUC^*(G)$ can be extended to a continuous function f' on $cl_H G$. Since $cl_H G$ is a compact group, it follows that $f \in AP(G)$, by 2.2.7. Thus, $LUC^*(G) = AP(G)$ (cf. 2.2.16). This shows that (iii) ⇒ (i) and that the final statement is true. □

A.3. Since G is a Tychonov space, the reflection $\beta_G: G \to \beta G$ of G in COMP is a topological embedding. Obviously, there is a unique continuous mapping $\bar{\alpha}: \beta G \to G^c$ such that $\alpha_G = \bar{\alpha} \circ \beta_G$. The following lemma describes groups G for which $\bar{\alpha}$ is a homeomorphism.

A.4. LEMMA. *The following conditions are equivalent:*

(i) *βG can be given the structure of a group in such a way that it becomes a topological group and $\beta_G\colon G \to \beta G$ a morphism of groups.*

(ii) $AP(G) = C^*(G)$.

(iii) *There exists a homeomorphism $\bar{\alpha}\colon \beta G \to G^c$ such that $\alpha_G = \bar{\alpha} \circ \beta_G$.*

(iv) *G is totally bounded and $LUC^*(G) = C^*(G)$.*

PROOF. (i) ⇒ (ii): Since $C^*(\beta_G)\colon f \mapsto f \circ \beta_G$ maps $C(\beta G)$ onto $C^*(G)$, this is an immediate application of lemma 2.2.7

(ii) ⇒ (iii): If (ii) is valid, then $C^*(\alpha_G)\colon f \mapsto f \circ \alpha_G$ maps $C(G^c)$ onto $C^*(G)$, by 2.2.18. Now use the fact that β_G is uniquely determined by the property that $C^*(\beta_G)$ is a surjection (cf. [GJ], 6.5).

(iii) ⇒ (i): Obvious.

(i) ⟺ (iv): Clear from A.2 and the equivalence of (i) and (ii). □

A.5. Recall that G is *pseudocompact* whenever $C(G) = C^*(G)$. It is well-known that G is pseudocompact iff the following condition is fulfilled (cf. [GJ], 6I1):

(i) Any non-void closed G_δ-set in βG meets G.

Notice, that this characterization is valid for any Tychonov space. For topological groups G, one can prove that G is pseudocompact iff

(ii) G is a dense subgroup of a compact group H and every non-void G_δ-set in H meets G.

This result is due to W.W. COMFORT & K.A. ROSS [1966]. For an elementary proof, cf. J. DE VRIES [1975b]. Using this characterization it is easy to prove the following theorem (which is also contained in the above mentioned paper).

A.6. THEOREM. *An arbitrary product of pseudocompact Hausdorff groups is again pseudocompact.* □

A.7. THEOREM. *G is pseudocompact iff one of the conditions in A.4 is fulfilled.*

PROOF. Cf. W.W. COMFORT & K.A. ROSS [1966]. □

A.8. Another question, which was considered in the paper of COMFORT and ROSS was, under which conditions on G one has $LUC^*(G) = C^*(G)$ (i.e. condition A.4(iv) without total boundedness). It turned out that the condition

$LUC^*(G) = C^*(G)$ is equivalent to the condition $LUC(G) = C(G)$. If this condition is fulfilled, then either G is pseudocompact, or G is a P-space (i.e. each G_δ-set in G is open). {For related results, cf. O.T. ALAS [1971], and also a forthcoming paper by W.W. COMFORT & A.W. HAGER.}

A.9. There exists an abundance of non-compact pseudocompact groups. Cf. the above mentioned paper by COMFORT and ROSS. See also H.J. WILCOX [1966; 1971]. For additional facts about pseudocompact groups, cf. W. MORAN [1970]: barring the existence of measurable cardinals, all groups which admit invariant means on $C(G)$ are pseudocompact (the converse is almost trivial).

APPENDIX B

Weight functions on sigma-compact locally compact Hausdorff groups

B.1. Throughout this appendix, let G denote a locally compact Hausdorff topological group. In addition, from B.4 on up to the end, G will be assumed to be sigma-compact, i.e. $G = \cup\{C_n : n \in \mathbb{N}\}$, where each C_n is a compact subset of G. Recall that a *weight function* on G is an element $w \in L^2(G)$ such that

(i) $\forall t \in G$: $w(t) > 0$.

(ii) $\forall s,t \in G$: $w(st) \geq w(s)w(t)$.

(iii) The function $t \mapsto w(t)^{-1}: G \to \mathbb{R}$ is bounded on compact subsets of G.

B.2. EXAMPLES. The following examples are taken from P.C. BAAYEN & J. DE GROOT [1968]; cf. also [Ba], section 4.2, where all proofs can be found.

(i) If G is compact, then the constant function $t \mapsto 1: G \to \mathbb{R}$ is a weight function on G.

(ii) The function $t \mapsto \exp(-|t|): \mathbb{R} \to \mathbb{R}$ is a weight function on the additive group $\mathbb{R}$.

(iii) The function $t \mapsto 2^{-|t|}: \mathbb{Z} \to \mathbb{R}$ is a weight function on the group $\mathbb{Z}$. More generally, let G denote the free group generated by the countable set $\{t_1, t_2, \ldots\}$. Every $t \in G$, $t \neq e$ can be written uniquely as a *reduced* word

$$t = t_{n_1}^{k_1} t_{n_2}^{k_2} \ldots t_{n_m}^{k_m};$$

then we put

$$w(t) := 2^{-\Sigma_{i=1}^{m} |k_i| n_i}.$$

If, in addition, we define $w(e) := 1$, then f is a weight function on the group G.

(iv) If $G = G_1 \times G_2 \times \ldots \times G_n$ where each G_i admits a weight function w_i, then $w\colon (t_1, t_2, \ldots, t_n) \mapsto w_1(t_1).w_2(t_2).\ldots.w_n(t_n)\colon G_1 \times G_2 \times \ldots \times G_n \to \mathbb{R}$ is a weight function on $G_1 \times G_2 \times \ldots \times G_n$.

B.3. THEOREM. *The following statements are equivalent:*

(i) G *is sigma-compact.*

(ii) G *admits a weight function.*

PROOF. This theorem and its proof are due to A.B. PAALMAN-DE MIRANDA [1971]. We shall confine ourselves here to the following remarks.

The proof of (ii) ⇒ (i) is based on the observation that in a locally compact group the closure of a sigma-compact subset is again sigma-compact, and on the well-known property that for any $f \in L^1(G)$, $f \geq 0$ (i.c. $f = w^2$, if w is the weight function on G), there exists an $f' \in L^1(G)$ such that $0 \leq f' \leq f$ on G, $\int_G f'(t)dt = \int_G f(t)dt$, and the set $\{t : t \in G \ \& \ f'(t) > 0\}$ is sigma-compact.

The proof of (i) ⇒ (ii) is much more complicated. Actually, in A.B. PAALMAN-DE MIRANDA [1971] the existence of an element $f \in L^2(G)$ has been proved, satisfying conditions (i) and (ii) of B.1. However, it follows immediately from the construction that there exist $V \in \mathcal{V}_e$ and $n_1 \in \mathbb{N}$ such that $f(t) \geq n_1^{-1}$ for all $t \in V$. Now any compact subset K of G can be covered by finitely many left translates of V. Hence the fact that $\sup\{f(t)^{-1} : t \in K\} < \infty$ follows from the observation that for each $s \in G$

$$\begin{aligned}\sup\{f(t)^{-1} : t \in sV\} &= \sup\{f(st)^{-1} : t \in V\} \\ &\leq \sup\{f(s)^{-1}f(t)^{-1} : t \in V\} \leq n_1 f(s)^{-1}. \quad \square\end{aligned}$$

B.4. From now on we shall assume that G is a sigma-compact, locally compact Hausdorff group. Then G admits a weight function w. The question may be raised, if G admits a *continuous* weight function. The construction in A.B. PAALMAN-DE MIRANDA [1971] does not necessarily produce a continuous weight function: if we apply that construction to $G = \mathbb{R}$, then we obtain the function $w\colon \mathbb{R} \to \mathbb{R}$ defined as follows:

$$w(t) = \begin{cases} 1 & \text{if } t = 0. \\ 3^{-k} & \text{if } k-1 < |t| \leq k \quad (k=1,2,\ldots). \end{cases}$$

On the other hand, $\mathbb{R}$ admits a continuous weight function (cf. B.2(ii)). More generally, it follows from the proof of Theorem 3.3 in P.C. BAAYEN &

J. DE GROOT [1968], that *every locally compact abelian Hausdorff group which is either separable or compactly generated admits a continuous weight function.*

We have not been able to improve on this result. In the following sequence of lemmas we provide some material showing how "nice" a weight function can always be chosen.

B.5. LEMMA. *There exists a weight function* w *on* G *satisfying the following additional conditions:*
(iv) $\forall t \in G : w(t) \leq 1$.
(v) $\forall t \in G : w(t) = w(t^{-1})$.

PROOF. (iv): In fact, we show that (iv) is *always* implied by the requirements that $w \in L^2(G)$ satisfies (i) and (ii) of B.1. If w is a weight function on G, then $\|w\|_2 > 0$ because of B.1(i). Then by B.2(ii) and right invariance of Haar measure, we obtain

$$\|w\|_2^2 = \int_G w(st)^2 ds \geq w(t)^2 \int_G w(s)^2 ds = w(t)^2 \|w\|_2^2.$$

Consequently, $w(t) \leq 1$ for all $t \in G$.

(v): Let w_0 be any weight function on G, set $w(t) := w_0(t) w_0(t^{-1})$ for all $t \in G$. Then w is obviously measurable. Since by (iv), $w_0(t^{-1}) \leq 1$ for all $t \in G$, it follows that $0 \leq w(t) \leq w_0(t)$, so that $w \in L^2(G)$. Now conditions (i), (ii) and (iii) of B.1 are easily verified for w. □

B.6. LEMMA. *There exist a lower semicontinuous weight function* w' *on* G *and an upper semicontinuous weight function* w" *such that* $w'(t) \leq w''(t)$ *for all* $t \in G$.

PROOF. Let w be a weight function on G. Define w' and w" by

$$w'(t) := \liminf_{s \to t} w(s); \quad w''(t) := \limsup_{s \to t} w'(s)$$

for each $t \in G$. Then the following inequalities are valid:

$$(1) \qquad w'(e)w(t) \leq w'(t) \leq w(t); \quad w'(t) \leq w''(t) \leq w(t).$$

Indeed, since $V_t = \{Ut : U \in V_e\}$, we have for each t:

$$w'(t) = \sup_{U\in \mathcal{V}_t} \left(\inf_{s\in U} w(s)\right) = \sup_{U\in \mathcal{V}_e} \left(\inf_{s\in U} w(st)\right)$$

$$\geq \sup_{U\in \mathcal{V}_e} \left(\inf_{s\in U} w(s)w(t)\right) = w'(e)w(t).$$

On the other hand, it is trivial that for each $U \in \mathcal{V}_t$, $\inf\{w(s) : s\in U\} \leq w(t)$, whence $w'(t) \leq w(t)$. This proves half of (1); the remaining part of (1) is trivial.

It is routine to check that w' is lower semicontinuous and that w'' is upper semicontinuous. In particular, w' and w'' are measurable, so that the inequalities $0 \leq w'(t) \leq w''(t) \leq w(t)$ $(t\in G)$ imply that $w', w'' \in L^2(G)$.

Next, observe that $w'(e) > 0$, because, by condition B.1(iii), the function w is bounded away from zero in a (compact) neighbourhood of e in G. Hence (1) implies that w' and w'' satisfy condition B.1(i). That they satisfy condition B.1(ii) follows from a straightforward computation, and B.1(iii) for w' and w'' is, again, an easy consequence of (1). □

B.7. As was remarked in the proof of B.5(iv), the functions w' and w'' satisfy $w'(t) \leq w''(t) \leq 1$ for each $t \in G$. If w in the proof of B.6 has property B.6(v), then so do w' and w''.

The process of "regularization" described in the proof of B.6 does in general not produce a continuous weight function. Indeed, if we take $w: \mathbb{R} \to \mathbb{R}$ as in B.4, then

$$w'(t) = \begin{cases} 3^{-1} & \text{if } t = 0. \\ 3^{-k} & \text{if } k-1 \leq |t| < k \quad (k=1,2,\ldots) \end{cases}$$

and

$$w''(t) = \begin{cases} 3^{-1} & \text{if } t = 0 \\ 3^{-k} & \text{if } k-1 < |t| \leq k \quad (k=1,2,\ldots). \end{cases}$$

So we gained only one point of continuity, namely, the point $t = 0$.

B.8. <u>LEMMA</u>. *Let w be a lower semicontinuous weight function on G. Then for every $\varepsilon > 0$ there exists $U \in \mathcal{V}_e$ such that*

(2) $$(1-\varepsilon)w(e)w(t) \leq w(s) \leq \frac{1}{1-\varepsilon}\frac{w(t)}{w(e)}$$

for all $t \in G$ and $s \in Ut$.

PROOF. Let $\varepsilon > 0$. By lower semicontinuity of w there exists $U \in \mathcal{V}_e$ such that $w(u) \geq (1-\varepsilon)w(e)$ for all $u \in U$. Thus, if $s \in Ut$ for some $t \in G$, say $s = ut$ with $u \in U$, then $w(s) \geq w(u)w(t) > (1-\varepsilon)w(e)w(t)$.

In addition, we may and shall assume that U is symmetric, i.e. $U = U^{-1}$. Then for $s \in Ut$ we have $ts^{-1} \in U$, hence $w(t) = w(ts^{-1}s) \geq w(ts^{-1})w(s) \geq (1-\varepsilon)w(e)w(s)$. □

B.9. COROLLARY. *A lower semicontinuous weight function* w *on* G *such that* $w(e) = 1$ *is right uniformly continuous.*

PROOF. Since $w(t) \leq 1$ for all $t \in G$, there exists for each $\delta > 0$ a real number $\varepsilon > 0$ such that $w(t)-\delta < (1-\varepsilon)w(t) < (1-\varepsilon)^{-1}w(t) < w(t)+\delta$. Now apply B.8. □

B.10. In 2.4.10 we gave another proof of the existence of an upper semi-continuous weight function on G. We do not know whether the weight function constructed there is actually continuous. For this, it would be sufficient to show the continuity of the norm, i.e. the mapping $\tau \mapsto \|\tau\|$, on the image of G in $GL(L^2(G))$. {Observe, that for a continuous weight function w with $w(e) = 1$ we have $\|\sigma^t\| = w(t)^{-1}$ for all $t \in G$ (cf. 2.4.10). In that case, the norm is actually continuous on the image of G in $GL(L^2(G))$.}

APPENDIX C

The weight of $C_c(X)$

C.1. In this appendix, X shall denote an infinite)1 locally compact Hausdorff space; so $w(X) \geq \aleph_0$ and $L(X) \geq \aleph_0$. We state our results only for $C_c(X)$. However, similar results (with the same proofs) are valid for $C_c^*(X)$ and for $C_c(X,[0,1])$. Most proofs are straightforward; they can be found in J. DE VRIES [1972 b].

The basic observation which enables us to determine the local weight of $C_c(X)$ is the following

C.2. LEMMA. *For any transfinite cardinal number* κ *the following conditions are equivalent:*

(i) $L(X) \leq \kappa$.

(ii) X *can be covered by* κ *relatively compact, open subsets.*

(iii) X *can be covered by* κ *compact sets.* □

C.3. LEMMA. $\ell w(C_c(X)) = L(X)$. □

C.4. COROLLARY. $C_c(X)$ *is metrizable iff* X *is sigma-compact. In that case,* $C_c(X)$ *is a Fréchet space*)2.

PROOF. If $C_c(X)$ is metrizable, then $L(X) = \aleph_0$, by C.3. Hence X is sigma-compact by C.2. Conversely, if X is sigma-compact, then it follows in a similar way that $\ell w(C_c(X)) = \aleph_0$. Since $C_c(X)$ is a locally convex topological vector space, it follows from [Sc], 6.1, that this implies that $C_c(X)$ is metrizable by means of an invariant metric d (i.e. a metric d such that

---

)1 If X is finite, then all results remain true if we add a factor $\aleph_0$ at the appropriate places.

)2 Of course, here $C_c(X)$ cannot be replaced by $C_c^*(X)$ or $C_c(X,[0,1])$: the former space is not complete, and the latter one is not a vector space.

$d(f+g,h+g) = d(f,h)$ for all $f,g,h \in C_c(X)$). In addition, the usual uniformity for $C_c(X)$ derived from this metric d coincides with the uniformity of uniform convergence on compact sets in X. With the latter, $C_c(X)$ is complete (cf. [Bo], Chap. X, §1.5, Theorem 1). Consequently, $C_c(X)$ admits a metric making it a locally convex vector space which is complete in this metric.

{An alternative proof is as follows: according to [Du], Chap. XII, 8.5, sigma-compactness of X implies that $C_c(X)$ is metrizable. It is quite easily checked that the metric indicated there, generates exactly the uniformity of uniform convergence on compact sets in X. Then proceed as above. This proof works also for $C_c(X,[0,1])$!}. □

C.5. <u>LEMMA</u>. $w(X) \geq d(C_c(X))$.

<u>PROOF</u>. For the compact case, cf. [Se], 7.6.5. Using this, the general case can be proved quite easily. □

C.6. <u>LEMMA</u>. $w(X) = L(X).d(C_c(X))$. □

C.7. <u>PROPOSITION</u>. $w(X) = w(C_c(X))$.

PROOF. First, observe that

$$w(C_c(X)) = d(C_c(X)).\ell w(C_c(X)). \tag{1}$$

This is due to the fact that $C_c(X)$ is a uniform space. In any uniform space Y it can be shown that $w(Y) \leq d(Y).u(Y)$, where $u(Y)$ is the uniform weight of Y (that is, the least cardinal number of a uniform base of Y). Since the uniform weight of $C_c(X)$ is equal to $\ell w(C_c(X))$, this proves that $w(C_c(X)) \leq d(C_c(X)).\ell w(C_c(X))$. In order to prove equality, use (3) in 0.2.10. Using (1), the desired equality follows easily from the preceding lemmas. □

C.8. <u>REMARK</u>. It follows from [Du], Chap. XII, Theorem 5.2, that $w(C_c(X)) \leq w(X).\aleph_0 = w(X)$. Conversely, C.6, C.3 and (1) (or rather the obvious "≥" in it; cf (3) in 0.2.10) imply that $w(X) \leq w(C_c(X))$. Thus, the use of "≤" in (1) can be avoided by this appeal to the theorem in [Du]. □

BIBLIOGRAPHY

Books and monographs

[Ba] P.C. BAAYEN: *Universal Morphisms*, Mathematical Centre Tracts no. 9, Mathematisch Centrum, Amsterdam, 1964.

[BH] J.F. BERGLUND & K.H. HOFMANN: *Compact Semitopological Semigroups and Weakly Almost Periodic Functions*, Lecture Notes in Mathematics, no. 42, Springer-Verlag, Berlin, Heidelberg, New York, 1967.

[Bo] N. BOURBAKI: *Elements de Mathematique, Livre* III, *Topologie generale*, Hermann, Paris, 1971.

[Br] G.E. BREDON: *Introduction to compact transformation groups*, Academic Press, London, New York, 1972.

[Bu] R.B. BURCKEL: *Weakly Almost Periodic Functions on Semigroups*, Gordon and Breach, New York, London, Paris, 1970.

[Ch] C. CHEVALLY: *The theory of Lie groups*, Princeton University Press, Princeton, New Jersey, 1946.

[Di] J. DIXMIER: *Les* C^**-algebres et leurs representations*, Gauthier-Villars, Paris, 1964.

[Du] J. DUGUNDJI: *Topology*, Allyn and Bacon, Inc., Boston, 1966.

[El] R. ELLIS: *Lectures on Topological Dynamics*, W.A. Benjamin, Inc., New York, 1969.

[En] R. ENGELKING: *Outline of General Topology*, North-Holland Publishing Company, Amsterdam, 1968.

[GH] W.H. GOTTSCHALK & G.A. HEDLUND: *Topological Dynamics*, Amer. Math. Soc. Colloquium Publications, Vol. 36, Providence, R.I., 1955.

[GJ] L. GILLMAN & M. JERISON: *Rings of Continuous Functions*, D. van Nostrand, New York, 1960.

[Go] R. GODEMENT: *Théorie des faisceaux*, Hermann, Paris, 1957.

[Ha] O. HAJEK: *Dynamical Systems in the Plane*, Academic Press, London, New York, 1968.

[He] H. HERRLICH: *Topologische Reflexionen und Coreflexionen*, Lecture Notes in Mathematics, no. 78, Springer-Verlag, Berlin, Heidelberg, New York, 1968.

[HM] K.H. HOFMANN & P.S. MOSTERT: *Elements of Compact Semigroups*, Chas. E. Merrill Books, Inc., Columbus, 1966.

[HR] E. HEWITT & K.A. ROSS: *Abstract Harmonic Analysis*, Vol. I, II, Springer-Verlag, Berlin, Heidelberg, New York, 1963/1970.

[HS] H. HERRLICH & G.E. STRECKER: *Category Theory*, Allyn and Bacon Inc., Boston, 1973.

[Hu] D. HUSEMOLLER: *Fibre Bundles*, McGraw-Hill, New York, 1966.

[Ju] I. JUHÁSZ (in collaboration with A. VERBEEK & N.S. KROONENBERG): *Cardinal functions in topology*, Mathematical Centre Tracts no 34, Mathematisch Centrum, Amsterdam, 1971.

[Is] J.R. ISBELL: *Uniform Spaces*, Amer. Math. Soc., Providence, 1964.

[Ke] J.L. KELLEY: *General Topology*, D. van Nostrand, New York, 1955.

[Ks] J.L. KOSZUL: *Lectures on groups of transformations*, Tata Institute of Fundamental Research, Bombay, 1965.

[Kw] H.-J. KOWALSKI: *Topologische Räume*, Birkhäuser Verlag, Basel, Stuttgart, 1961.

[Lo] L. LOOMIS: *An introduction to abstract harmonic analysis*, Van Nostrand, New York, 1953.

[Ma] W. MAAK: *Fastperiodische Funktionen*, Springer-Verlag, Berlin, Heidelberg, New York, 1950.

[ML] S. MACLANE: *Categories for the Working Mathematician*, Springer-Verlag, Berlin, Heidelberg, New York, 1971.

[MZ] D. MONTGOMERY & L. ZIPPIN: *Topological Transformation Groups*, Interscience, New York, 1955.

[Na] J. NAGATA: *Modern dimension theory*, Noordhoff N.V., Groningen/North-Holland Publishing Company, Amsterdam, 1965.

[Pa] B. PAREIGIS: *Categories and Functors*, Academic Press, New York, London, 1970.

[Sc] H.H. SCHAEFER: *Topological Vector Spaces*, Mac Millan, New York, London, 1966. Springer-Verlag, Berlin, Heidelberg, New York, 1971.

[Se] Z. SEMADENI: *Banach Spaces of Continuous Functions, Vol.* I, PWN, Warszawa, 1971.

[SK] I. SEGAL & R.A. KUNZE: *Integrals and Operators*, McGraw-Hill, New York, 1968.

[St] N. STEENROD: *The topology of Fibre Bundles*, Princeton University Press, Princeton, New Jersey, 1951.

[We] A. WEIL: *l'Intégration dans les groupes topologiques et ses applications*, Hermann, Paris, 1940.

Proceedings and seminars

[I] A. BOREL et al: *Seminar on Transformation Groups*, Annals of Mathematics Studies 46, Princeton University Press, Princeton, New Jersey, 1960.

[II] P.S. MOSTERT (ed.): *Proceedings of the Conference on Transformation Groups, New Orleans, 1967*, Springer-Verlag, Berlin, Heidelberg, New York, 1968.

[III] J. AUSLANDER & W.H. GOTTSCHALK (ed.): *Topological Dynamics, An International Symposium,* W.A. Benjamin, Inc., New York, Amsterdam, 1968.

[IV] B. ECKMANN (ed.): *Seminar on Triples and Categorical Homology Theory*, Lecture Notes in Mathematics, no. 80, Springer-Verlag, Berlin, Heidelberg, New York, 1969.

[V] P. HILTON (ed.): *Category Theory, Homology Theory and their Applications* III, Lecture Notes in Mathematics, no. 99, Springer-Verlag, Berlin, Heidelberg, New York, 1969.

[VI] J.A. YORKE (ed.): *Seminar on Differential Equations and Dynamical Systems*, II, Lecture Notes in Mathematics, no. 144, Springer-Verlag, Berlin, Heidelberg, New York, 1970.

[VII] D. CHILLINGWORTH (ed.): *Symposium on Differential Equations and Dynamical Systems*, 1969, Lecture Notes in Mathematics, no. 206, Springer-Verlag, Berlin, Heidelberg, New York, 1971.

[VIII] *General Topology and its Relation to Modern Analysis and Algebra,* Proc. 1961 Prague Symposium, Prague, 1972.

[IX] A. BECK (ed.): *Recent Advances in Topological Dynamics, Proceedings 1972.* Lecture Notes in Mathematics, no. 318, Springer-Verlag, Berlin, Heidelberg, New York, 1973.

[X] P.C. BAAYEN (ed.): *Topological Structures,* Mathematical Centre Tracts no. 52, Mathematisch Centrum, Amsterdam, 1974.

Papers

ALAS, O.T. [1971]: Topological groups and uniform continuity, *Portugal. Math.* 30 (1971), 137-143.

ALFSEN, E.M. & P. HOLM [1962]: A note on compact representations and almost periodicity in topological groups, *Math. Scand.* 10 (1962), 127-136.

ANDERSON, R.D. [1968]: Universal and quasi-universal flows [III], p.1-16.[1)]

ARENS, R. [1946a]: Topologies for homeomorphism groups, *Amer. J. Math.* 68 (1946), 593-610.

- [1946b]: A topology for spaces of transformations, *Ann. of Math.* 47 (1946), 480-495.

AUSLANDER, L. & F. HAHN [1963]: Real functions coming from flows on compact spaces and concepts of almost periodicity, *Trans. Amer. Math. Soc.* 106 (1963), 415-426.

AUSLANDER, J. & F. HAHN [1967]: Point transitive flows, algebras of functions and the Bebutov system, *Fund. Math.* 60 (1967), 117-137.

BAAYEN, P.C. [1967]: Topological linearization of locally compact transformation groups, *Report no.* 2, *Wiskundig Seminarium, Free University,* Amsterdam, 1967.

BAAYEN, P.C. & J. DE GROOT [1968]: Linearization of locally compact transformation groups in Hilbert space, *Math. Systems Theory* 2 (1968), 363-379.

BAGLEY, R.W. & J.S. YANG [1966]: On k-spaces and function spaces, *Proc. Amer. Math. Soc.* 17 (1966), 703-705.

)1 Roman numerals refer to the list of proceedings and seminars.

BAUM, J.D. [1953]: An equicontinuity condition for transformation groups, *Proc. Amer. Math. Soc.* 4 (1953), 656-662.

BOCHNER, S. [1926]: Beiträge zur Theorie der fastperiodischen Funktionen, I. Teil. Funktionen einer Variabeln, *Math. Ann.* 96 (1926), 119-147.

BOHR, H. [1924]: Zur Theorie der fastperiodische Funktionen, *Acta Math.* 45 (1924), 29-127.

BROOK, R.B. [1970]: A construction of the greatest ambit, *Math. Systems Theory* 4 (1970), 243-248.

CARLSON, D.H. [1971]: Extensions of dynamical systems via prolongations, *Funkcial. Ekvac.* 14 (1971), 35-46.

- [1972]: Universal dynamical systems, *Math. Systems Theory* 6 (1972), 90-95.

CHU, H. [1962]: On universal transformation groups, *Illinois J. Math.* 6 (1962), 317-326.

- [1973]: On the embedding problem and the Hilbert-Smidt conjecture, [IX], p.78-85.

COMFORT, W.W. & K.A. ROSS [1966]: Pseudocompactness and uniform continuity in topological groups, *Pacific J. Math.* 16 (1966), 483-496.

COPELAND, A.H. & J. DE GROOT [1961]: Linearization of a homeomorphism, *Math. Annalen* 144 (1961), 80-92.

DUGUNDJI, J. & H.A. ANTOSIEWICZ [1961]: Parallelizable flows and Lyapunov's second method, *Ann. of Math.* 73 (1961), 543-555.

EBERLEIN, W.F. [1949]: Abstract ergodic theorems and weakly almost periodic functions, *Trans. Amer. Math. Soc.* 67 (1949), 217-240.

EILENBERG, S. & J.C. MOORE [1965]: Adjoint functors and triples, *Illinois J. Math.* 9 (1965), 381-398.

ELLIS, R. [1957]: Locally compact transformation groups, *Duke Math. J.* 24 (1957), 119-125.

- [1959]: Equicontinuity and almost periodic functions, *Proc. Amer. Math. Soc.* 10 (1959), 637-643.

- [1961]: Point transitive transformation groups, *Trans. Amer. Math. Soc.* 101 (1961), 384-395.

ELLIS, R. & W.H. GOTTSCHALK [1960]: Homomorphisms of transformation groups, *Trans. Amer. Math. Soc.* 94 (1960), 258-271.

ELLIS, R. & H. KEYNES [1971]: A characterization of the equicontinuous structure relation, *Trans. Amer. Math. Soc.* 161 (1971), 171-183.

FELDMAN, J. & F.P. GREENLEAF [1968]: Measurable transversals in locally compact groups, *Pacific J. Math.* 25 (1968), 455-461.

FLOR, P. [1967]: Über eine Kompaktifizierung topologischer Gruppen, *J. Reine Angew. Math.* 228 (1967), 193-198.

FURSTENBERG, H. [1967]: Disjointness in ergodic theory, minimal sets, and a problem in Diophantine approximation, *Math. Systems Theory* 1 (1967), 1-49.

GAIT, J. [1972]: Transformation groups with no equicontinuous minimal set, *Compositio Math.* 25 (1972), 87-92.

GLICKSBERG, I. [1959]: Stone-Čech compactifications of products, *Trans. Amer. Math. Soc.* 90 (1959), 369-382.

GOTTSCHALK, W.H. [1958]: Minimal sets: an introduction to topological dynamics, *Bull. Amer. Math. Soc.* 64 (1958), 336-351.

- [1964]: A survey of minimal sets, *Ann. Inst. Fourier* (Grenoble) 14 (1964), 53-60.

- [1968]: Dynamical aspects of orbit closures, [III], p.217-224.

- [1973]: Some general dynamic notions, [IX], p.120-125.

DE GROOT, J. [1959]: The action of a locally compact group on a metric space, *Nieuw Arch. Wisk.* (3) 7 (1959), 70-74.

- [1962]: Linearization of mappings, [VIII], p.191-193.

DE GROOT, J. & R.H. MC DOWELL [1960]: Extension of mappings on metric spaces, *Fund. Math.* 68 (1960), 251-263.

HAJEK, O. [1968]: Categorical concepts in Dynamical System Theory, [III], p.243-257.

- [1970]: Prolongations in topological dynamics [VI], p.79-89.

- [1971]: Representation of dynamical systems, *Funkcial. Ekvac.* 14 (1971), 25-34.

- [1971]: Parallelizability revisited, *Proc. Amer. Math. Soc.* 27 (1971), 77-84.

HEDLUND, G.A. [1969]: Endomorphisms and automorphisms of the shift dynamical system, *Math. Systems Theory* 3 (1969), 320-375.

HERRLICH, H. [1965]: Wann sind alle stetigen Abbildungen in Y constant? *Math. Z.* 90 (1965), 152-154.

HOLM, P. [1964]: On the Bohr compactification, *Math. Ann.* 156 (1964), 34-46.

JONES, G.D. [1972]: The embedding of homeomorphisms of the plane in continuous flows, *Pacific J. Math.* 41 (1972), 421-436.

KAKUTANI, S. [1968]: A proof of Bebutov's theorem, *J. Differential Equations* 4 (1968), 194-201.

KEESLING, J. [1971]: Locally compact full homeomorphism groups are zero-dimensional, *Proc. Amer. Math. Soc.* 29 (1971), 390-396.

KENT, J.F. [1972]: A characterization of distal and point-distal minimal transformation groups. *Proc. Amer. Math. Soc.* 32 (1972), 304-308.

KEYNES, H.B. [1972]: Disjointness in transformation groups, *Proc. Amer. Math. Soc.* 36 (1972), 253-259.

KNAPP, A.W. [1964]: Distal functions, *Proc. Nat. Acad. Sci.* U.S.A. 52 (1964), 1409-1412.

- [1966]: Decomposition theorem for bounded uniformly continuous functions on a group, *Amer. J. Math.* 88 (1966), 902-914.

- [1967]: Distal functions on groups, *Trans. Amer. Math. Soc.* 128 (1967), 1-40.

LANDSTAD, M.B. [1972]: On the Bohr compactification of a transformation group, *Math. Z.* 127 (1972), 167-178.

LANGE, K., A. RAMSAY & G.-C. ROTA [1971]: Frobenius reciprocity in ergodic theory, *Bull. Amer. Math. Soc.* 77 (1971), 713-718.

DE LEEUW, K. & I. GLICKSBERG [1961]: Applications of almost periodic compactifications, *Acta Math.* 105 (1961), 63-97.

- [1965]: The decomposition of certain group representations, *J. Analyse Math.* 15 (1965), 135-192.

LINTON, F.E.J. [1969]: Coequalizers in categories of algebras, [IV], p.75-90.

MACKEY, G. [1952]: Induced representations of locally compact groups I, *Ann. of Math.* 55 (1952), 101-139.

MANES, E. [1969a]: Minimal subalgebras for dynamic triples, [V], p.419-447.

- [1969b]: A triple theoretic construction of compact algebras, [IV], p. 91-118.

MAXWELL, C.N. [1966]: Homomorphisms of topological transformation groups into function spaces, *Duke Math. J.* 33 (1966), 567-574.

MICHAEL, E. [1959]: Convex structures and continuous selections, *Canad. J. Math.* 11 (1959), 556-575.

MORAN, W. [1970]: Invariant means on C(G), *J. London Math. Soc.* (2), 2 (1970), 133-138.

MORRIS, S.A. [1971]: Free products of topological groups, *Bull. Austral. Math. Soc.* 4 (1971), 17-29.

MOSTERT, P.S. [1953]: Local cross sections in locally compact groups, *Proc. Amer. Math. Soc.* 4 (1953), 645-649.

- [1956]: Sections in principal fibre spaces, *Duke Math. J.* 23 (1956), 57-71.

MOSTOW, G.D. [1957]: Equivariant embedding in Euclidean space, *Ann. of Math.* 65 (1957), 432-446.

NEMYCKIĬ, V.V. [1949]: Topological problems of the theory of dynamical systems, *Uspehi Mat. Nauk.* 4 (1949), no. 6 (34), 91-153. English translation in: AMS Translation Series 1, Vol. 5, p.414-497.

NEUMANN, J. VON [1934]: Almost periodic functions in a group I, *Trans. Amer. Math. Soc.* 36 (1934), 445-492.

ORDMAN, E.T. [1974]: Free products of topological groups with equal uniformities, I, *Coll. Math.* 31 (1974), 37-43.

PAALMAN-DE MIRANDA, A.B. [1971]: A Note on W-Groups, *Math. Systems Theory* 5 (1971), 168-171.

PALAIS, R.S. [1960]: Slices and equivariant imbeddings, [I], p.101-115.

- [1961]: On the existence of slices for actions of non-compact Lie groups, *Ann. of Math.* 73 (1961), 295-323.

PELEG, R. [1972]: Weak disjointness of transformation groups, *Proc. Amer. Math. Soc.* 33 (1972), 165-170.

POGUNTKE, D. [1970]: Epimorphisms of compact groups are onto, *Proc. Amer. Math. Soc.* 26 (1970), 503-504.

PYM, J.S. [1963]: On almost periodic compactifications, *Math. Scand.* 12 (1963), 189-198.

ROEDER, D.W. [1974]: Category theory applied to Pontryigen duality, *Pacific J. Math.* 52 (1974), 519-527.

STEENROD, N.E. [1967]: A convenient category of topological spaces, *Michigan Math. J.* 14 (1967), 133-152.

THOMAS, B.V.S. [1974]: Free topological groups, *General Topology and Appl.* 4 (1974), 51-72.

VRIES, J. DE [1970]: Equivalence of almost periodic compactifications, *Compositio Math.* 22 (1970), 453-456.

- [1972a]: A note on topological linearization of locally compact transformation groups in Hilbert space, *Math. Systems Theory* 6 (1972), 49-59.

- [1972b]: Cardinal functions on topological groups, *Math. Centrum, Amsterdam, Afd. Zuivere Wisk.*, ZW 12, 1972.

- [1975a]: A universal topological transformation group in $L^2(G\times G)$, *Math. Systems Theory* 9 (1975).

- [1975b]: Pseudocompactness and the Stone-Čech compactification for topological groups, *Nieuw Arch. Wisk.* (3), 23 (1975), 35-48.

- [1975c]: Can every Tychonov G-space equivariantly be embedded in a compact G-space? *Math. Centrum, Amsterdam, Afd. Zuivere Wisk.*, ZW 36, 1975.

WILCOX, H.J. [1966]: Pseudocompact groups, *Pacific J. Math.* 19 (1966), 365-379.

- [1971]: Dense subgroups of compact groups, *Proc. Amer. Math. Soc.* 28 (1971), 578-580.

WILLIAMS, R.F. [1968]: Compact Non-Lie Groups, [II], p.366-369.

WU, T.-S. [1966]: Left almost periodicity does not imply right almost periodicity, *Bull. Amer. Math. Soc.* 72 (1966), 314-316.

WYLER, O. [1971]: On the categories of general topology and topological algebra, *Arch. Math. (Basel)*, XXII (1971), 7-17.

INDEX

Action, 24
  bounded, 206
  discrete, 27
  effective, 28
  equicontinuous, 40
  ergodic, 148
  free, 29
  linear, 214
  minimal, 147
  point-transitive, *cf. ambit*
  proper, 125, 224
  strongly effective, 28
  transitive, 206
  trivial, 27
  weakly mixing, 148
adjunction, 12
  of a monad and a comonad, 180
adjoint (left or right), 13
  of L_ψ, 100, 162
  of R_ψ, 100, 162
  of S_1, 116
  of S_1^G, 103
algebra, 16
  morphism of, 17
  in KR, 161
  in KRGRP×KR, 158
  in TOP^G, 95
  in TOPGRP×TOP, 88
almost periodic, 60, 62
  Bohr, 60, 62
  Von Neumann, 62

ambit, 148
  greatest (= maximal = universal), 145, 148
approximate unit, 69
  cardinality of, 70
ASCOLI, theorem of, 8

Bilateral compact-open topology, 34
bilateral shift, 188
bisequence, 188
Bohr almost periodic, 60, 62
Bohr compactification, 23, 65, 134, 139
bounded action, 206
  metrically, 206
boundedness and compactifications, 211

Cardinal invariant, 9
coalgebra, 20
  in KR, 179
  in $KRGRP^{op}$×KR, 175
  in TOP, 183
  in TTG, 92
cocomplete, 12
  subcategories of TTG, 126, 127, 132
codomain, 2
coequalizer, *cf. colimit*
co-E-small, 14
cogenerator, 184
  in k-TTG_*, 186
  in subcategories of TTG_*, 187

relation with comprehensive objects, 189
colimits in subcategories of TTG, 126, 127, 132
comonad, 19
in KR, 179
in $KRGRP^{op} \times KR$, 173
in TOP, 183
in TTG, 92
comorphism, 48, 165, 171
compactification, 146, 211
Bohr, 23
of G-spaces, 211
Stone-Čech, 22
compact-open topology, 6
complete category, 12
subcategories of TTG, 120, 125
comprehensive object, 189
in TOP, 191
in TOP^G, 194, 200, 203, 221, 222
relation to cogenerators, 189
counit, 14
cross-section, 26, 41, 92

Density (of a topological space), 9
of $C_c(X)$, 235
of $L^2(G)$, 70
dimension of $L^2(G)$, 70, 71
discrete ttg, 27
domain (of a function), 2

Effective, 28
ELLIS, theorem of, 36
embedding problem, 105
$\mathcal{E}$-$\mathcal{M}$-factorization, 14
enveloping semigroup, 39
epimorphisms in subcategories of TTG, 122, 128
equalizers in subcategories of TTG, 128
equicontinuous ttg, 40, 140
equicontinuous factor, 141
equivariant, 43
ergodic, 148

Factorization, $\mathcal{E}$-$\mathcal{M}$-, 14
free algebra, 17
free coalgebra, 20
free k-ttg, 159
free ttg, 29, 91

Greatest ambit, 148
group component, 42, 48
G-space, 28

HILBERT-SMITH conjecture, 105, 123
homeomorphism group, 33
full, 33
topological, 33

Induced action, 97
invariant,
equivalence relation, 50
point, 37
subset, 37
inverse image, 2
isomorphism,
of compactifications, 146
of G-spaces, 42
of ttgs, 42

K-action, 155
k-group, 153
k-refinement, 151
k-space, 150
k-ttg, 156
morphism of, 157

Left adjoint, *cf. adjoint*
left almost periodic, 62
left uniformity, 11
limits in subcategories of TTG, 120, 125, 128, 132
Lindelöf degree, 10
linear ttg, 214
linearization, 215
  in a Fréchet space, 217
  in a Hilbert space, 217, 219, 221, 222
  strict, 215
list of categories, 12, 250
locally compact Hausdorff groups, 180
local weight, 9

Maximal equicontinuous factor, 141, 147
maximal G-ambit, 148
metrically bounded, 206
minimal G-space, 147
monad, 16
  in KR, 161
  in KRGRP×KR, 158
  in TOP, 95
  in TOPGRP×TOP, 86
monomorphisms in subcategories of TTG, 120, 121, 128
morphism of algebras, 17, 97
  of G-spaces, 42
  of k-ttgs, 157
  of monads, 18, 97
  of ttgs, 42

Norm in $C_u(X)$, 9
  in $L^p(G)$, 66

Opposite category, 164
orbit, 37
  closure, 39
  space, 38

Perfect mapping, 4
phase group, 25
phase space, 25
point-open topology, 6
point-transitive ttg, *cf. ambit*
preservation of reflections, 133, 138, 143
products in subcategories of TTG, 128
proper action, 125, 224

Quotient mapping, 4
  products of, 5

Range, 2
reflection, 14
  of a G-space in $COMP^G$, 138
  of a G-space in $HAUS^G$, 137
  of a ttg in $\overleftarrow{K}[A\times B]$, 135
  of a ttg in COMPEQ, 140
reflective subcategory, 14
  of TTG, 132, 140
relatively dense, 60
right adjoint, *cf. adjoint*
right almost periodic, 60
right invariant, 55
right uniformity, 11
right translation, 55

Shift, 188
space component, 42, 48
stability group, 29
stabilizing set, 30
Stone-Čech compactification, 22
strict linearization, 215
strongly effective ttg, 28
  is not free, 38
structure group, 141
syndetic, *cf. relatively dense*

Topological transformation group, 25
transition, 25
  group, 26
  mapping, 26
transitive, 206
trivial action, 27
ttg, *cf. topological transformation group; also: action*

Uniform convergence, 7
unit of adjunction, 14
universal ambit, 148
universal arrow, 13

Weight, 9
  of $C_c(G)$, 235
  of $L^2(G)$, 70, 71
weight function, 72, 229
weighted translation, 72

LIST OF SYMBOLS

The following list includes only those non-standard notations which are of a more than local application in this book (i.e. which are used not only immediately after the definition). For notational conventions concerning set-theory and topology, see pp. 1-3 and 9.

$AP(G)$, 60

$(.)_{bc}$, 34

$C(X,Y)$, 6

$C^*(X,Y)$, 7

$C_c(X,Y)$, 6

$C_p(X,Y)$, 6

$C_u(X,Y)$, 7

$C_{kc}(X,Y)$, 151

C_π, 37

c_π, 38

$(.)_c$, 7

$E_{<G,X,\pi>}$, 40

$\mathcal{e}<G,X,\pi>$, 30

G^c, 23

$\mathcal{H}(X,X)$, 25

$\mathcal{H}_{bc}(X,X)$, 34

K_π, 39

$M(K,\alpha)$, 6

$N(K,U)$, 6

$(.)_p$, 7

$U_f(K,\alpha)$, 7

$(.)_u$, 7

α_G, 23

η_X^G, 24

λ, 10

μ_X^G, 24

π^x, 2

π_y, 2

$\bar{\pi}$, 26

$\underline{\pi}$, 58

$\tilde{\rho}$, 55

A list of the categories which are considered as "known" can be found on p. 12. In this book, we have defined the following categories and functors:

COMPEQ, 140

$COMP^G$, 119

$HAUS^G$, 119

G, 84, 119, 158

G_*, 165, 171

K, 85, 119, 158

K_*, 165, 171

k-KR^G, 161

k-TTG, 157

k-TTG_*, 171

L_ψ, 100, 162

R_ψ, 98, 162

S, 84, 119, 158

S_*, 165, 171

S^G, 94, 119, 161

TTG, 84

TTG_*, 165

TOP^G, 94

OTHER TITLES IN THE SERIES MATHEMATICAL CENTRE TRACTS

A leaflet containing an order-form and abstracts of all publications mentioned below is available at the Mathematical Centre, 2e Boerhaavestraat 49, Amsterdam-1005, The Netherlands. Orders should be sent to the same address.

MCT 1 T. VAN DER WALT, *Fixed and almost fixed points*, 1963. ISBN 90 6196 002 9.

MCT 2 A.R. BLOEMENA, *Sampling from a graph*, 1964. ISBN 90 6196 003 7.

MCT 3 G. DE LEVE, *Generalized Markovian decision processes, part I: Model and method*, 1964. ISBN 90 6196 004 5.

MCT 4 G. DE LEVE, *Generalized Markovian decision processes, part II: Probabilistic background*, 1964. ISBN 90 6196 006 1.

MCT 5 G. DE LEVE, H.C. TIJMS & P.J. WEEDA, *Generalized Markovian decision processes, Applications*, 1970. ISBN 90 6196 051 7.

MCT 6 M.A. MAURICE, *Compact ordered spaces*, 1964. ISBN 90 6196 006 1.

MCT 7 W.R. VAN ZWET, *Convex transformations of random variables*, 1964. ISBN 90 6196 007 X.

MCT 8 J.A. ZONNEVELD, *Automatic numerical integration*, 1964. ISBN 90 6196 008 8.

MCT 9 P.C. BAAYEN, *Universal morphisms*, 1964. ISBN 90 6196 009 6.

MCT 10 E.M. DE JAGER, *Applications of distributions in mathematical physics*, 1964. ISBN 90 6196 010 X.

MCT 11 A.B. PAALMAN-DE MIRANDA, *Topological semigroups*, 1964. ISBN 90 6196 011 8.

MCT 12 J.A.TH.M. VAN BERCKEL, H. BRANDT CORSTIUS, R.J. MOKKEN & A. VAN WIJNGAARDEN, *Formal properties of newspaper Dutch*, 1965. ISBN 90 6196 013 4.

MCT 13 H.A. LAUWERIER, *Asymptotic expansions*, 1966, out of print; replaced by MCT 54.

MCT 14 H.A. LAUWERIER, *Calculus of variations in mathematical physics*, 1966. ISBN 90 6196 020 7.

MCT 15 R. DOORNBOS, *Slippage tests*, 1966. ISBN 90 6196 021 5.

MCT 16 J.W. DE BAKKER, *Formal definition of programming languages with an application to the definition of ALGOL 60*, 1967. ISBN 90 6196 022 3.

MCT 17 R.P. VAN DE RIET, *Formula manipulation in ALGOL 60, part 1*, 1968. ISBN 90 6196 025 8.

MCT 18 R.P. VAN DE RIET, *Formula manipulation in ALGOL 60, part 2*, 1968. ISBN 90 6196 038 X.

MCT 19 J. VAN DER SLOT, *Some properties related to compactness*, 1968. ISBN 90 6196 026 6.

MCT 20 P.J. VAN DER HOUWEN, *Finite difference methods for solving partial differential equations*, 1968. ISBN 90 6196 027 4.

MCT 21 E. WATTEL, *The compactness operator in set theory and topology*, 1968. ISBN 90 6196 028 2.

MCT 22 T.J. DEKKER, *ALGOL 60 procedures in numerical algebra, part 1*, 1968. ISBN 90 6196 029 0.

MCT 23 T.J. DEKKER & W. HOFFMANN, *ALGOL 60 procedures in numerical algebra, part 2*, 1968. ISBN 90 6196 030 4.

MCT 24 J.W. DE BAKKER, *Recursive procedures*, 1971. ISBN 90 6196 060 6.

MCT 25 E.R. PAERL, *Representations of the Lorentz group and projective geometry*, 1969. ISBN 90 6196 039 8.

MCT 26 EUROPEAN MEETING 1968, *Selected statistical papers, part I*, 1968. ISBN 90 6196 031 2.

MCT 27 EUROPEAN MEETING 1968, *Selected statistical papers, part II*, 1969. ISBN 90 6196 040 1.

MCT 28 J. OOSTERHOFF, *Combination of one-sided statistical tests*, 1969. ISBN 90 6196 041 X.

MCT 29 J. VERHOEFF, *Error detecting decimal codes*, 1969. ISBN 90 6196 042 8.

MCT 30 H. BRANDT CORSTIUS, *Excercises in computational linguistics*, 1970. ISBN 90 6196 052 5.

MCT 31 W. MOLENAAR, *Approximations to the Poisson, binomial and hypergeometric distribution functions*, 1970. ISBN 90 6196 053 3.

MCT 32 L. DE HAAN, *On regular variation and its application to the weak convergence of sample extremes*, 1970. ISBN 90 6196 054 1.

MCT 33 F.W. STEUTEL, *Preservation of infinite divisibility under mixing and related topics*, 1970. ISBN 90 6196 061 4.

MCT 34 I. JUHASZ a.o., *Cardinal functions in topology*, 1971. ISBN 90 6196 062 2.

MCT 35 M.H. VAN EMDEN, *An analysis of complexity*, 1971. ISBN 90 6196 063 0.

MCT 36 J. GRASMAN, *On the birth of boundary layers*, 1971. ISBN 90 6196 064 9.

MCT 37 G.A. BLAAUW a.o., *MC-25 Informatica Symposium*, 1971. ISBN 90 6196 065 7.

MCT 38 W.A. VERLOREN VAN THEMAAT, *Automatic analysis of Dutch compound words*, 1971. ISBN 90 6196 073 8.

MCT 39 H. BAVINCK, *Jacobi series and approximation*, 1972. ISBN 90 6196 074 6.

MCT 40 H.C. TIJMS, *Analysis of (s,S) inventory models*, 1972. ISBN 90 6196 075 4.

MCT 41 A. VERBEEK, *Superextensions of topological spaces*, 1972. ISBN 90 6196 076 2.

MCT 42 W. VERVAAT, *Success epochs in Bernoulli trials (with applications in number theory)*, 1972. ISBN 90 6196 077 0.

MCT 43 F.H. RUYMGAART, *Asymptotic theory of rank tests for independence*, 1973. ISBN 90 6196 081 9.

MCT 44 H. BART, *Meromorphic operator valued functions*, 1973. ISBN 90 6196 082 7.

MCT 45 A.A. BALKEMA, *Monotone transformations and limit laws*, 1973. ISBN 90 6196 083 5.

MCT 46 R.P. VAN DE RIET, *ABC ALGOL, A portable language for formula manipulation systems, part 1: The language*, 1973. ISBN 90 6196 084 3.

MCT 47 R.P. VAN DE RIET, *ABC ALGOL, A portable language for formula manipulation systems, part 2: The compiler*, 1973. ISBN 90 6196 085 1.

MCT 48 F.E.J. KRUSEMAN ARETZ, P.J.W. TEN HAGEN & H.L. OUDSHOORN, *An ALGOL 60 compiler in ALGOL 60, Text of the MC-compiler for the EL-X8*, 1973. ISBN 90 6196 086 X.

MCT 49 H. KOK, *Connected orderable spaces*, 1974. ISBN 90 6196 088 6.

* MCT 50 A. VAN WIJNGAARDEN, B.J. MAILLOUX, J.E.L. PECK, C.H.A. KOSTER, M. SINTZOFF, C.H. LINDSEY, L.G.L.T. MEERTENS & R.G. FISKER (eds.), *Revised report on the algorithmic langauge ALGOL 68*. ISBN 90 6196 089 4.

MCT 51 A. HORDIJK, *Dynamic programming and Markov potential theory*, 1974. ISBN 90 6196 095 9.

MCT 52 P.C. BAAYEN (ed.), *Topological structures*, 1974. ISBN 90 6196 096 7.

MCT 53 M.J. FABER, *Metrizability in generalized ordered spaces*, 1974. ISBN 90 6196 097 5.

MCT 54 H.A. LAUWERIER, *Asymptotic analysis, part 1*, 1974. ISBN 90 6196 098 3.

MCT 55 M. HALL JR. & J.H. VAN LINT (eds.), *Combinatorics, part 1: Theory of designs, finite geometry and coding theory*, 1974. ISBN 90 6196 099 1.

MCT 56 M. HALL JR. & J.H. VAN LINT (eds.), *Combinatorics, part 2: Graph theory; foundations, partitions and combinatorial geometry*, 1974. ISBN 90 6196 100 9

MCT 57 M. HALL JR. & J.H. VAN LINT (eds.), *Combinatorics, part 3: Combinatorial group theory*, 1974. ISBN 90 6196 101 7.

MCT 58 W. ALBERS, *Asymptotic expansions and the deficiency concept in statistics*, 1975. ISBN 90 6196 102 5.

MCT 59 J.L. MIJNHEER, *Sample path properties of stable processes*, 1975. ISBN 90 6196 107 6.

* MCT 60 F. GÖBEL, *Queueing models involving buffers*. ISBN 90 6196 108 4.

* MCT 61 P. VAN EMDE BOAS, *Abstract resource-bound classes, part 1*. ISBN 90 6196 109 2.

* MCT 62 P. VAN EMDE BOAS, *Abstract resource-bound classes, part 2*. ISBN 90 6196 110 6.

MCT 63 J.W. DE BAKKER (ed.), *Foundations of computer science*, 1975. ISBN 90 6196 111 4.

MCT 64 W.J. DE SCHIPPER, *Symmetric closed categories*, 1975. ISBN 90 6196 112 2.

* MCT 65 J. DE VRIES, *Reflections on topological transformation groups*. ISBN 90 6196 113 0.

* MCT 66 H.G.J. PIJLS, *Locally convex algebras in spectral theory and eigenfunction expansions*. ISBN 90 6196 114 9.

An asterisk before the number means "to appear".